LIFE AND LEARNING XVIII

PROCEEDINGS OF THE EIGHTEENTH UNIVERSITY FACULTY FOR LIFE CONFERENCE
at
MARQUETTE UNIVERSITY
2008

edited by
Joseph W. Koterski, S.J.

University Faculty for Life

Bronx NY

Published by University Faculty for Life
c/o Philosophy Department
Fordham University
Bronx NY 10458

Printed in the United States of America
ISSN 1097-0878

Table of Contents

Preface

VOLUME EIGHTEEN of *Life and Learning* presents a selection of papers from UFL's 2008 conference. We are deeply grateful to Marquette University for providing a wonderful venue for this meeting, and especially to our indefatigable local host, Prof. Richard Fehring as well as to the Marquette Chapter of UFL. As the Program Chair for this conference, Prof. Frank Beckwith deserves our heartfelt thanks for arranging a fine program. We would also like to express our grateful appreciation to Our Sunday Visitor Institute for a special grant in support of the 2008 UFL Conference and to all the benefactors of UFL who have made possible its annual meetings as well as the publication of its newsletter and of its annual volume of proceedings. Without their generous contributions this organization would not be able to continue its work.

Let me also offer special thanks to Prof. Carol Nevins Abromaitis (Loyola College of Maryland) and to Prof. Jacqueline Nolan-Haley (Fordham University Law School), for their invaluable help yet again this year in the reviewing the papers submitted for this volume.

Electronic versions of these papers and many of those delivered at previous UFL conferences are available on our web site at www.uffl.org. For additional copies of this volume or for bound versions of the proceedings of our earlier conferences, please contact me at koterski@fordham.edu.

Joseph W. Koterski, S.J.

BIOETHICS

Engaging the Whole Breadth of Reason: Catholic Bioethics in the University and in the Post-Secular World

Edmund D. Pellegrino, M.D.

ABSTRACT: From its beginnings, bioethics has been a secular enterprise. Scholars who hold religious beliefs are often disenfranchised in debate or writing as incapable of rational discourse. This antipathy has been extended to the disenfranchisement of "Catholic bioethics" as an illegitimate university discipline. This essay examines that claim in light of 450 years of Catholic scholarship in questions now often subsumed under the rubric of bioethics.

> *The West has long been endangered by this aversion to the questions that underlie its rationality, and can only suffer harm thereby. The courage to engage the whole breadth of reason, and not denial of its grandeur–this is the program with which theology grounded in Biblical Faith enters the debates of our times.*
>
> – Pope Benedict XVI, 12 September 2006[1]

IS CATHOLIC BIOETHICS a viable university discipline?[2] Or is it, as some aver, merely a set of religious prejudices disguised as rational

---

[1] Pope Benedict XVI, "Three Stages in the Program of De-Hellenization," papal address, University of Regensburg, 12 September 2006.

[2] This paper was originally delivered in 2009 at Blackfriars College, Oxford University, at the invitation of Dr. Richard Finn, O.P., Regent of Blackfriars.

discourse? Is Catholic bioethics ready for the capacious dustbin of outmoded classical-medieval notions that positive science long ago put to rest?

In the past half century I have been increasingly asked this question in the university and in the public square. I have seen important principles of ethics marginalized simply because they have been the heritage of five hundred years of serious cogitation by Catholic scholars. And I have witnessed the growing conviction that man is the ultimate source of morality, that moral truth is only ascertained by positive science, and that the Roman Catholic Church is the last repository of resistance to man's realization of the dream of enlightened moral freedom.

What is at issue is the growing societal schism between moral and epistemological doctrines of militant skepticism and a balanced view of the place of both reason and faith. This schism is not likely to be healed in the years immediately ahead. The only road to peaceful co-existence is a productive dialectic and dialogue between secular and religious world views. For this to occur, Catholic bioethics must have a place in the university–the locus at which the necessary reasoned engagement is, and will be, taking place.

This dialogue is essential to humanity's common need to respond intelligently to the central question posed by the new biology. How are we to use our new powers for the betterment of human life without being overshadowed by our own ingenuity? What do we mean by "betterment" of human life? What indeed makes life truly human? By what means shall we determine its moral content?

This question has increasing significance for the future of bioethics and not just for Roman Catholics. At its beginnings in the U.S., bioethics had strong roots in the Protestant religion as well as the Catholic.[3] Few of us then suspected how rapidly those religious roots

---

[3] Thomas K. McElhinney and Edmund D. Pellegrino, "The Institute on Human Values in Medicine: Its Role and Influence in the Conception and Evolution of Bioethics," *Theoretical Medicine* 22 (2001): 291-317.

would be weakened by the growth of secularism with its traditional skepticism and relativism, and now by the militant anti-religious spirit that characterizes some of the writing in academia today.

Militant secularism has cast religiously grounded bioethics in the role of a social evil whose influence in academia is deleterious to progress and societal good. This attitude is reflected in the subtle disenfranchisement of Catholic bioethics in academic discourse. Moral conclusions cohering with a religious perspective have become *ipso facto* intellectually suspect in the minds of many.

There is every indication that this situation will continue in the years ahead into what some have called the "post secular age,"[4] an age in which secular and religious world views will live side by side. In this circumstance, if there is to be civil accord on some of our most pressing moral issues, productive dialogue between opposing world views is essential. In this dialogue Catholic bioethics has a central role. Since the intellectual locus of the debate will be in the universities, Catholic bioethics must be represented in the academic milieu. To ignore or banish it as academically disreputable deprives the university of a rich and relevant tradition of medical morality. It deprives millions of believers of an intellectual forum representing their world view. It also assumes, without justification, that radical secularism and militant rationalism have already demolished two millennia of religious moral discourse in the West.

I will begin by considering the root of the fundamental schism between the rationalist and the religious world views as well as the way that schism has contributed to the fractiousness of today's bioethics debates. I shall close by outlining why and how Catholic bioethics must occupy an unavoidable place in the moral controversy and the university. Throughout I shall maintain that Catholic bioethics, and other religiously connected systems of bioethics, must be in

---

[4] K. Eder, "Europäische Säkular Isierung-Sonderweg in die Postsäkular Gesellschaft?" *Berliner Journal für Soziologie* 3 (2002): 321-43; M. King, *Postsecularism: The Hidden Challenges to Extremism* (Cambridge UK: James Clark & Co., 2009).

[illegible] discourse with secular bioethics. This interchange is [illegible] if we are to find agreement on the practical ethical guidelines we [illegible]ed to modulate the unprecedented powers modern biology puts before us.

In biology we face the same issue that Einstein touched on in the physical sciences when he said:

> For the scientific method can teach us nothing else beyond how facts are related to and conditioned by each other. The aspiration toward such objective knowledge belongs to the highest of which man is capable and you will certainly not suspect me of wishing to belittle the achievements and heroic efforts of man in this sphere. Yet it is equally clear that knowledge of what is does not open the door directly to what should be.[5]

Although he was not a "believer" in the usual sense, Einstein's distinction is just as true for the biological as it is for the physical sciences. To confuse or conflate their respective epistemologies imperils the credibility of both. Empirical science and ethics must respect each other's domain even while examining the overlapping truths between them.

In a post-secular world neither the naturalistic nor the religious worldview can assume *prima facie* advantage over the other. Continuing interactions between secular and religious worldviews must be sought if these views are to live peaceably with one another. Humankind shares a powerful and continuing need to agree on how to channel the power and the opportunities of biotechnology so that all may benefit and all may be protected against the misuse of that power. For this, some source of criticism outside of science is essential.

Catholic Bioethics as an Academic Discipline

A valid discipline must, at a minimum, possess an organized body of knowledge and a distinctive method for the study of that body of knowledge. On this view Catholic bioethics is an academic discipline.

---

[5] Alfred Einstein, *Out of My Later Years* (Secaucus NJ: Citadel, 1974), pp. 21-22.

It is a branch of ethics whose specific focus is right and good action in the use of biological knowledge in human affairs. It shares with other studies subsumed under the rubric of ethics an orderly, systematic, critical, and definable body of knowledge aimed at a cognitive grasp of right and wrong, good and bad human conduct. Catholic bioethics as an organized body of knowledge is examined by trained professionals who belong to professional organizations and publish their work in available journals open to public and scholarly criticism. Catholic bioethics conducts its inquiries with a variety of analytic methods, both philosophical and theological. It has roots in classical, medieval, and contemporary philosophy. Many of the principles and methods that Catholic bioethics uses are shared by secular philosophers, even when their pre-logical presuppositions are different.

That Catholic bioethics differs in important ways from secular ethical systems of analyses and their conclusions does not *per se* make it either irrational or an exercise of religious prejudice. Measured by the usual criteria, Catholic bioethics is as valid an academic discipline as any other organized body of knowledge now accepted on university campuses. Humanity's need for the fullest examination of the ethical issues in contemporary biology and biotechnology is incomplete without the participation of Catholic bioethics. This inquiry is as crucial for believers as it is for non-believers. In a post-secular world the exile of Catholic bioethics from academia would be a loss for the whole of society.

This is not to suggest that to be legitimate academically *Catholic* bioethics must be reducible to secular bioethics. Like secular bioethics, Catholic bioethics argues its propositions from the point of view of reason. Its conclusions are open to reasoned objection. The fact that its conclusions are also consistent with Church teaching does not *per se* invalidate them. Like any other philosophical endeavor Catholic bioethics answers reasons with reasons. It does not offer scripture, tradition, church teaching or papal encyclicals as evidence against reasoned objections by those who do not accept such evidence.

In a sense, then, Catholic bioethics is a "bipolar" discipline, i.e., [illegible] line of thought extending from reason to revelation. At [illegible] can be engaged by reason alone unaided by theology. At the oth[illegible]nd, it is compatible with theological ethics. How far one goes along this continuum is dependent on how far the inquirer wishes to go. Catholic bioethics engages the intellect through reason at one end and through faith on the other. Faith complements reason, while reason complements faith.[6]

That there is in Catholic bioethics a congruence between faith and reason does not *per se* invalidate it either as philosophy or theology. Each end of its bipolar structure can be engaged on its own terms. This bipolarity equips Catholic bioethics to serve as a linch pin in the current and future dialogue between the secular and religious world views.

Secular and Catholic Bioethics: The Widening Gap

Before turning to the ways by which Catholic bioethics can engage in productive dialogue and dialectic with secular bioethics, a very brief summarization of the forces driving them apart is in order. I need not repeat here the extraordinary efforts of Pope John Paul II and now Pope Benedict XVI to encourage dialogue with contemporary culture in all its manifestations.

Despite some progress this encounter has been difficult in academic circles. Here the gap has been made dialogue difficult, or even impossible in some cases, by narrowing the legitimacy of reason itself as a means of ascertaining truth. Until the Enlightenment, classical human reason could engage the whole world of things and events in search of the truth. Since the Enlightenment human reason has gradually been reduced to scientific reason, to only those truths judged valid by the criterion of falsifiability. This narrowing has now come to include morality and ethics, thus eroding their underpinning in moral philosophy as well.

---

[6] John Paul II, *Fides et Ratio*, 1998.

This limitation of reason to scientific reason has dealt a double blow to bioethics, which must consider the moral dimensions of biology when it is used to re-shape our notions of *being* human, and human *being*. Moral truths, if any are left, are further reduced to psychology, axiology, or evolutionary biology. With the societal revolution of the mid-sixties of the last century morality became the province of social or cultural construction. Here the repudiation of received traditions and authority has led to atomization of moral standards. They have become matters of personal preference instead.

This trajectory leaves little room for sources beyond man that can bind the moral life of all humans as humans. Total freedom of choice reduces the moral life solely to personal "values" that are as such inarguable by reason alone. Given that this, or something like it, is presently the case, what is the status of today's moral discourse?

The Fractiousness of Current Bioethical Discourse

In 1997, H.T. Engelhardt, Jr. viewed the state of ethical discourse in bioethics with a mixture of satisfaction and foreboding. He was pleasantly surprised that bioethicists without a shared moral narrative were, nonetheless, able to engage in a productive degree of ethical discourse. His satisfaction, however, was tempered by his longstanding conviction that rational discourse could not long survive without a shared, content-full, moral consensus. He phrased his doubts in clearly apodictic terms:"In particular, the project of discovering a shared normative consensus in general secular terms must always fail."[7] Bereft of a shared moral yardstick, Engelhardt argued, bioethicists must be "moral strangers," incapable of meaningful moral discourse between, or among, communities with opposing values.[8]

---

[7] H.T. Engelhardt, "Bioethics and Philosophy Reconsidered" in *Philosophy and Medicine Reconsidered, A Twenty Year Retrospective and Critical Appraisal*, ed. Ronald Carson and Chester Burns (Dordrecht: Kluwer, 1997), pp. 85-105.

[8] H.T. Engelhardt, *The Foundations of Bioethics*, 2nd Edition (New York NY: Oxford Univ. Press, 1996).

...stic appraisal of the trajectory of discourse in bioethics ... give testimony to Engelhardt's prescience. Moreover, tod... discord in bioethics is not limited to failure to agree on a secular moral vision. The same failure is becoming evident between and within religion-inspired moral narratives as well. One example is the sad division between liberal and conservative Catholics on some of the most crucial human life issues (e.g., abortion, embryonic stem cell research).

The current discord between "moral strangers" impedes discourse on topics of common concern–e.g., physician-patient relationships, health care reform, the care of the very young and the very old, human enhancement, end-of-life decisions, abortion, euthanasia, and virtually every other biomedical issue of importance. These divisions become most acute when important bioethical issues of the day are debated in the public square or the venue of public policy. In that venue, both private and public disagreements have too often ended in socially ruinous eventualities: capitulation, unacceptable compromise, or incommensurability, all lethal to productive discourse.

We are indeed becoming the "moral strangers" that Engelhardt predicted. In democratic societies the tendency is often to think that legislative judicial fiat or a simple majority plebiscite will "settle" the issues. This tendency for Americans to seek juridical resolution was recognized in our country's early history by de Tocqueville a long time ago in these words: "Scarcely any political question arises in the United States which is not resolved, sooner or later, into a judicial question."[9]

When we resort to the resolution of debated moral issues by legislation or the courts, there is the additional danger that de Tocqueville also saw of conflict between equality and freedom, between conformity to the majority rule and the power of the majority over individual freedoms. De Tocqueville put it this way: "I have

---

[9] Alexis de Tocqueville, *Democracy in America*, ed. Richard Heffner (New York NY: New American Library, 1956), p. 126.

sought to point out the dangers to which the principle of equality exposes the independence of man...because I firmly believe that these dangers are the most formidable."[10]

This is an issue in the United States now. There are currently pressures to equate legality with morality. In the case of abortion, some argue that physicians, being licensed by the State, are legally compelled to do what they believe intrinsically wrong. Some bioethicists insist that all physicians must be "morally neutral" on the human most serious human life issues.[11] The central Catholic teaching on conscience and moral accountability is thus imperiled.[12]

One Mechanism for Accord: "Consent and Forbearance"

Fortunately, at the international level the process of decision-making in the absence of consensus on a moral narrative has had some genuine success. Engelhardt describes this as the "consent and forbearance method." Using this method, the participants eschewed debating the foundational questions and justifications on which they based their opposing positions. Instead, they focused on those aspects of the issues on which they could agree. To these they gave their consent and practiced the forbearance necessary to actualize particular undertakings to which their consent could be given. For Engelhardt, the free consent of the participants and their moral forbearance counted as valid moral permission. Differences of opinion then centered on the validity of the consent process. The ideological, metaphysical, and theological differences grounding the particular undertaking on which agreement was sought were voluntarily set aside and not engaged.

This method succeeded in gaining consent to a variety of

---

[10] Ibid., p. 315.

[11] J. Blustein and A.R. Fleishman, "The Pro-Life Maternal-Fetal Medicine Physician: A Problem of Integrity," *Hastings Center Report* (Jan.-Feb., 1995).

[12] W.J. Smith, "Pulling the Plug on the Conscience Clause," *First Things* (Dec. 2009): 41-44.

agreements between nations and individuals representing a wide variety of cultures, legal philosophies, and religious beliefs. Some examples are these: the 1929 International Declaration on the Rights of Man of the Institute of International Law, the 1948 U.N. Declaration on the Rights of Man, the UNESCO Universal Declaration on Bioethics and Human Rights,[13] the 1946 Nuremberg Code on Permissible Medical Experiments, and the 2003 Revised Declaration of Helsinki of the World Medical Association.

These bodies came to agreements despite their moral and cultural diversity and the complexity of the issues. However, it is important to recognize that at the outset the participants shared certain practical perspectives, were willing to work together cooperatively, and held moral positions at least in part amenable to compromise. These conditions rarely obtain in academe or "public debates" involving bioethics today. They are most notably missing in attempts at dialogue between secular and Catholic viewpoints on the human life issues.

CONSENT AND FORBEARANCE: SOME PROBLEMS

Today, the aforementioned conditions favoring constructive collaboration have become difficult for a variety of reasons. A more diverse cadre of younger bioethicists has taken the place of the more experienced participants of the earlier discourses. Their moral viewpoints are more diverse, and more sharply divided, than those of their predecessors. Their partisan political sympathies are more overtly expressed. Self-designated ethical "progressives" or "retrogressives" array themselves against each other. Thus loyalty to political ideology is often confused with ethical consistency. Common consent and forbearance–and, at times, even common civility–are thus harder to achieve.

---

[13] E. D. Pellegrino, "Article 4: Benefit and Harm" in *The UNESCO Universal Declaration on Bioethics and Human Rights: Background, Principles and Application*, ed. H.A. ten Have and M.S. Jean (UNESCO Publishing, 2009), pp. 99-109.

Today's bioethicists come from a wide variety of disciplines in the humanities, social sciences, political science, the law, and medicine. They have had varying degrees of formal education in ethics or bioethics. Some interpret bioethics as a discipline; for others it is a public forum within which to shape societal mores in ways that would justify their own political views.

This variety of backgrounds has enhanced and enriched bioethical discourse and fostered interdisciplinary dialogue. But it has also diluted the ethical rigor of the discourse and increased the possibilities for discord in debate. In the past philosophical or theological ethics enjoyed intellectual stature. For many "bioethicists" today, those disciplines are demeaned as retrogressive, too abstract, or too close to religion. Moral arguments today are often shaped in terms of "values" rather than moral principle or reasoning. Some bioethicists want to be "comfortable" with their conclusions rather than being rationally convinced by them.

This de-emphasis on ethics *per se* tends to weaken the process of dialectic that is essential to the kind of argumentation needed to distinguish compromise from capitulation and to recognize when arguments have reached the state of incommensurability and can no longer be pursued productively.

Elsewhere I have detailed the current trajectory toward normative decay in bioethics, together with the difficulties of retrieving its normative status.[14] Unfortunately traditionalists, modernists, and postmodernists have each contributed to this normative decadence. Whenever bioethics fails to engage the deeper issues (classically the domain of metaphysics and theology), it succumbs easily to moral nihilism. This is not a plea for nostalgia but simply recognition of a cultural heritage within the perennial philosophy still latent in the major philosophical systems today. Rather, it is to recognize the obstacles that must be dealt with for secular and religiously oriented

---

[14] E. D. Pellegrino, "Bioethics at Century's End: Can Normative Ethics be Retrieved?" in *Journal of Medicine and Philosophy* 25/6 (2000): 655-75.

views to engage each other.

Catholic Bioethics, the University and the Post Secular Age

I will turn from these reflections to the necessity for Catholic bioethics to engage in productive discourse with the rationalist world view. This can only be accomplished in an intellectually serious way if Catholic bioethics is a full partner in academia with the bioethics of Western rationalism and skepticism. Full academic partnership does not mean mere tolerance, but a true mutually respectful dialectic between mature scholars, like that between Jürgen Habermas and Joseph Ratzinger.[15] I will use their dialectic as an example of how mature scholars with fundamentally different worldviews can engage in a productive discourse.

It is difficult to imagine the productive relationship exhibited in the dialectic between Habermas and Pope Benedict XVI without the academic presence of Catholic bioethics. If we are ever to overcome the barriers between the "moral strangers" described by Engelhardt, universities must play a leadership role in sustaining the requisite discourse. To label reasoned approaches that look to theology or classical philosophy as off-limits ignores the most serious questions of philosophical anthropology implicit and explicit in what we may aspire to be as humans.[16] To assume, on the other hand, that the secularized perspective is unwarranted or without merit, or to deny that it can contribute to philosophical anthropology is similarly mistaken.

What is more, to exclude Catholic bioethics from academia deprives the university community of contact with the *philosophia perennis*, the longest continuous repository of philosophy and ethics,

---

[15] Joseph Cardinal Ratzinger and Jürgen Habermas, *Dialectic of Secularization, On Reason and Religion* with a foreword by Florian Schuller, trans. Brian McNeill (San Francisco CA: Ignatius, 2006).

[16] E. D. Pellegrino, "Toward a Richer Bioethics: A Conclusion" in *Health and Human Flourishing*, ed. Carol R. Taylor and Roberto Dell'Oro (Washington, D.C.: Georgetown Univ. Press, 2006), pp. 247-69.

dating from classical times, through the middle ages, to the contemporary era. This is not to suggest that immediate answers to contemporary problems are ready for picking from the mature tree of Western philosophical reflection. Rather, it is to afford the secular ethicist an insight into ideas that once flourished and some of which can still enrich contemporary thought.

Then, there is an array of concepts crucial to any creditable moral philosophy that is currently interpreted solely in naturalist terms. The modern rationalist and naturalist interpretations of scientific evidence are crucial. But so, too, are the ways in which they have been interpreted by philosophers and theologians over the ages in the classical and Catholic moral traditions. I refer here to such concepts crucial to any philosophical anthropology like dignity, mind, spirit, soul, self, virtue, consciousness, responsibility, and so on. Of late, these concepts have received much attention from psychology, neurophysiology, and phenomenology. The possible correlations between localized brain activity observed by MRI and the mind-body problem are current cases in point. Our understandings of these concepts have been expanded by contemporary imaging techniques. Our knowledge of neurophysiology does not exhaust our understanding of the human experiences with which they may correlate experimentally.

Exiling Catholic bioethics also ignores the five-hundred-year old history of Catholic efforts in bioethics *per se*.[17] Beginning with the penitential books of the thirteenth century, the Church encouraged the study of medical morals. It fostered the earliest moral discussions about the responsibilities of physicians regarding embryology, abortion, euthanasia, craniotomy, medical fees, and futile treatment, for example. Even if one disagrees with Catholic ethical positions, their intellectual history cannot be lightly ignored.

In the modern history of bioethics, even before it was recognized

---

[17] D. Kelly, *The Emergence of Roman Catholic Bioethics in North America* (New York NY: Cambridge Univ. Press, 1987).

by the secular world, a wide range of bioethics problems were examined in depth by the Church. Contemporary issues like the duties of confidentiality, organ donation, ordinary-extraordinary means, the principle of double effect, the physician's ethics, etc. were discussed in the teachings of Pope Pius XII. Indeed I think it no exaggeration to call him the "first modern bioethicist." He addressed these issues more than a decade before bioethics was "born."

The scholarly contributions of Catholic scholars worldwide, especially since Pius XII, have covered every imaginable topic germane to the field of bioethics. No scholar can responsibly set these aside as mere religious prejudices. We also add the enormously influential encyclicals of John Paul II. These together with numerous reports of the Pontifical Academy for Science and the Pontifical Academy for Life, as well as the writings of numerous Catholic scholars cannot be responsibly ignored as mere "religious prejudice."

Yet, as recently as 2008, this is what occurred at Rome's Sapienza University where the irrational and intemperate objections of students and faculty forced cancellation of a speech by Benedict XVI.[18] More subtle forms of disenfranchisement are not rare when the human life issues are discussed in academe.

Fortunately, not all secularists are so openly disdainful of ideas with which they do not agree. Some are closer to the position of Jürgen Habermas, philosopher and committed secularist as he was, expressed in his extraordinary dialectic with Joseph Ratzinger (now Benedict XVI). Habermas argued that

> ...in the public arena, naturalistic world views which owe their genesis to a speculative assimilation of scientific information and are relevant to the ethical self-understanding of the citizens do not in the least enjoy a *prima facie* advantage over competing world views or religious understandings.[19]

---

[18] Pope Benedict XVI, "Planned Lecture at La Sapienza," *Catholic online*, 1 (2008): 20.

[19] Ratzinger and Habermas, op. cit., p. 51.

Ratzinger for his part of the dialectic expressed an equally reasonable openness to rational dialogue:

> Accordingly, I would speak of a necessary relatedness between reason and faith and between reason and religion which are called to purify and help one another. They need each other and they must acknowledge their mutual need.[20]
>
> Religion must continually allow itself to be purified and structured by reason and this was the view of the Church Fathers too. However, we have also seen in our reflections that there are also pathologies of reason.[21]

If more secularists are to be open to genuine discourse like Habermas, Catholic bioethicists will have to settle some of their differences in interpretation of natural law.[22] The traditional Aristotelian-Thomist themes that have characterized natural law in the past are currently subject to contested interpretations. The core themes, moral and epistemological, remain but their inter-relationships are more intricate than previously suggested.

In his conversation with Habermas, Benedict XVI made some pointed comments on the present state of natural law. He was quite frank in saying that natural law had become a "blunt" instrument. He questioned the notion that nature and reason overlap since nature was thought to be rational. Evolution seems to indicate otherwise, in Benedict's opinion. What remains, he suggests, is the modern notion that man *qua* man has rights simply by virtue of being human. Moreover, Benedict would expand the case for human rights to include

---

[20] Ratzinger and Habermas, op. cit., p. 78.

[21] Ratzinger and Habermas, op. cit., p. 77.

[22] Matthew Levering, *Biblical Natural Law: A Theocentric and Teleological Approach* (New York NY: Oxford Univ. Press, 2008); D. F. Kelly, *The Emergence of Roman Catholic Medical Ethics in North America* (New York NY: Cambridge Univ. Pres, 1981); Paul J. Griffiths, "The Nature of Desire," *First Things* 198 (2009): 27-30; Martin Rhonheimer, "Natural Law and the Thomistic Root of John Paul's Ethics of Human Life," *The National Catholic Bioethics Quarterly* 3 (2009): 517-39; J. Finnis, J. Boyle, and G. Grisez, *Nuclear Deterrance, Morality and Realism* (New York NY: Oxford Univ. Press, 1987), pp. 281-87.

obligations and limitations.[23]

Clearly, Benedict's reflections call for a greater clarity in our use of natural law as an instrument of engagement. The central epistemological and ethical themes remain, but their interrelationships deserve re-inspection. William Wallace, in a carefully analyzed account of the ancient notion of philosophy of nature, identifies it with the philosophy of science. Indeed Wallace admits that the "essential task of the philosopher of science is to assist in the task of disengaging valid physical knowledge from the logical and mathematical scaffolding in which it may be embedded."[24] This the scientist does but there is also room here for the philosopher of science "in uncovering the presuppositions and constructions wherewith the puzzling and enigmatic results are being obtained."[25]

This disengagement becomes crucial in the bioethics surrounding our rapidly emerging knowledge of the physiology of the human brain. Here the capacity to visualize brain tracts and nuclei in action too easily invites premature conclusions about the meanings of body, mind, and soul.[26] A disciplined philosophy of science can help to keep the different orders of abstraction separated in the interests of both secular and Catholic bioethics. Each, after all, seeks to understand these phenomena in their reality.

For myself, having engaged in the dialogue and dialectic as it pertains to bioethics and the human life issues especially, there is hope that the tensions of a post-secular world will not end in an intellectual or spiritual impasse. These issues will prove tendentious in the post-secular world. And it is only with Catholic bioethics *in situ* as a

---

[23] Op. cit., pp. 69-71.

[24] William Wallace, *The Modeling of Nature: Philosophy of Nature and Philosophy of Science in Synthesis* (Washington, D.C.: The Catholic Univ. of America Press, 1996), p. 236.

[25] Wallace, p. 236.

[26] Martin Rhonheimer, "Natural Law and the Thomistic Root of John Paul's Ethics of Human Life," *National Catholic Bioethics Quarterly* 3 (2009): 517-39.

university discipline that the requisite dialogue and dialectic can be accomplished.

Thus, my answer to the question at the heart of this essay is that Catholic bioethics satisfies the criteria of a valid university discipline and that, more than most university disciplines, it addresses the most crucial questions arising in modern biology as they affect the nature and meaning of human life. Despite the current emergence of skeptical rationalism and secular naturalism, the long tradition of Catholic medical-moral scholarship cannot be banished from the university. Were it to be banished or marginalized, irreparable damage would occur to the ideals of the *Universitas* itself. Without the university intact as the critic of society, society itself will become the child of unrestrained intellectual hubris.

Questions of Conscience and Law

Rights of Conscience vs. Peer-Driven Medical Ethics: ACOG and Abortion

Lynn D. Wardle[1]

ABSTRACT: Each generation must rediscover the foundational principles upon which our democracy is built, including respect for rights of conscience. ACOG Opinion No. 385 is moderate in tone and recognizes the ethical dilemma of physicians with conscience objections to patient requests for controversial provisions. However, the substance of the Opinion is biased against rights of conscience, presents a weakened version of the physicians' right-of-conscience position, assumes away the real dilemmas, presents ethical arguments for only one side of the issue, and portrays the controversy as a toggle-switch matter, fails to consider many relevant considerations and alternative solutions, and is conclusory throughout. The history of the settling of America and the founding of our nation show the importance of protecting rights of conscience. The Founders viewed conscience as protected by right, not by tolerance. The First Amendment was intended to protect rights of conscience. By fostering virtue, protecting conscience protects our constitutional liberties.

---

[1] Bruce C. Hafen Professor of Law, J. Reuben Clark Law School, Brigham Young University. This paper was prepared by the author and read in his absence by Professor Richard Myers at the 18th Annual Conference of the University Faculty for Life at Marquette University on 30 May 2008. Much of the third part of this paper was first presented at a conference on "Diverse Visions in American Health Care: Conflict, Conscience and the Law" at the Catholic University of America in April 2003. The valuable assistance of Brittany Howick, Justin W. Starr, William J. Perkins and Malisa King is gratefully acknowledged. After this paper was first presented, Notre Dame Law School student Paul Harold shared with me some additional material about rights of conscience which I have used with permission of Nik Nikas, General Counsel, Americans United for Life Legal Defense and Education Fund, for whom that research was done.

I. Ten Generations of Rediscovery of Basic Values

Each generation must discover for itself the value and worth of the principles and liberties that it has inherited from preceding generations. Each generation must, in effect, fight anew the War of Independence, and debate and decide anew, as in Philadelphia in 1787, the fundamental principles upon which its government will be founded and the fundamental freedoms that will be protected and perpetuated. Each generation must study the past in order to preserve for the future the legacy of liberties and of effective constitutional government that the Founders of the United States of America established for themselves and their posterity more than two hundred twenty years ago.[2]

For over two centuries, protection for rights of conscience–not just rights of belief or of worship but the right to live and act according to the deepest principles of religious and moral belief–has been among the core values and central liberties protected by the Constitution of the United States. It is amazing that so many consecutive generations of Americans have been able to rediscover, revive, and renew strong commitment to the principle of protection of rights of conscience. However, there have been numerous lapses and exceptions, some of which served as painful reminders of the importance of protecting rights of conscience.

It should, therefore, come as no surprise that in our day we are experiencing another controversy over rights of conscience–in this instance the rights of health care professionals not to participate in the provision of elective abortions and other medical services that they believe to be deeply immoral and to be avoided as the result of what they believe to be a fundamental moral duty imposed by God. While

---

[2] Neal A. Maxwell, "Some Thoughts about our Constitution and Government" in *By the Hands of Wise Men: Essays on the U.S. Constitution*, ed. Ray C. Hillam (Provo UT: Brigham Young Univ. Press, 1979), pp. 111, 114: "The Constitution depend[ed] on a sufficient number of strong citizens for its very establishment; it will depend, likewise, on a crucial mass of strong and able citizens for its preservation.... Societies composed of strong citizens willing and able to maintain freedom and to cope with its frustrations are not common."

there are many dimensions of the current controversy, if we are to be true to our legacy of liberty we must remember the history of protection for rights of conscience in our legal system and decide the current controversies according to the principles that undergird and sustain our constitutional system of liberties.

II. Current Controversy Over ACOG Ethics Opinion No. 385

A. *Background of the Current Controversy*

The tension between the rights of patients and the rights and responsibilities of healthcare providers is as old as the history of medicine. Hypocrites attempted to address and resolve the tension over 2400 years ago with his famous Oath.[3] In recent years, developments making abortion safer and assisted reproduction more effective have increased the occasion for such conflicts in the provision of "reproductive" medicine.[4]

The current rights-of-conscience controversy came to a head in November 2007 when the Committee on Ethics of the American College of Obstetricians and Gynecologists published its Opinion No. 385, entitled "The Limits of Conscientious Refusal in Reproductive

---

[3] See, e.g., *Encyclopedia Britannica Online*, "Hippocratic oath," available at http://www.britannica.com/eb/article-9040542/Hippocratic-oath (last seen 14 May 2008); NOVA Online, "Hippocratic Oath–Classical Version," available at http://www.pbs.org/wgbh/nova/doctors/oath_classical.html (last seen 14 May 2008).

[4] See generally Lynn D. Wardle, "Protecting the Rights of Conscience of Health Care Providers," 14 *Journal of Legal Medicine* (1993): 177; Robin Fretwell Wilson, "The Limits of Conscience: Moral Clashes over Deeply Divisive Healthcare Procedures," 34 *American Journal of Law & Medicine* 41 (2008); Jessica D. Yoder, Note, "Pharmacists' Right of Conscience: Strategies for Showing Respect for Pharmacists' Beliefs While Maintaining Adequate Care for Patients," 41 *Valparaiso University Law Review* 975, 1009 (2006).

Medicine."[5] The Opinion strongly curtails exercise of the rights of conscience of healthcare providers involving reproductive medicine.

B. *Some Positive Aspects of Opinion No. 385*

There are some positive aspects of Opinion No. 385. First, it is a public acknowledgment by an influential professional organization, the American College of Obstetricians and Gynecologists (herein "ACOG"), of the existence of some of the ethical dilemmas in this area. Second, it gives some tacit recognition (if weak and superficial) to the existence of moral claims of conscience by healthcare providers in some of these dilemmas. Third, it purports to try to balance and protect the interests conscience of healthcare providers. Fourth, the opinion avoids nasty hyperbole and name-calling and generally is professional in tone. All of these points represent important, if small, steps in the right direction for which ACOG deserves due credit.

C. *Some of the Flaws of ACOG Ethics Opinion No. 385*

The flaws and failings of Opinion No. 385, however, are substantial and far outweigh its few and slender merits.[6] First, the language of the Opinion No. 385 is heavily slanted. For example, a computer search of the document reveals that the term "right" appears in the five-page text of the Opinion ten times; seven times in reference to (unqualified)

---

[5] American College of Obstetricians and Gynecologists, Committee on Ethics, Committee Opinion No. 385, "The Limits of Conscientious Refusal in Reproductive Medicine" (Nov. 2007), available http://www.acog.org/from home/ publications/ ethics/co385.pdf (last seen 12 May 2010).

[6] For some additional critiques of the ACOG Opinion, see, e.g., Christopher Kaczor, "Pro-Life Doctors: A New Oxymoron," *First Things* (online), April 8, 2008, available at http://www.firstthings.com/onthesquare/?p=1021 (last seen 12 May 2008); "Letter written to ACOG President from Christian Medical and Dental Association (CMDA) President" (7 December 2007) http://www.cmda.org/AM/Template.cfm? Section= Right of Conscience&TEMPLATE=/CM/ContentDisplay.cfm&CONTENTID=1 1270 (last seen 12 May 2008); Felipe E. Vizcarrondo, "Physicians Freedom of Conscience Threatened," available at http://www. physiciansforlife.org/content/ view/1548/83/ (last seen 12 May 2008).

"patients' rights" (including "women's rights" and "reproductive rights"); twice in reference to physician's *claimed* right to refuse to provide abortion services (not even acknowledging that healthcare providers actually have a *bona fide* right of conscience, but only that they claim such a right),[7] and once in suggestively warning that healthcare providers' "[r]ights to withdraw from caring for an individual should not be a *pretext* for interfering with patients' rights to healthcare services"[8] (rhetorically labeling the exercise of a right of conscience to refuse to provide abortion service, for example, as a "*withdraw[al] of caring* for an individual" and suggesting that it may be a mere "*pretext* for interfering with patient's rights"). This is hardly the language of honest, fair, even-handed, unbiased (or ethical) analysis.

The substance of Opinion No. 385 is seriously flawed, incomplete, and profoundly prejudiced. Paragraph two gives four examples of cases where healthcare providers declined to provide service but casts three of the four as toggle-switch either-or dilemmas, without even mentioning any possible alternative.[9] Two of the examples involved pharmacists who declined to provide "emergency contraception," but the Opinion failed to indicate whether other pharmacists in the pharmacy were available to provide the service, or whether other pharmacies were nearby that were willing to fill the prescriptions. Another example involved a doctor who declined to provide artificial insemination for a lesbian seeking to become a mother with her same-sex partner, but the Opinion failed to indicate whether other doctors were available in the area who might be willing to provide the

---

[7] *Id.* at 1 ("claim a right to refuse"); *id.* at 2 ("the particular claim to a provider's right to protect his or her moral integrity...").

[8] Opinion No. 385, at 5 (emphasis added). This is the only time that genuine right-versus-right is acknowledged, and it is coupled with the biased suggestion that the physician's conscience claim may be "pretextual."

[9] *Id.* at 1.

service.[10] This failure is important because it means that the Opinion initially casts the issue as one in which the alternatives available and the burdens involved are largely irrelevant to professional ethics; the only significant variables are the patient's desire for a medical service that is legal and that a healthcare provider is competent to provide. For persons seriously interested in analyzing real moral conflicts, the ability to resolve a dilemma with only minor inconvenience to the patient (such as a patient making a telephone call to ascertain the facts, or driving down the street to another pharmacy or another ob/gyn clinic) or to the provider (such as expecting the provider to clearly post and advertise the moral policy boundaries and practical limits of the services offered) is not insignificant. The extent of the burden or damage caused or avoided is a legitimate moral consideration.

The Opinion states its intent to "maximize accommodation of an individual's religious or moral beliefs *while avoiding* impositions of these beliefs on others or interfering with the safe, timely, and financially feasible access to reproductive health care that all women deserve."[11] However, the qualification of the initial stated objective –"to maximize accommodation"–creates a very different objective–one in which "accommodation" is guaranteed to lose. The poison is in the "while avoiding" language, which states an absolute condition– namely, "avoiding" what follows. The "imposition of beliefs upon others" and "interfering with the safe, timely, and financially feasible access to reproductive health care" are absolutely to be avoided. To "avoid" means "to remove, to quit,"[12] "to clear out, put away,

---

[10] The fourth example did mention that the patient was transferred to another hospital where the abortion was performed, thus acknowledging an alternative, but it emphasized hardship (transfer by ambulance), delay ("ultimately") and health risk ("a life-threatening pulmonary embolism").

[11] *Id.* at 2 (emphasis added).

[12] Oxford English Dictionary online, *avoid, v.*, at II, available at http:// dictionary.oed.com.proxlaw.byu.edu/cgi/entry/50015569?query_type=word&queryword=avoid&first=1&max_to_show=10&sort_type=alpha&result_place=3&search_id=KrhO-PFyVLV-10753&hilite=50015569 (last seen 14 May 2008).

remove,"[13] "to get rid of, clear away, do away with, put an end to,"[14] to "expel, banish, dismiss, send or drive away,"[15] "to "keep away from, keep from,"[16] and "to prevent, to obviate, to keep off."[17] Thus, the conscience of providers is to be accommodated only to the ("maximum") point at which such accommodation prevents, keeps away from, removes, quits, puts an end to, gets rid of, banishes, and obviates imposing beliefs upon patients or interference with a patient's safe, timely, and financially feasible access to abortion, for example. Taking those assumptions as "givens" that must be avoided, the result of "accommodation" of the rights of conscience of providers–namely, subordination and sacrifice of conscience to the dominant goal of insuring easy access to abortion–is assured.

The Opinion posits that failure of a particular healthcare provider to facilitate or provide a particular service to a particular patient at a particular time for an affordable price constitutes an act of interference. That is a flawed assumption. For example, it fails altogether to consider whether the distinction between active and passive behavior, long recognized in moral and ethical discourse, might be relevant to the moral analysis.[18] Moreover, why should a person who qualifies for

---

[13] *Id.* at 4.

[14] *Id.* at 4.c.

[15] *Id.* at 5.

[16] *Id.* at III.

[17] *Id.* at 10.

[18] See, e.g., Tom L. Beauchamp & James F. Childress, *Principles of Biomedical Ethics* (New York NY: Oxford University Press, 1979), pp. 82-85; James Rachels, "Active and Passive Euthanasia" in *Ethical Issues in Death and Dying*, ed. Tom L. Beauchamp & Seymour Perlin (Englewood Cliffs NJ: Prentice-Hall, 1978), p. 240; Tom L. Beauchamp, "A Reply to Rachels on Active and Passive Euthanasia," *id.* at p. 246; John A. Robertson & Norman Frost, "Passive Euthanasia of Defective Newborn Infants: Legal and Moral Considerations," *id.* at p. 259; but see Barry Furrow, et al., *Health Law* No. 17-74 at 762 (1995) (distinction is vague and anachronistic).

a medical license be morally or ethically required to provide any patient with any service the patient wants if it is legal? Do all state-licensed anesthetists have an ethical duty if called upon (or if employed) by the government to administer lethal drugs to fulfill a death sentence imposed by a court? Do all gynecologists or family doctors have an ethical duty to perform female circumcision at the behest of parents where it is legal? Do all surgeons have a duty to perform sex-change surgery when their patients want it? Does the failure to provide those requested medical services constitute acts of interference? Why? The Opinion simply assumes the answer without analyzing it.

The Opinion also assumes a broad "right" of patients to physician assistance in obtaining abortions. In fact, the Supreme Court has never held that there is a constitutional right to abortion, only that other general constitutional rights (such as the right of privacy, the right to "liberty," or, arguably, a right to "autonomy") prevent the state from criminally prohibiting or unduly burdening access to abortion services. Abortion is merely a means to that constitutionally protected end, not the end "right" itself.[19] Nor has the Court ever held that healthcare providers have general legal or constitutional duty to perform, assist, or facilitate abortion, as Opinion Number No. 385 mistakenly assumes.

The notion that all obstetricians and all gynecologists have a duty to avoid interference with a patient's safe, timely, and financially feasible access to reproductive healthcare is, at the least, a very tenuous and highly debatable proposition. For example, Congress has generally prohibited (and the Supreme Court has upheld those restrictions on) "partial birth abortion,"[20] which ACOG officially considers to be legitimate reproductive healthcare. ACOG's leaders adopted a formal policy opposing laws restricting partial-birth

---

[19] See *Planned Parenthood of Southern Pennsylvania v. Casey* 510 US 1309 (1994), *Planned Parenthood of Central Missouri v. Danforth* 428 US 52 (1976), and *Roe v. Wade* 412 US 113 (1973).

[20] *Gonzales v. Carhart*, 127 S. Ct. 1610 (2007).

abortion.[21] ACOG also filed an unsuccessful brief with the Supreme Court of the United States in the *Gonzales v. Carhart* case arguing that the federal law restricting partial-birth abortion was unconstitutional.[22] ACOG's brief argued that not only the Act of Congress prohibiting partial-birth abortion was unconstitutional, but noted that ACOG has "consistently opposed bans such as the Act [of Congress],"[23] on the basis of health-risk allegations that the Supreme Court resoundingly rejected as unconvincing as applied to women seeking partial-birth abortions generally.[24]

There are numerous other flaws in the ACOG Ethics Opinion. The definition of "conscience" given in the Opinion is a weak, subjective version (e.g., "I wouldn't be able to sleep at night").[25] It fails even to consider the much stronger matter of divine or moral compulsion claimed by healthcare providers of faith (e.g., "I will disobey God and be eternally damned"). Opinion No. 385 adds a cheap, if politically obligatory, suggestion that claims of conscience "are not always genuine." That diversion simply evades consideration of the real dilemma and suggests a fallacious justification for failure to adequately protect rights of conscience (one that is repeated in the recommendations of the Opinion). Because "referral to another provider *need not be* conceptualized as a repudiation or compromise of one's own values,"[26] the Opinion declines to analyze the issue morally. Of course, the moral dilemma arises because it *can be* so

---

[21] "ACOG Statement of Policy, Abortion Policy" (July 2004), reprinted in ACOG, *2006 Compendium of Selected Publications* (2006), cited in Brief of the American College of Obstetricians and Gynecologists, *infra* note 18.

[22] Brief of the American College of Obstetricians and Gynecologists as Amicus Curiae Supporting Respondents, in *Gonzales v. Carhart* (Sept. 20, 2006), available in Westlaw at 2007 WL 1135596 (last seen 14 May 2008).

[23] *Id.* at 1.

[24] 127 S.Ct. at 1635-37.

[25] ACOG Opinion, *supra* note 5, at 2.

[26] *Id.*

conceptualized; it adds nothing to serious moral analysis to dismiss an argument just because "it need not be" so viewed, or just because other people can view it differently.

In defining the limits upon healthcare providers' exercise of conscience, the Opinion, again, assumes the answer to the question it is asking. It states that in all cases in which a providers' "conscientious refusals conflict with moral obligations that are central to the ethical practice of medicine, ethical care requires either that the physician provide care despite reservations or that there be resources in place to allow the patient to gain access to care...."[27] That is because the provider's conscience "is only a *prima facie* value, which means it can and should be overridden" when necessary to protect patient autonomy.[28] Why do consumer-patient claims to specific medical services (particularly elective services) override the moral claim of a particular healthcare provider to exercise her right of conscience not to engage in what she considers morally reprehensible practices? Again, the Opinion fails to analyze (let alone justify) the conclusion, but merely asserts a set of conclusory assumptions.

This section of the Opinion discusses four criteria that ACOG advises should be considered in the ethical analysis: potential for imposition on the autonomy of patients, effect on the health of the patient, consistency of the moral claim with scientific integrity and knowledge, and potential for discrimination in the distribution of medical services to the poor and members of unpopular groups. These are valid considerations, but all fall on only one side of the ledger–in favor of subordination of health provider's rights of conscience.[29] There is no discussion of similar considerations on the other side of the question, such as degree of imposition on the conscience of the provider, effect on the moral self-identify and human dignity of the

---

[27] *Id.* at 3.

[28] *Id.*

[29] See generally Letter, *supra* note 6 (emphasizing one-sided bias in the Opinion).

provider, consistency of claims of access with medical knowledge about the necessity of the service to the health of the patient and upon the welfare of others affected (such as co-parents of the embryo or fetus, or the children created by Artificial Reproductive Techniques (ART), and the potential for discrimination against unpopular or minority groups (such as doctors of faith, or of a particular faith). The analysis in this section of the Opinion is not merely incomplete, it is blatantly dishonest and biased (presenting the case for one side of the issue but not presenting the other side of the issue). It fails the minimum ethical standards for serious academic or professional analysis. It is nothing more than an advocacy brief for one side of a complex issue.

The next section posits that institutions and organizations should work to "ensure nondiscriminatory access" to all professional services.[30] Rather than attempting to implement its asserted concern for "accommodation" of provider conscience, the Opinion boldly suggests that "individuals and organizations should support" discriminatory hiring, assignment, and institutional approval practices that would deny individual and institutional healthcare providers of faith or moral conscience the opportunity to provide healthcare services.[31] The easiest way to resolve the dilemma is to eliminate from medical practice those who claim rights of conscience, according to the Opinion. That may be cynical, but it is hardly a responsible ethical position.

The final section recommends seven principles, including a call for legal action "ensuring timely, effective, evidence-based and safe access to all women seeking reproductive services."[32] That is fine political rhetoric but shabby moral analysis. The first principle, not surprisingly, is that:

---

[30] *Id.* at 4-5.

[31] *Id.* at 5.

[32] *Id.*

In the provision of reproductive services, the patient's well-being must be paramount. Any conscientious refusal that conflicts with a patient's well-being should be accommodated only if the primary duty to the patient can be fulfilled.[33]

So much for "maximum accommodation" of rights of conscience. Actually, if the standard of "patient's well-being" were not defined on the basis of such avidly pro-abortion ideological assumptions, and if the living human embryo or fetus ("unborn child" as we like to say) were included within the class covered by the term "patients," this principle would merit serious consideration. However, in the context of Opinion No. 385, this high-sounding language amounts to little more than political code words for pressuring and marginalizing healthcare providers with moral objections to abortion-on-demand. The rhetoric simply masks and deceives by assumption and definition but without analysis.

The Opinion also recommends that healthcare provides have a duty to "disclose" information that conforms to ACOG's value-based characterizations, to give prior notice of their conscience commitments, to refer patients to providers who will provide services that the first provider will not provide, to provide all "emergency" case "regardless of the provider's personal moral objections,"[34] and a duty of providers in resource poor areas to practice near providers who will provide the morally offensive services, or by referral to "ensure...that patients have access to the service...."[35] In short, all of the elements necessary to facilitate full access to abortion-on-demand at the hands of all medical professionals are dressed up as principles to justify the suppression and elimination of the rights of conscience of healthcare providers to object to performing or facilitating abortion-on-demand. It seeks to compel all members of ACOG to become accessories to abortion regardless of their moral convictions.

---

[33] *Id.*

[34] *Id.* at number 5.

[35] *Id.* at number 6.

Thus, the flaws of ACOG Ethics Opinion No. 385 are numerous. As a matter of ethical analysis, it is weak, biased, evades the central issues, filled with conclusory assumptions and provides little serious analysis. It is written more like a press release for the advocates of a political campaign than a careful consideration of the competing concerns underlying the moral and ethical issues.

Perhaps the most serious defect of the ACOG Opinion is its failure to grasp, let alone to analyze, the nature, depth and dimensions of the claim for protection of healthcare providers' rights of conscience. ACOG presents that merely as a claim for accommodation, based on principles of professional expediency. That flies in the face of the legal positions that can be traced back to critical decisions made by the Founders of the American Republic. The Founders of our Constitution recognize that protection for rights of conscience involves a matter of basic human *rights*, not mere policy expediency.

When our nation was established, the Founders had two different models for protecting conscience. One addressed the issue as a matter of political balancing, accommodation, and toleration. The other saw it as a matter of protection of inalienable *rights*. The Founders chose the latter, and our Nation has flourished to the extent it has been true to that vision of *rights* of conscience. The drafters of the ACOG Opinion espouse a position about protecting conscience that has been rejected and repudiated for over two centuries in our legal tradition.

III. The Pre-Constitutional and Constitutional Foundations for Protection of Conscience

The wide swath of protection of conscience in the history of the settling of America and the founding of the Constitution is directly relevant to the protection of rights of conscience of healthcare providers today. In at least six ways the history of rights of conscience in colonial- and founding-era America have profound implication for protection of rights of conscience in healthcare provision by constitutional values if not constitutional rights today.

First, the settling of America by many colonies of religious communities and individuals seeking freedom of conscience provided the moral foundation for the rights and structures of the Constitution of the United States that evolved out of those experiences. That history gives our current system of constitutional liberties coherent meaning. "Stories of origins have great significance in any society...."[36] From the Pilgrims, the Puritans and other religious groups who immigrated to and congregated in America that they might live according the precepts of their dissenting religious consciences, to Roger William's remarkably successful attempt to establish a colony in which rights of conscience were fully protected, to the establishment of Maryland as a place where other unpopular religious communities could live the tenets their religions unmolested, to the founding of Pennsylvania as a place where Quakers could freely practice their beliefs, to the amazing influx of Anabaptists, Dutch Calvinists, Scotch Irish Presbyterians, Quakers, and others, the story of the settling of America is in very significant part the story of a quest for a place, a community, and a polity in which rights of conscience would be fully protected.[37] Protection of religious conscience was a major reason for the settling

---

[36] Aviam Soifer, "Full and Equal Rights of Conscience," 22 *University of Hawaii Law Review* 469, 473-77 (2000), reviewing story of importance of rights of conscience in the Founding of America. See also Timothy L. Hall, "Roger Williams and the Foundations of Religious Liberty," 71 *Brigham Young University Law Review* 455 (1991), reviewing the importance of Roger Williams's contribution to religious liberty, how it contrasted with the approach of Thomas Jefferson).

[37] Michael W. McConnell, "The Origins and Historical Understanding of Free Exercise of Religion," 103 *Harvard Law Review* 1409, 1421-1430 (1990), reviewing colonial history of protection of rights of conscience; see generally Harrop A. Freeman, "A Remonstrance for Conscience," 106 *University of Pennsylvania Law Review* 806, 806 n.1 (1958), describing incident that led to the Flushing Remonstrance of 1657 in which citizens of that New York community defied their governor to protect their rights of conscience and those of the persecuted Quakers who came to preach among them, and sequel incident involving the conviction, ordered deportation, and subsequent acquittal of John Bowne who joined the Quakers and let them meet in his home.

of America and central concern in colonial America.[38] Six of the American colonies (not counting any of the New England settlements) had been initially founded to provide havens for religious dissenters.[39] As young John Adams explained, "[s]oon after the Reformation a few people came over into the new world *for conscience sake.*"[40] From that foundation in pursuit of conscience, the nineteen year-old Harvard College student presciently predicted that "*this (apparently) trivial incident may transfer the great seat of empire into America.*"[41] Adams, like his contemporaries, saw a direct link between protection of conscience and political-economic progress and prosperity.

Second, recent scholarship by Noah Feldman sheds light on the tremendous influence of liberty of conscience, derived from Lockean philosophy, in the colonial and founding eras.[42] Feldman shows that Locke's argument for liberty of conscience had religious roots

> in the Protestant idea of the primacy of the individual conscience in decisions about matters of religious faith. Its philosophical roots lay in the division of the world into differently-constituted temporal and spiritual realms. Under this division, the temporal power lacked legitimate authority to compel dissenters' conscience in the realm of religion, because no one had alienated to the temporal government their rights in matters of religion....[43]

Professor Feldman's article traces "the archeology" of the idea of liberty of conscience in Western thought, from biblical text and

---

[38] See "Bloudy Tenent of Persecution for Cause of Conscience Discussed" (Roger Williams, 1644), and "The Great Cause of the Liberty of Conscience" (William Penn, 1650) cited in Freeman, *supra* note 37, at 808.

[39] McConnell, *supra* note 37, at 1424-1425, citing Rhode Island, Maryland, Pennsylvania (and its offshoot, Deleware) and the Carolinas.

[40] David McCullough, *John Adams* (New York NY: Simon & Schuster, 2001), p. 39 (emphasis added).

[41] *Id.* (Emhasis added).

[42] Noah Feldman, "The Intellectual Origins of the Establishment Clause," 77 *New York University Law Review* 346 (2002).

[43] Feldman, *supra* note 42, at 350–51.

exegesis,[44] through the foundational Christian theologians,[45] through the Reformation,[46] and into arguments for government toleration of dissenting religions in seventeenth-century England and America.[47] Locke's powerful *A Letter Concerning Toleration* built an argument from the premises that governments are formed by individuals to protect their life, liberty, and property and have no authority over other matters, including religion or conscience, and that since "no man can, if he would, conform his faith to the dictates of another," because salvation results only from freely-made choices, so government has no authority to compel religion even for the salvation of souls.[48] Feldman points out that Locke's "dependence on religious arguments, grounded in reason," presented what had previously been articulated as a theological principle of Christian liberty in political and legal terms, laying the foundation for the later recognition of personal conscience as a natural right.[49] He shows that despite centuries of differing interpretations and theologies, by the founding era Americans of all

---

[44] Feldman, *supra* note 42, at 355-56, Jerome's commentary on Ezekiel 1:14.

[45] Feldman, *supra* note 42, at 356-57, emphasizing Thomas Aquinas's notion that acting against conscience was to sin.

[46] Feldman, *supra* note 42, at 358-63, noting Luther's notion of Christian liberty through Christ to follow conscience instead of law, Calvin's doctrine primacy of internal conscience in religious matters over "indifferent" external things like law, and Cambridge Puritan William Perkin's teaching that only God could bind conscience regarding matters of salvation.

[47] Feldman, *supra* note 42, at 363-67, noting Baptist pamphlets, the Westminster Confession chapter "Of Christian Liberty, and Liberty of Conscience" declaring that "God alone is Lord of the Conscience" and that human law only may restrain conscience according to God's word or as to indifferent things, and the debate between John Cotton and Roger Williams , who argued that his expulsion and the punishment of dissenting religionists was a denial of liberty of conscience.

[48] Feldman, *supra* note 42, at 368-69. Locke's influence on American ideas also came through his drafting of the "Fundamental Constitutions" of Carolina for Lord Ashby, which broadly protected rights of conscience not only of mainstream and dissenting Christians, but also of Jews and heathens. McConnell, *supra* note 37, at 1428-30.

[49] Feldman, *supra* note 42, at 369-72.

creeds and persuasions had united in the belief, based on Lockean principles, that in matters of religious duty the state had no authority to compel individual conscience.[50] With Locke, the protection of rights of conscience took a giant step forward.

Third, it is critical to understand that in America in the late eighteenth century, two different views about matters of conscience and religion were competing.[51] One view was that protection of conscience was a matter of utilitarian tolerance, just policy, and prudent political accommodation.[52] In some of his early writing, at least, Thomas Jefferson advocated this approach: Respect matters of conscience and religion was a matter of *toleration*–sound public policy, neighborliness, good will, and expedient politics. As Jefferson wrote in his draft of the Virginia Bill for Establishing Religious Freedom:

> Almighty God hath created the mind free, and manifested his supreme will that free it shall remain by making it altogether unsusceptible of restraint; that all attempts to influence it by temporal punishments, or burthens, or by civil incapacitations, *tend only to beget habits of hypocrisy and meanness,* and are a departure from the plan of the holy author of our religion.[53]

---

[50] Feldman, *supra* note 42, at 350–51. "Major portions of Jefferson's Bill for Establishing Religious Freedom derived from passages in Locke's first *Letter Concerning Toleration*." McConnell, *supra* note 37, at 1430-31

[51] Dawn Hendrickson Steadman, "The Free Exercise Clause and Original Intent: A View Toward Exemptions," for *Origins of the Constitution*, Winter Semester 2000.

[52] "Locke recognized that religious intolerance was inconsistent with both public peace and good government, and deemed religious revelry and intolerance to be among the most severe political problems of his day.... The way to avoid such strife[, wrote Locke,] is by assuring toleration and liberty of religious practice for all." J. David Bleich, "The Physician as a Conscientious Objector," 30 *Fordham Urban Law Journal* 245, 248-49 (2002). However, Locke advocated "legislative supremacy with respect to conflicts between public power and individual conscience and reject[ed] religious exemptions." McConnell, *supra* note 37, at 1433.

[53] Thomas Jefferson, A Bill for Establishing Religious Freedom (1779), reprinted in *The Papers of Thomas Jefferson*, vol. 2, ed. Julian P. Boyd (Princeton NJ: Princeton University Press, 1950), pp. 545-56, cited in Feldman, *infra*, note 42, at 392.

From this perspective, liberty of conscience should be respected to avoid "hypocrisy and meanness."

On the other hand, James Madison spoke of matters of conscience and religion not merely as toleration but as fundamental, natural *rights*.[54] It makes a big difference whether respect for another's moral convictions is given simply as a matter of tolerance (to be suspended when outweighed by other political considerations, for example, in time of emergency), or whether it is a matter of your neighbor's basic civil rights. Fortunately, Madison's view prevailed and the Founders ultimately concluded that protection for conscience was a matter of fundamental right. Early colonial charters and state constitutions spoke of it as a right.[55] The Virginia Declaration of Rights was initially drafted to guarantee "fullest toleration" of religion; but Madison amended it and when it passed, it provided that "all men are *entitled to* the full and free exercise of [religion] according to the dictates of conscience." Madison's *Memorial and Remonstrance* expressed the language of rights, not toleration: "The equal *right* of every citizen to the free exercise of his Religion according to the dictates of conscience is *held by the same tenure with all our other rights*."[56] He explained:

> The Religion then of every man must be left to the conviction and conscience of every man; and it is the right of every man to exercise it as these may dictate.... It is

---

[54] McConnell, *supra* note 37, at 1449, contrasting Jefferson's and Madison's views of conscience protection.

[55] McConnell, *supra* note 37, at 1449, Locke's view of tolerance of conscience took the view of the government, while the American proponents of rights of conscience took the view of the believer; Founders took the latter view also.

[56] James Madison, *Memorial and Remonstrance Against Religious Assessments*, ¶15, reprinted in *Everson v. Bd. of Ed.*, 330 U.S. 1, 65-66 (Rutledge, J., dissenting) (emphasis added). *Id.* at ¶ 1: "The Religion then of every man must be left to the conviction and *conscience* of every man; and it is the *right* of every man to exercise it as these may dictate. This *right* is in its nature an *unalienable right*" (emphasis added).

the duty of every man to render to the Creator such homage, and such only, as he believes to be acceptable to him.[57]

Madison saw the individual's right of conscience tied to and derive from his pre-existing and superior duty to God.[58]

In Federalist No. 10 Madison further acknowledged that one way to prevent the abusive influence of "factions" in government would be "by giving to every citizen the same opinions, the same passions, and the same interest."[59] But he summarily rejected this solution as both unwise and impractical because he considered "[t]he protection" of such "diversity" of "faculties," "interests,' and "views" to be "the first object of government...."[60] The principal duty of government in Madison's view is to protect not only the difference in talents, interests, and abilities that produce differences in wealth, education, and influence, but also to protect the different "sentiments and views of the respective proprietors [that] ensures a division of the society into different interests and parties."[61] He also noted that the "liberty" that producces factions "is to faction what air is to fire...,"[62] but to eliminate liberty in order to control faction would be a "remedy that...was worse than the disease."[63]

Fortunately, the protection-of-conscience-as-a-policy-of-tolerance was superseded by protection-of-conscience-as-a-fundamental-right.[64]

---

[57] *Id.* at ¶ 1.

[58] See *supra* note 56 and accompanying text. See also McConnell, *supra* note 37, at 1494-1500.

[59] *The Federalist Papers* No. 10 (Madison), ¶4 (New York NY: New American Library 1961), p. 78.

[60] *Id.* at ¶6.

[61] *Id.*

[62] *Id.* ¶5.

[63] *Id.*

[64] "George Washington, in his famous address to the Hebrew Congregation of

(Ironically, some courts and most commentators today have slipped into using the language of toleration and accommodation. It is time for us to reassert emphatically the language of rights.)

Fourth, protection for rights of conscience underlay and historically preceded the First Amendment.[65] The Revolutionary War spurred the quest for protection of rights of conscience in several ways. In June 1776, even before the Declaration of Independence, the Virginia Declaration of Rights provided, *inter alia*, that "all men are equally entitled to the free exercise of religion, according to the dictates of conscience...."[66] During the War of Independence, rather than suspend respect for divergent moral views, many states granted exemptions from conscription to persons with religious scruples against war, such as Quakers and Mennonites.[67] In 1775, the Continental Congress granted a general exemption from military conscription to religious groups.[68] Also, the main established church

---

Newport, RI, stated: 'It is now no more that toleration is spoken of, as if it was by the indulgence of one class of people, that another enjoyed the exercise of their inherent natural rights. More pungently, Thomas Paine commented: 'Toleration is not the *opposite* of intolerance, but is the *counterfeit* of it. Both are despotisms. One assumes to itself the right of withholding liberty of conscience, and the other of granting it.'" McConnell, *supra* note 37, at 1434-44.

[65] Joseph L. Hassan, "Freedom of Conscience in Early Virginia: A Precursor to the Religion Clauses of the First Amendment," paper submitted for *Origins of the Constitution*, Apr. 17, 1998 (copy in author's possession).

[66] Kermit Hall, et al., American Legal History: Cases and Materials 70 (1996).

[67] This was not the first time conscientious objection from military service had been recognized. Many of the 600 colonial laws establishing and regulating militias had "regularly embodied clauses exempting conscientious objectors, either absolutely or conditionally." Freeman, *supra* note 37, at 809.

[68] "General recognition of the importance of conscience at the time of the Revolution is illustrated by the resolution of the Continental Congress, July 18, 1775: "As there are some people, who, from religious principles, cannot bear arms in any case, this Congress intend no violence to their consciences, but earnestly recommend it to them, to contribute liberally in this time of universal calamity, to the relief of their distressed brethren in the several colonies, and to do all other services to their oppressed country, which they can consistently with their religious principles."

in America (Anglican), which had opposed rights of conscience, was associated with the oppressive enemy, and the break with England enhanced the status of the fiercely patriotic dissenting religious communities who advocated protection for their rights of religious conscience, such as the Baptists.[69] After centuries of government support for the state church in Virginia, the Baptists led a petition campaign demanding that "every tax upon conscience...be abolished."[70] In 1779, Thomas Jefferson introduced his Bill for Establishing Religious Freedom in the Virginia Legislature (House of Burgesses). It declared that "to compel a man to furnish contributions of money for the propagation of opinions which he disbelieves, is sinful and tyrannical."[71] (If Jefferson thought that about merely funding things against one's will, one can imagine what he would say about being compelled to perform, provide, or facilitate delivery of services or products like abortion or the "morning after pill" (MAP) against one's conscience!) Jefferson's Bill did not pass for over six years, but in December 1785, while Jefferson was Minister to France, James Madison engineered passage of Jefferson's Bill. As finally enacted it declared that "no man shall be...molested or burdened in his body or his good, nor shall otherwise suffer on account of his religious opinions or belief...and that the same shall in no wise diminish, enlarge

---

Freeman, *supra* note 37, at 809.

[69] McConnell, *supra* note 37, at 1436-42.

[70] Hassan, *supra* note 65, at 12.

[71] Preamble to the Virginia Bill for Religious Liberty, cited in *Everson v. Bd. of Ed.*, 330 U.S. 1, 12-13 (1946).

or effect their civil capacity."[72] Thus, it provided expansive protection for rights of religious conscience.

Professor John Witte concurs that at the time of the Founding of America freedom of conscience guaranteed "a freedom and exemption from human impositions and legal restraints in matters of religion and conscience,"[73] and that it required that persons be exempt or immune from civil duties and restrictions that they could not, in good conscience, accept or obey.[74] Professor Michael W. McConnell has noted that before the Constitution was adopted, every state except Connecticut had adopted state constitutional protection for rights of religious exercise "in terms of the conscience of the individual believer and the actions that flow from that conscience."[75]

Thus, protection of rights of conscience is deeply rooted in and intertwined with the fundamental First Amendment rights guaranteeing free exercise of religion and no establishment of religion.[76] Of course, the best example is the protection of conscience as a right is inclusion of the right to free exercise of religion in the First Amendment of the Bill of Rights.[77] While there is room for debate over the degree to

---

[72] Thomas Jefferson, "A Bill for Establishing Religious Freedom – June 12, 1779," in *The Founders' Constitution*, vol. 5, ed. P. Kurland and R. Lerner (Chicago IL: Univ. of Chicago Press, 1987), p. 77. So proud was Jefferson of his role in securing protection for rights of conscience that he asked that his gravestone be inscribed: "Thomas Jefferson, Author of the Declaration of Independence, of the Statute of Virginia for Religious Freedom, and Father of the University of Virginia."

[73] John Witte, "The Essential Rights and Liberties in the American Constitutional Experiment," 71 *Notre Dame Law Review* 371, 391, quoting John Mellen, *The Great and Happy Doctrine of Liberty* (1795), p. 17.

[74] Witte, *supra* note 73, at 391-92.

[75] McConnell, *supra* note 37, at 1458-59; see generally *id.* at 1455-66.

[76] See generally McConnell, *supra* note 37, at 1466-1500, reviewing history of Free Exercise clause.

[77] James Madison was the Father of the Bill of Rights. See generally Richard G. Wilkins, "The Structural Role of the Bill of Rights," 6 *Brigham Young University Journal of Public Law* 525 (1992).

which the "free exercise" of religion clause of the First Amendment protects rights of conscience,[78] it is clear that

> [t]he phrase "liberty of conscience" was often conflated with the phrase "free exercise of religion," "religious freedom," "religious liberty," "religious privileges," or "religious rights." James Madison, for example, simply rolled into one linguistic heap "religious freedom" or "the free exercise of religion according to the dictates of conscience."[79]

Indeed, the state "conciliatory amendments" (ratifying the Constitution but asking that it be amended to explicitly protect certain fundamental rights) which led to the drafting of the First Amendment expressly asked for "rights of conscience" to be protected in the Bill of Rights.[80] That is the purpose for which the religion clauses of the First Amendment were drafted.

Even the Establishment Clause was intended to protect rights of conscience. Noah Feldman has challenged the conventional wisdom about the reasons for the Establishment Clause of the Constitution (i.e., that rationalists thought state control of churches was bad for the state, religionists thought it bad for churches, even though republicans generally believed civic virtue essential and looked to religion to cultivate virtue).[81] Instead he makes a strong case that the Lockean

---

[78] The history of the writing of the First Amendment and the differing language used in the various drafts "casts doubt on the suggestion of some commentators that the constitutional term "religion" should be broadly interpreted in order to encompass secular claims of conscience. Regardless of whether such a broad interpretation would be a good idea, such a step would constitute an amendment, not an interpretation, of the First Amendment, and one that the Framers specifically considered, debated, and ultimately rejected." Michael W. McConnell, "The Problem of Singling Out Religion," 50 *DePaul Law Review* 1, 12 (2000)(citations omitted). See also *id.* at 1494-1500.

[79] Witte, *supra* note 73, at 390, quoting Va. Bill of Rights of 1776, art. XVI.

[80] Freeman, *supra* note 37, at 810, citing language from the New Hampshire, Virginia, North Carolina, Rhode Island, and New York ratifying conventions.

[81] Feldman, *supra* note 42, at 349-50.

value of "[l]iberty of conscience...was the central value invoked by the states that proposed constitutional amendments on the question of religion, and the purpose that underlay the Establishment Clause when it was enacted."[82] He shows that "by the late eighteenth century, American rationalists and evangelicals alike argued, in terms identifiably derived from Locke, that the purpose of non-establishment was to protect the liberty of conscience of religious dissenters from the coercive power of government."[83] Despite earlier differences in ideology and policy among the communities and colonies, "*by the late eighteenth century it was broadly agreed in the colonies that there was a basic, indeed natural, right called liberty of conscience.*"[84] "[O]n the eve of the Constitution" regardless of religious or ideological faction, Americans all "shared a basic theory of religious liberty and drew on the same sources and Lockean ideas to express their views."[85] From 1787, when the Constitution was proposed, to 1789 when the Bill of Rights was proposed by the First Congress, "the predominant, not to say exclusive, argument against established churches was that they had

---

[82] Feldman, *supra* note 42, at 351.

[83] Feldman, *supra* note 42, at 350–51. Feldman's article suggests that Howe's taxonomy of competing strands of religious thought in colonial America has obscured "the broad agreement in post-revolutionary America on a Lockean concept of liberty of conscience." *Id.* at 373. Feldman traces the development of consensus on the right of conscience from about 1690 until "by the late eighteenth century, some version of Locke's basic view of the nature of the liberty of conscience had been formally embraced by nearly every politically active American writing on the subject of religion and the state." *Id.* at 378 Reviewing the well-documented differences in state patterns of creating and supporting established churches in the eighteenth century are reviewed, Feldman notes that "liberty of conscience" was invoked in the battles over support of established churches in Massachusetts and Virginia. *Id.* at 379-84.

[84] Feldman, *supra* note 42, at 374 (emphasis added).

[85] Feldman, *supra* note 42, at 384. Writings of eighteenth-century Puritans (both criticizing and defending the New England Way), Baptists (John Leland, Isaac Backus, William McLoughlin, and others), Enlightened Deists (Thomas Jefferson and James Madison), and Civil Republicans (whose purported endorsement of government support for established religion is questioned by Feldman) broadly agreed that liberty of conscience was the key to church-state relations. *Id.* at 384-98.

the potential to violate liberty of conscience."[86] The Virginia ratifying convention proposed an amendment to the Constitution linking protection of conscience directly to non-establishment:

> That religion, or the duty which we owe to our Creator, and the manner of discharging it, can be directed only by reason and conviction, not by force of violence; and therefore all men have an equal, natural, and unalienable *right to the free exercise of religion, according to the dictates of conscience,* and that no particular religious sect of society ought to be favored or establish, by law, in preference to others.[87]

Likewise, multiple drafts of the First Amendment in Congress reflected the linkage among conscience, freedom of religion, and establishment.[88] While the term "conscience" was dropped from the final version of the First Amendment, the inclusion of free exercise of religion and no establishment of religion together "were thought to cover all the ground required to protect the liberty of conscience,"[89] and the theoretical basis for both religion clauses in protection of rights of conscience remained "even after the word "conscicnce" disappeared from the draft language."[90] There was "broad agreement that liberty of conscience was a basic, inalienable right," and "[l]iberty of conscience was the basic principle that underlay the arguments for non-establishment at the federal level."[91] Other scholars agree that the

---

[86] Feldman, *supra* note 42, at 398.

[87] Feldman, *supra* note 42, at 401, quoting *The Debates in the Several State Conventions on the Adoption of the Federal Constitution, as Recommended by the General Convention at Philadelphia, in 1787*, vol. 3, ed. Jonathan Elliot (Philadelphia PA: J.B. Lippincott, 1901), p. 659. North Carolina and Rhode Island "proposed almost identical language." Feldman, *supra* note 42, at 401.

[88] Feldman, *supra* note 42, at 401-04.

[89] Feldman, *supra* note 42, at 404.

[90] *Id.*

[91] Feldman, *supra* note 42, at 405. Likewise, both neo-federalist and post-modern structuralist arguments that the First Amendment was intended to bar Congress for interfering with state establishment of religion or to take any position on the problem

ultimate dropping of the term "conscience" from the First Amendment resulted from "later revisions [that] were revisions only of language which all agreed carried out the [intent to protect religious conscience]."[92]

Professor Feldman's work places liberty of conscience at the core of First Amendment jurisprudence, especially central to the Establishment Clause.[93] While it does not guarantee outcomes in particular cases,[94] and while the modern conception of liberty of conscience includes some deeply held secular principles as well as purely religious principles,[95] "knowing how these ideas got their start in our constitutional context makes all the difference in the world."[96] Certainly, it holds significance for the debate over protecting rights of conscience of healthcare providers.

Fifth, the principle of liberty of conscience underlay the notion of a self-governing republic. Thus, when an effort to revive the religion tax in Virginia was made after the War of Independence, James Madison drafted his famous *Memorial and Remonstrance* declaring that certain things like religious duties "must be left to the conviction and conscience of every man; and it is the right of every man to

---

of funding of religion fail the test of historical evidence. *Id.* at 406-12.

[92] Freeman, *supra* note 37, at 812. Professor McConnell suggests that "conscience" was dropped to limit the protection to religiously-motivated acts. McConnell, *supra* note 37, at 1494-1500.

[93] Feldman, *supra* note 42, at 412-17, examining "coercion" as possible test for Establishment suggesting advantages with caution.

[94] "While the Framers certainly understood protection of liberty of conscience to undergird the Establishment Clause, and all agreed that, in principle, coercion of conscience was wrong, there was, we have seen, no clear consensus on hard questions of whether certain forms of government support of religion should be understood as coercing conscience." Feldman, *supra* note 42, at 416. *Id.* at 416-27, examining funding of religious institutions.

[95] Feldman, *supra* note 42, at 424-27, noting trend toward and historical and logical problems of secularizing the protection of conscience.

[96] Feldman, *supra* note 42, at 428.

exercise it as these may dictate."[97] He explained why in terms that underscore the foundational nature of rights of conscience:

> Before any man can be considered as a member of Civil Society, he must be considered as a subject of the Governor of the Universe: And if a member of a Civil Society, who enters into any subordinate Association, must always do it with reservation of his duty to the general authority; much more must every man who becomes a member of any particular Civil Society, do it with a saving of his allegiance to the Universal Sovereign.[98]

Here Madison brilliantly linked the moral tradition of a right to tolerance traceable from John Locke with the basic human rights tradition that had blossomed and evolved powerfully in America, especially since the Declaration of Independence. Madison clearly understood that if men are not loyal to themselves, to their conscience, to their God and their moral duty as they see it, it is utterly irrational folly to expect them to be loyal to less compelling moral obligations of legal rules, statutes, judicial orders, or the claims of citizenship and civic virtue, much less professional duties.[99] If you demand that a man betray his conscience, you have eliminated the only moral basis for his fidelity to the rule of law and have destroyed the moral foundation for democracy.[100]

---

[97] *Id.*

[98] James Madison, *Memorial and Remonstrance*, *supra* note 56, at ¶1.

[99] "[T]he evidence suggests that the theoretical underpinning of the free exercise clause, best reflected in Madison's writings, is that the claims of the "universal sovereign" precede the claims of civil society, both in time and in authority, and that when the people vested power in the government over civil affairs, they necessarily reserved their unalienable right to the free exercise of religion, in accordance with the dictates of conscience. Under this understanding, the right of free exercise is defined in the first instance not by the nature and scope of the laws, but by the nature and scope of religious duty." McConnell, *supra* note 37, at 1512.

[100] Jefferson agreed. He famously explained: "The rights of conscience we never submitted, we could not submit. We are answerable for them to our God." Thomas Jefferson, "Notes on Virginia," in *The Life and Selected Writings of Thomas Jefferson*, ed. Adrienne Koch & William Peden (New York NY: Modern Writings

Seventh, the founders understood that requiring men to violate and disregard their conscience resulted in the loss of virtue, which undermined the basis for self-government.[101] Most of the political traditions the Founders consulted emphasized that no self-governing republic could exist without a high degree of virtue in the citizenry.[102] Thus, the founders of the American Constitution were convinced that virtue in the citizenry was absolutely essential, indispensable for this system of government to function and survive. A few quotes from the Founders makes this point.

George Washington famously noted: "Tis substantially true, that virtue or morality is a necessary spring of popular government. The rule indeed extends with more or less force to every species of Free Government. Who then is a sincere friend to it, can look with indifference upon attempts to shake the foundation of the fabric?"[103]

Samuel Adams agreed that "neither the wisest constitution nor the wisest laws will secure the liberty and happiness of a people whose manners are universally corrupt."[104]

Benjamin Franklin, in the Constitution Convention of 1787, voiced his concern that although the new government would likely "be well administered for a course of years," it would "end in Despotism, as other forms have done before it, when the people have become so corrupted as to need some despotic Government, being incapable of

---

1944), p. 275, cited in Steven D. Smith, "The Rise and Fall of Religious Freedom in Constitutional Discourse," 140 *University of Pennsylvania Law Review* 149, 164 n. 58 (1991).

[101] Richard Vetterli & Gary Bryner, *In Search of the Republic, Public Virtue and the Roots of American Government*, rev. ed. (Totowa NJ: Rowman & Littlefield, 1996).

[102] Charles L. de Secondat (Baron de Montesquieu), *The Spirit of the Laws*, Book 3, ch. 3, tr. T. Nugent (New York NY: Hafner, 1952): "[I]n a popular state, one spring more is necessary..., namely, *virtue*."

[103] George Washington, Washington's Farewell Address from Saul Padover, *The Washington Papers* (searched Sept. 9, 1999).

[104] *Id.*

any other." On another occasion, he said: "Only a virtuous people are capable of freedom. As nations become corrupt and vicious, they have more need of masters."[105]

James Madison told delegates to Virginia's ratifying convention: "To suppose that any form of government will secure liberty or happiness without any virtue in the people, is a chimerical idea."[106] He also wrote in *Federalist* No. 57: "The aim of every political Constitution is or ought to be first to obtain for rules men who possess most wisdom to discern, and most virtue to pursue, the common good of society; and in the next place, to take the most effectual precautions for keeping them virtuous whilst they continue to hold their public trust."

John Adams clearly warned: "Our constitution was made only for a moral and religious people. It is wholly inadequate to the government of any other."[107] He also said: "Liberty can no more exist without virtue and independence than the body can live and move without a soul."[108]

Edmund Burke, the English contemporary of and sympathizer with the American Founders, may have explained it best when he wrote:

> Men are qualified for civil liberty in exact proportion to their disposition to put moral chains on their own appetites; in proportion as their love of justice is above their rapacity; in proportion as their soundness and sobriety of understanding is above their vanity and presumption; in proportion as they are more disposed to listen to the councils of the wise and good, in preference to the flattery of knaves. Society cannot exist unless a controlling power upon the will and appetite be placed somewhere, and the less of it there is within, the more there must be without. It is ordained in the

---

[105] Richard Vetterli & Gary Bryner, "Public Virtue and the Roots of American Government," 27 *BYU Studies*, 29, 41 (Summer 1987).

[106] *Id.*

[107] J. Howe, *The Changing Political Thought of John Adams* (Princeton NJ: Princeton Univ. Press, 1966), p. 165.

[108] *The Works of John Adams*, vol. 10, p. 284.

eternal constitution of things, that men of intemperate minds cannot be free. Their passions forge their fetters.[109]

The political philosophy of the Founding directly linked virtue with republication (self-) government; if the constitutional republic was to survive, virtue had to be cultivated in the populace. If virtue were to be cultivated, individual conscience had to be nurtured and protected, for only the free exercise of conscience can generate the virtue necessary to sustain a free republic. Thus, protection of the rights of conscience went to the core of the Constitution.

This also explains the limitation on protection of conscience from the colonial era, through the Founding era, and down to the present. That is a limitation for acts that are licentious and contrary to good morals or disruptive of the public peace or safety.[110] The protection of conscience to cultivate virtue does not provide a "wild card" to let people engage in behavior that is destructive of the political community.

V. Conclusion

There are good utilitarian reasons for protecting the rights of conscience of all healthcare providers. As one commentator put it, "a physician's professional conscience, derived from personal and professional experiences, plays a vital role in the way in which a doctor interacts with his or her patients."[111] Of course, this is not

---

[109] R. Vetterli & G. Bryner, "Introduction: Public Virtue and the Roots of Republican Government," *In Search of the Republic, Public Virtue and the Roots of American Government* at p. 1, quoting from *The Works of the Right Honorable Edmund Burke* (Boston MA: Little, Brown & Co., 1866), pp. 51-52.

[110] McConnell, *supra* note 37, at 1461, describing state constitutional protections of conscience' "nine of the states limited the free exercise right to actions that were 'peaceable' or that would not disturb the 'peace' or 'safety' of the state."; see generally *id.* at 1461-1466, describing the limitations in state constitutions on protection of religious conscience.

[111] Judith F. Daar, "A Clash at the Bedside: Patient Autonomy v. A Physician's Professional Conscience," 44 *Hastings Law Journal* 1241, 1245 (1993), suggesting

limited to physicians; the same principle is true of other healthcare providers as well. Likewise, "[i]f patient autonomy is to have meaning, recognition must also be given to a physician's moral autonomy," because without protection of conscience medical response is constrained.[112]

But the more important reason why rights of conscience of healthcare providers must be protected is much deeper and much more fundamental than optimizing medical service. It is because rights of conscience are basic human rights, and protection of rights of conscience goes to the very core of the history, purpose, and structure of our system of liberties and of our constitutional government. As one commentator put it: "Integrity of conscience and professional judgment are moral rights of physicians. Society and patients have an obligation to respect them."[113]

In an infamous law review article about the marginalization of religion and toleration only of innocuous religious practices in the public square, Professor Michael W. McConnell identified one reason why such blatant disregard of the rights of conscience of healthcare providers seems to be so rampant today. It relates to the cultural values that dominate our time:

> In *Thus Spake Zarathustra*, Nietzsche's mythic hero carries the... message–"God is dead!"–throughout the earth, in a parody of the gospels, calling it his "gift" to mankind. But there is one exception. The book begins with an encounter between Zarathustra and a holy man living alone in the forest. Zarathustra asks the hermit

---

need to hear, recognize and address health providers moral concerns, and favoring transfer when possible; at 1245; see also Bryan A. Dykes, Note, "Proposed Rights of Conscience Legislation: Expanding to Include Pharmacists and other Health Care Providers," 36 *Georgia Law Review* 565, 565 (2002): "the emphasis on patient autonomy has created an environment in which some patients request and expect to receive whatever treatments they desire."

112 Daar, *supra* note 111, at 1289.

113 Edmund D. Pellegrino, "Patient and Physician Autonomy: Conflicting Rights and Obligations in the Physician-Patient Relationship," 10 *Journal of Contemporary Health Law & Policy* 47, 68 (1993).

what he does in the forest, and the hermit replies: "I make hymns and sing them; and in making hymns I laugh and weep and mumble: thus do I praise God. With singing, weeping, laughing, and mumbling do I praise the God who is my God.' The hermit then asks Zarathustra what he had brought as a "gift." Zarathustra, surprisingly, does not take up this invitation to tell the hermit the terrible truth of the death of God. Instead he says, evasively, "What should I have to give thee! Let me rather hurry hence lest I take aught away from thee!" And Zarathustra leaves the old man to worship in peace. This is the story of religious freedom in the post-modern world...

Zarathustra's toleration was toward one who neither participated in public life nor entered public discourse. No such forbearance was shown to anyone in the village. If the hermit left the forest and attempted to enter into public discussion and debate, he would be given the news of God's death like everyone else.

Can we recognize in Zarathustra the enlightened attitude toward religious faith in our age? Religious freedom is to be protected, strongly protected–so long as it is irrelevant to the life of the wider community. But allow religion to affect the law pertaining to, say, abortion; or allow religion to affect the way we educate our children in our communities' schools; even allow religion to affect the way we celebrate holidays in public, and there is trouble. When these quaint and discredited beliefs spill over into the life of the community, we have crossed the line. Religion, the Supreme Court has told us on more than one occasion, is "a private matter for the individual, the family, and the institutions of private choice." Religion in public is at best a breach of etiquette, at worst a violation of the law. Religion is privatized and marginalized. It has nothing to offer to the public sphere. We will not interfere with solitary hermits in the forest, but they must stay out of the public square.[114]

Healthcare providers who assert rights of conscience are not like the quaint and impotent hermit in Nietzsche's tale. Rather, their exercise of their beliefs can upset and threaten the worldview and the plans of those who seek to normalize and facilitate controversial medical procedures such as abortion (to name one practice) as much as the abolitionists' exercise of their beliefs upset and threatened the worldview and wishes of slave-owners in 1859. So it is unlikely that those who oppose protection of rights of conscience for healthcare providers will simply change their minds and cease their attacks in the near future.

---

[114] Michael W. McConnell, "God is Dead and We Have Killed Him!": Freedom of Religion in the Post-Modern Age," 1993 *Brigham Young University Law Review* 163, 163-65.

The history of the founding of our nation and the intellectual history of the ideas upon which it was erected reveal that protection of rights of conscience is the keystone in the arch of our constitutional system. Conscience and the virtue it nurtures hold the entire system of constitutional rights together. Thus, what ultimately is at stake in the growing disputes over healthcare providers' rights of conscience, and concerning ACOG Ethics Opinion No. 385, is more than just the interests of those individuals and that industry. The structure of our system of individual liberties is founded on respect for liberty of conscience.

Thomas Jefferson said: "We may consider each generation as a distinct nation, with a right, by the will of its majority, to bind themselves, but none to bind the succeeding generation, more than the inhabitants of another country."[115] It was also Jefferson who said: "Nothing...is unchangeable but the inherent and inalienable rights of man."[116] Jefferson apparently believed that each generation would have to discover for itself those unchangeable, inherent, and inalienable basic human rights, such as rights of conscience. Our generation must discover those truths. We must defend rights of conscience of healthcare providers against attacks such as that presented by ACOG Ethics Opinion No. 385 not only to protect those individuals, and not merely to be faithful to the legacy of liberty we have inherited, but we must do so for the sake of future generations whose constitutional liberties depends upon preservation of rights of conscience.

---

[115] Thomas Jefferson to John Wayles Eppes, 1813, in *Favorite Jefferson Quotes*, available at http://www.whatreallyhappened.com/RANCHO/POLITICS/DOCUMENTS/JEFFERSON/jeff1.html (last seen 12 May 2008).

[116] Thomas Jefferson to John Cartwright, 1824, in *Favorite Jefferson Quotes*, *id.*

Assessing the Legal Bases for Conscientious Objection in Healthcare

Richard S. Myers

ABSTRACT: The problem of rights of conscience in healthcare is one of the most serious religious freedom issues in the United States. There are increasing pressures on healthcare professionals to conform their conduct to a secular vision of healthcare, even in situations when such professionals have a conscientious objection to facilitating, participating in, or performing various procedures. This paper evaluates the legal bases for conscientious objection in healthcare. Under current law, there is inadequate protection for those healthcare professionals who have religious and moral objections to governmental mandates. There is a pressing need for comprehensive protection for rights of conscience. Perhaps paradoxically, an effort to protect religious conscience has some risks because of the current pressures to privatize religion. In the long run, rebuilding a pro-life culture is the only sure protection for pro-life healthcare professionals.

I. INTRODUCTION

It is a pleasure for me to serve as one of the commentators on Lynn Wardle's paper.[1] Lynn has been one of the leading legal commentators on these issues for quite some time; he wrote an influential article on this topic back in 1993.[2] His most recent paper is another very helpful contribution to the debate on rights of conscience. I think the principal virtue of the paper is its very effective and

---

[1] Lynn D. Wardle, "Rights of Conscience Versus Peer-Driven Medical Ethics: ACOG and Abortion," in *Life & Learning XVIII: Proceedings of the Eighteenth University Faculty for Life Conference*, ed. J. Koterski (2011), pp. 21-51.

[2] Lynn D. Wardle, "Protecting the Rights of Conscience of Healthcare Providers," 14 *Journal of Legal Medicine* 177 (1993).

compelling critique of the ACOG statement.[3] That statement is being re-evaluated and I believe that criticisms such as Lynn's will prompt a revision in that statement. Lynn's paper also is quite effective in detailing the historical background and support for rights of conscience.

One thing that is noteworthy about Professor Wardle's paper is that he says very little about the current legal situation. That may be because the news is so depressing. Despite the historical support for conscience, the current situation provides very little protection, at least not as a matter of constitutional law.[4]

In these comments, I will explain the current legal situation. I will also explain why the movement to protect religious conscience has some risks. I will explain why I think this effort to protect conscience ought still to be pursued while we also pursue the strategy of rebuilding a pro-life culture, which in the long-run is the only sure protection for healthcare professionals who are pro-life.

II. BACKGROUND: THREATS TO CONSCIENCE

The problem of rights of conscience in healthcare is one of the most serious religious freedom issues that now exists in the United States. In many ways, there are profound ironies about this. The

---

[3] In November 2007, the Committee on Ethics of the American College of Obstetricians and Gynecologists issued an Opinion (No. 385) entitled "The Limits of Conscientious Refusal in Reproductive Medicine." http://www.acog.org/from home/publications/ethics/co385.pdf.

[4] See generally, Richard S. Myers, "United States Law and Conscientious Objection in Healthcare," in *Cooperation, Complicity, and Conscience: Moral Problems in Healthcare, Science, Law, and Public Policy*, ed. Helen Watt (London UK: Linacre, 2005), pp. 296-315. [Hereinafter Myers, Linacre paper.] This paper is largely drawn from my earlier treatment of the topic in the Linacre paper. I will update the analysis here as appropriate. For a more extended treatment of recent developments, see also Richard S. Myers, "Current Legal Issues Regarding Rights to Conscience in Healthcare," *Josephinum Journal of Theology* 16/2 (2009): 394-410.

legal system in the United States has been characterized as "A Republic of Choice."[5] Appeals to choice (and personal autonomy) tend to dominate public policy debates. The rhetoric of choice is exceedingly powerful, and it is difficult to resist its appeal. I think this point is evidenced by the way in which "choice" is invoked by all sides of the political spectrum. It is no accident that those in favor of abortion rights and those in favor of school vouchers both refer to themselves as movements of "choice."[6]

Appeals to choice are very common in bioethics. Perhaps the most infamous judicial example occurred in the Court's decision in *Planned Parenthood v. Casey*.[7] There the Court noted: "At the heart of liberty is the right to define one's own concept of existence, of meaning, of the universe, and of the mystery of human life."[8]

This line of thinking has also played a role in the assisted suicide area. In the mid-1990s, one of the lower court opinions addressed the constitutionality of the State of Washington's ban on assisted suicide thus: "This Court finds the reasoning in *Casey* highly instructive and almost prescriptive on the...issue [of a terminally ill person's choice to commit suicide]. Like the abortion decision, the decision of a terminally ill person to end his or her life 'involv[es] the most intimate and personal choices a person may make in a lifetime' and constitutes a 'choice...central to personal

---

[5] Lawrence M. Friedman, *The Republic of Choice: Law, Authority, and Culture* (Cambridge MA: Harvard University Press, 1990).

[6] For a discussion of choice in education, see Richard S. Myers, "School Choice: The Constitutional Issues," *Catholic Social Science Review* 8 (2003): 167. It is noteworthy that in early 2003, one of the major abortion rights organizations, the National Abortion and Reproductive Rights Action League, changed its name to NARAL Pro-Choice America. See http://www.naral.org.

[7] 505 U. S. 833 (1992). For criticism of Casey, see Michael Stokes Paulsen, "The Worst Constitutional Decision of All Time," 78 *Notre Dame Law Review* 995 (2003).

[8] 505 U. S. at 851.

dignity and autonomy.'"[9]

In its 1997 decisions on assisted suicide,[10] the Supreme Court did reject reliance on this broad language from *Casey* in concluding that there was no federal constitutional right to assisted suicide.[11] The Court's majority there seemed to confine the use of the language to the limited context of abortion.[12]

Somewhat surprisingly, however, the Supreme Court resurrected this language in its decision in *Lawrence v. Texas*.[13] In *Lawrence*, the Texas case involving homosexual sodomy, the Court relied on *Casey*'s more expansive approach without so much as mentioning the assisted suicide cases.[14] As Justice Scalia pointed out in his *Lawrence* dissent, this language (which he described as

---

[9] *Compassion in Dying v. Washington*, 850 F. Supp. 1454, 1459-1460 (W. D. Wash. 1994)(quoting Casey, 505 U. S. at 851), rev'd, 49 F. 3d 586 (9th Cir. 1995), rev'd, 79 F. 3d 790 (9th Cir. 1996)(en banc), rev'd sub nom. *Washington v. Glucksberg*, 521 U. S. 702 (1997).

[10] See *Washington v. Glucksberg*, 521 U. S. 702 (1997); *Vacco v. Quill*, 521 U. S. 793 (1997).

[11] *Glucksberg*, 521 U. S. at 728.

[12] *Id.* The *Glucksberg* Court seemed to adopt a far more restrained approach to judicial review. See Richard S. Myers, "Physician-assisted Suicide: A Current Legal Perspective," *National Catholic Bioethics Quarterly* 1 (2001): 349; Michael W. McConnell, "The Right to Die and the Jurisprudence of Tradition," 1997 *Utah Law Review* 665.

[13] 539 U. S. 558, 573-574 (2003).

[14] In Justice Kennedy's majority opinion, there is neither a citation to nor a discussion of the assisted suicide cases. In his dissenting opinion, Justice Scalia noted that "Roe and Casey have been equally 'eroded' by *Washington v. Glucksberg*, ...which held that *only* fundamental rights which are 'deeply rooted in this Nation's history and tradition' qualify for anything other than rational basis scrutiny under the doctrine of 'substantive due process.'" 539 U. S. at 588 (Scalia, J., dissenting). For a detailed discussion of the ways in which Lawrence departs from *Glucksberg*, see Robert C. Post, "Foreword: Fashioning the Legal Constitution: Culture, Courts, and Law," 117 *Harvard Law Review* 4, 91-107 (2003).

the Court's "famed sweet-mystery-of-life passage"[15]) threatens the constitutionality of nearly all morals legislation.[16] We see, yet again, the almost overwhelmingly powerful appeal of the language of choice and of "an autonomy of self."[17]

The idea is, of course, that the state must remain neutral on these basic moral choices. In fact, some even celebrated the statement in *Casey* as support for the idea that moral relativism is a constitutional command.[18] Under this view, morality is purely private, purely subjective. The state must remain neutral about the content of the individual's choice. The state must remain indifferent toward whether the pregnant woman chooses life or death.[19] It is considered a sufficient answer to these questions to leave these matters entirely to the realm of subjective choice. You see this on bumper stickers: "Don't like abortion, don't have one"–as if that adequately resolved the underlying moral question.

Yet, this is a false neutrality. On the issue of abortion, for example, the state must decide whether an unborn child is a person entitled to the full protection of the law. This is not a matter that can adequately be dealt with by falsely pretending not to decide whether an unborn child is a human being entitled to legal protection.[20] For

---

[15] 539 U. S. at 588 (Scalia, J., dissenting).

[16] Justice Scalia noted that the Court's approach "effectively decrees the end of all morals legislation." 539 U. S. at 599 (Scalia, J., dissenting).

[17] See generally Richard S. Myers, "Pope John Paul II, Freedom, and Constitutional Law," 6 *Ave Maria Law Review* 61 (2007). This article comments critically on the Supreme Court's cases that embody the extreme autonomy view. The article discusses the impact of *Lawrence v. Texas* and notes that most subsequent lower court opinions have not yet read *Lawrence* broadly. Myers, *supra*, at 72-77.

[18] See Stephen G. Gey, "Is Moral Relativism a Constitutional Command?," 70 *Indiana Law Journal* 331 (1995).

[19] Myers, *supra* note 12, at 346.

[20] This error is common. In *Roe v. Wade*, 410 U. S. 113 (1973), Justice Blackmun

as Pope John Paul II stated in *Evangelium Vitae*, "when freedom is detached from objective truth it becomes impossible to establish personal rights on a firm rational basis; and the ground is laid for society to be at the mercy of the unrestrained will of individuals or the oppressive totalitarianism of public authority."[21] Cardinal Ratzinger, before he became Pope Benedict XVI, made this point with great force a number of years ago. He stated: "One sees...that the idea of an absolute tolerance of freedom of choice for some destroys the very foundation of a just life for men together. The separation of politics from any natural content of right, which is the inalienable patrimony of everyone's moral conscience, deprives social life of its ethical substance and leaves it defenseless before

---

noted: "We need not resolve the difficult question of when life begins. When those trained in the respective disciplines of medicine, philosophy, and theology are unable to arrive at a consensus, the judiciary, at this point in the development of man's knowledge, is not in a position to speculate as to the answer." 410 U. S. at 159. In an article published several years ago, Professor Whitman made the same error. She stated: "The constitutional question posed by abortion cannot be 'when does life begin.' Legal analysis cannot answer that question, so it cannot be the test or doctrinal structure on which the right to abortion hinges." Chris Whitman, "Looking Back on Planned Parenthood v. Casey," 100 *Michigan Law Review* 1791, 1995 (2002). The problem with this false gesture of humility is that a decision is being made about the status of the unborn. The *Roe* Court later noted that "we do not agree that, by adopting one theory of life, Texas may override the rights of the pregnant woman that are at stake." 410 U. S. at 162. The Court reached this conclusion because it had its own theory of human life that it enshrined into the law. The Court in *Roe* was in fact concluding that the unborn child could not legally be regarded as a human person entitled to the full protection of the law. Whatever this is, it is assuredly not a failure to decide the question. For a critique of Professor Whitman's article, see Richard S. Myers, "Reflections on "Looking Back on *Planned Parenthood v. Casey*," in *Life and Learning XIII: The Proceedings of the Thirteenth University Faculty for Life Conference*, ed. J. Koterski (Washington, D.C.: UFL, 2003), pp. 3-19.

[21] Pope John Paul II, *Evangelium Vitae* (1995) §96, available at http://www.vatican.va/holy_father/john_paul_ii/encyclicals/documents/hf_jp_ii_enc_25031995_evangelium-vitae_en.html.

the will of the strongest."[22]

We see this playing out in the United States. What begins with an appeal to "choice" and to freedom quickly moves to the will of the strongest prevailing, in large part by certain powerful individuals turning to the "oppressive totalitarianism of public authority." We have seen this in dramatic fashion with regard to abortion. Defended first as a private choice, we quickly saw moves to require that taxpayers (even those with a moral objection) pay for abortions.[23] Although the Supreme Court rejected the view that this was required by the Constitution,[24] this has been mandated by a number of states.[25] We have also increasingly seen moves to make participation in or facilitation of abortion mandatory.[26] We now see "choice" becoming compulsory.[27] These efforts to violate con-

---

[22] Joseph Cardinal Ratzinger, "Doctrinal Document on Threats to Life Proposed," *Origins* 20 (1991): 757, available at http://www.priestsforlife.org/magisterium/threatstohumanlife.htm#ratzinger.

[23] John T. Noonan, Jr., *A Private Choice: Abortion in America in the Seventies* (New York NY: Free Press, 1979), p. 191.

[24] *Harris v. McRae*, 448 U. S. 297 (1980); *Maher v. Roe*, 432 U. S. 464 (1977).

[25] In *Humphreys v. Clinic for Women, Inc.*, 796 N. E. 2d 247 (Ind. 2003), the Indiana Supreme Court concluded that the Indiana Constitution required the funding of abortions in certain limited cases. One Justice, who thought that the majority's opinion did not go far enough, noted that "[t]welve of the seventeen state courts that have considered the issue in published opinions have concluded that denial of benefits to indigent women for medically necessary abortions is a violation of their state constitutions. Under prevailing constitutional doctrine in this state, I would reach the same result." *Id.* at 264-65 (footnote omitted)(Boehm, J., concurring in part and dissenting in part). As Justice Boehm notes, this conclusion has been rejected by some states. See, e.g., *Bell v. Low Income Women of Texas*, 95 S. W. 3d 253 (Tex. 2002).

[26] See, e.g., "The Campaign to Force Hospitals to Provide Abortion" (September 2003), Fact Sheet prepared by United States Conference of Catholic Bishops, Secretariat for Pro-Life Activities, available at http://www.usccb.org/prolife/issues/abortion/threat.pdf.

[27] See Myers, Linacre paper, *supra* note 4, at 300.

science are becoming increasingly widespread, as the ACOG statement illustrates.[28]

The trends in this area are quite troublesome.[29] There is an increasing pressure to conform to the secular vision of healthcare and morality. While some of these initiatives have been defeated and while some of these measures contain exemptions for those with an objection to being forced to participate in these procedures, the plight of those who adhere to a moral vision that was widely shared a hundred years ago is becoming more and more serious.

III. Current Legal Situation

We are increasingly witnessing a comprehensive assault on religious freedom in healthcare. The protection for religious freedom in the United States is, perhaps surprisingly, not comprehensive. The United States is associated with religious freedom. Yet, in most of the situations described above, constitutional protections for religious freedom in the United States provide little protection.

A. *Free Exercise Clause*

To demonstrate this point, I will provide a brief summary of the law in the United States on religious liberty, with a primary focus on the Constitution of the United States. In general, the free exercise clause of the First Amendment provides very little judicially enforceable protection against state laws that mandate conduct that

---

[28] See Christopher Kaczor, "Pro-Life Doctors: A New Oxymoron?," (blog post of April 8, 2008), http://www.firstthings.com/onthesquare/?p=1021. Kaczor notes that under the ACOG Ethics Committee's Opinion, *supra* note 3, doctors would in certain cases be required to perform abortions despite a conscientious objection.

[29] See Myers, Linacre paper, *supra* note 4, at 300-02; see also Wesley J. Smith, "Pulling the Plug on the Conscience Clause," *First Things* 198 (Dec. 2009): 41-44.

might be viewed as interfering with the religious liberty of an individual or an institution. If the state requirement is a "neutral law of general applicability," then (under current law) there is no realistic argument that the Constitution provides any basis to resist the mandate.

The leading case is *Employment Division v. Smith.*[30] *Smith* involved two individuals who were denied unemployment compensation because of work-related misconduct. The workers were fired from their jobs with a drug rehabilitation organization due to their use of peyote, an illegal drug, even though they used peyote for religious purposes. The Supreme Court, in an opinion by Justice Scalia, concluded that Oregon could "include religiously inspired peyote use within the reach of its general criminal prohibitions on use of that drug...."[31] To allow an exemption from laws prohibiting "socially harmful conduct"[32] would allow an individual with a religious objection to such laws "'to become a law unto himself.'"[33]

Under this approach, so long as the state mandate is a neutral

---

[30] 494 U. S. 872 (1990). The *Smith* decision was tremendously controversial. For support of the outcome in *Smith*, see Gerard V. Bradley, "Beguiled: Free Exercise Exemptions and the Siren Song of Liberalism," 20 *Hofstra Law Review* 245 (1991); Lino A. Graglia, "Church of the Lukumi Babalu Aye: Of Animal Sacrifice and Religious Persecution," 85 *Georgetown Law Journal* 1 (1996); Philip A. Hamburger, "A Constitutional Right of Religious Exemption: An Historical Perspective," 60 *George Washington Law Review* 915 (1992); John Harrison, "The Free Exercise Clause as a Rule about Rules," 15 *Harvard Journal of Law & Public Policy* 169 (1992); William P. Marshall, "In Defense of Smith and Free Exercise Revisionism," 58 *University of Chicago Law Review* 308 (1991). For criticism, see, e.g., Douglas Laycock, The Remnants of Free Exercise, 1990 Sup. Ct. Rev. 1; Michael W. McConnell, "Free Exercise Revisionism and the Smith Decision," 57 *University of Chicago Law Review* 1109 (1990); Michael W. McConnell, "The Origins and Historical Understanding of Free Exercise of Religion," 103 *Harvard Law Review* 1409 (1990).

[31] 494 U. S. at 874.

[32] *Id.* at 885.

[33] *Id.*, quoting *Reynolds v. United States*, 98 U. S. 145, 167 (1879).

law of general applicability, then there is no prospect of a court finding that someone with a religious objection to the mandate is exempted from the mandate.

One seeking an exemption from such a mandate would be limited to seeking an exemption from the legislature. Justice Scalia noted that "leaving accommodation to the political process will place at a relative disadvantage those religious practices that are not widely engaged in; [he concluded, though]...that [that] unavoidable consequence of democratic government must be preferred to a system in which conscience is a law unto itself or in which judges weigh the social importance of all laws against the centrality of all religious beliefs."[34]

B. *Free Exercise Clause: Recent litigation involving conscientious objection in healthcare*

Most of the recent litigation dealing with claims of conscience in the area of healthcare has involved the contraceptive mandate issue.[35] Many states have required that employers that provide their employees with health insurance or disability insurance coverage that includes prescription drug benefits must include prescription

---

[34] 494 U. S. at 890.

[35] There has also been much focus on the plight of pharmacists. See generally Jennifer E. Spreng, "Pharmacists and the 'Duty' to Dispense Emergency Contraceptives," 23 *Issues in Law & Medicine* 215 (2008); Nell O. Kromhout, Note, "Crushed at the Counter: Protection for a Pharmacist's Right of Conscience," 6 *Ave Maria Law Review* 265 (2007). Another significant recent case involved doctors who asserted a religious basis for refusing to provide artificial insemination to a lesbian couple. In *North Coast Women's Care Medical Group, Inc. v. San Diego Count Superior Court*, 189 P. 3d 959 (Cal. 2008), the California Supreme Court rejected the argument that the doctors had a free exercise defense to California's law prohibiting discrimination based on a person's sexual orientation. For discussion of this case, see Richard S. Myers, "Current Legal Issues Regarding Rights to Conscience in Healthcare," *Josephinum Journal of Theology* 16/2 (2009): 399-400.

contraceptives in the coverage. These laws typically apply even to most employers with a religious objection to providing such coverage. As long as the contraceptive mandate is applied across the board, those employers with a religious objection to providing such coverage do not have much of a chance of resisting these mandates under the U.S. Constitution. The highest courts of New York and California have rejected religious freedom claims in cases brought by Catholic Charities of the Diocese of Albany and Catholic Charities of Sacramento.[36]

If the mandate is not viewed as a neutral law of general applicability, then the state must satisfy the "strict scrutiny" test, which means that the mandate must be narrowly tailored to meet a compelling government interest. How to decide whether a law fails this "neutral law of general applicability" requirement is an unsettled question.[37] The one Supreme Court case on the issue–*Church of the Lukumi Babalu Aye, Inc. v. City of Hialeah*[38]–involved local laws that were directed at outlawing animal sacrifice as practiced by the Santeria religion. Under the local laws, one could kill an animal for almost any reason except for a religious one,[39] and the laws therefore, were treated and invalidated as a transparent effort to shut down a religion.[40]

---

[36] *Catholic Charities of Sacramento, Inc. v. Superior Court*, 85 P. 3d 67 (Cal.), ccrt .denied, 543 U. S. 816 (2004); *Catholic Charities of Diocese of Albany v. Serio*, 859 N. E. 2d 459 (N. Y. 2006), cert. denied, 128 S. Ct. 97 (2007). See generally Myers, Linacre paper, *supra* note 4, at 305-07.

[37] See generally Christopher C. Lund, "A Matter of Constitutional Luck: The General Applicability Requirement in Free Exercise Jurisprudence," 26 *Harvard Journal of Law & Public Policy* 627 (2003). This article provides citations to the voluminous literature on this topic.

[38] 508 U. S. 520 (1993).

[39] The Supreme Court stated: "[T]he ordinances are drafted with care to forbid few killings but those occasioned by religious sacrifice." 508 U. S. at 543.

[40] The Court stated: "We conclude, in sum, that each of Hialeah's ordinances

In the California and New York cases noted above, the plaintiffs argued that the contraceptive mandates ought to be regarded as transparent efforts to target particular religions (principally the Catholic Church) and that therefore employers with religious objections to these mandates ought to be entitled to an exemption.[41] There were two basic arguments, and the arguments were so closely related that they were really just different versions of the same argument. One argument relied on the fact that the contraceptive mandates contain legislative exemptions, and so arguably the laws fail the "neutral law of general applicability" requirement.[42] The other argument was based on "legislative intent." According to this view, these contraceptive mandates (with or without legislative exemptions) are in reality efforts to attack the Catholic Church and should be viewed as failing the "neutral law of

---

pursues the city's governmental interests only against conduct motivated by religious belief. The ordinances 'have every appearance of a prohibition that society is prepared to impose upon [Santeria worshippers] but not upon itself.'" Id. at 545 (quoting *Florida Star v. B. J. F.*, 491 U. S. 525, 542 (1989)(Scalia, J., concurring in part and concurring in the judgment)). There is a great deal of debate in the literature about whether laws will fail the "general applicability" requirement only in cases that are as extreme as Lukumi. For example, Professor Gedicks interprets Smith and Lukumi narrowly. He has stated: "a religiously neutral law does not fail the test of general applicability merely by being modestly or even substantially underinclusive; rather, the law must be so dramatically underinclusive that religious conduct is virtually the only conduct to which the law applies. The Court will tolerate a tremendous amount of underinclusion before finding that a law is not generally applicable, so long as the underinclusion stops short of religious targeting." Frederick Mark Gedicks, "The Normalized Free Exercise Clause: Three Abnormalities," 75 *Indiana Law Journal* 77, 114 (2000)(footnote omitted). Others take a far broader view. See Richard F. Duncan, "Free Exercise is Dead, Long Live Free Exercise: *Smith*, *Lukumi* and the General Applicability Requirement," 3 *University of Pennsylvania Journal of Constitutional Law* 850 (2001).

[41] *Catholic Charities of Sacramento, Inc. v. Superior Court*, 85 P. 3d at 82-87 (describing and rejecting this argument); *Catholic Charities of the Diocese of Albany*, 859 N. E. 2d at 463-64.

[42] *Catholic Charities of Sacramento, Inc.*, 85 P. 3d at 82-84.

general applicability" requirement.[43]

Both aspects of this argument were considered and rejected in the lawsuit involving California's contraceptive mandate.[44] The law requires that employers that provide their employees with health insurance that includes prescription-drug benefits must include prescription contraceptives in the coverage.[45] The law does contain an exemption for religious employers, but the exemption is basically a smokescreen. In order to qualify for this exemption, an employer needs to satisfy each of the following requirements: (1) the inculcation of religious values is the purpose of the entity, (2) the entity primarily employs persons who share the religious tenets of the entity, (3) the entity serves primarily persons who share the religious tenets of the entity, and (4) the entity is a non-profit organization pursuant to the Internal Revenue Code.[46] It is quite clear that this exemption, which has been characterized as "narrow" by those supporting such mandates,[47] would cover very few–if any–Catholic organizations. It is doubtful, for example, whether many Catholic organizations that provide social services would be able to maintain that the purpose of their entity was to inculcate religious values. Many of these organizations do not employ or serve primarily persons who share the religious tenets of the entity. Think about a hospital or a parish elementary school in the inner city or a

---

[43] *Id.* at 84-87.

[44] *Id.* See also *Catholic Charities of the Diocese of Albany*, 859 N. E. 2d at 463-64.

[45] *Catholic Charities of Sacramento*, 85 P. 3d at 73-75 (describing California's statute).

[46] *Id.*

[47] See "Protecting the Rights of Conscience of Healthcare Providers and a Parent's Right to Know: Hearing on H. R. 4691 Before the House Committee on Energy and Commerce, 107th Cong." (2002)(statement of Catherine Weiss, Director, ACLU Reproductive Freedom Project), available at http://energycommerce.house.gov/107/hearings/07112002Hearing632/Weiss1088print.htm.

soup kitchen or a homeless shelter, none of which likely serves primarily persons who share the religious tenets of the entity. Moreover, the exemption would be very difficult to administer–is the Capuchin soup kitchen supposed to inquire whether the individuals it serves "share the religious tenets of the entity?"[48]

Catholic Charities of Sacramento filed a lawsuit challenging the constitutionality of the California law. As the suit explained, Catholic Charities is not covered by the law's religious exemption. The suit contended that the strict scrutiny test ought to apply because the law should not be treated as a "neutral law of general applicability" since the law, unlike Oregon's prohibition on peyote use involved in the *Smith* case, does contain an exemption and since the law allegedly was "gerrymandered" to reach only Catholic employers.[49] The California courts rejected these arguments,[50] and the Supreme Court refused to intervene.[51]

The California court rulings are not in any way idiosyncratic. I think most courts in the United States would reach the same conclusion.[52] Most courts would agree that the contraceptive

---

[48] In the California litigation, the California Supreme Court explained that "Catholic Charities does not qualify as a 'religious employer' under the...[Act] because it does not meet any of the [statutory] definition's four criteria." *Catholic Charities of Sacramento*, 85 P. 3d at 76. Catholic Charities admitted that it didn't qualify for the exemption. *Id.* The same conclusion was reached in the New York litigation. *Catholic Charities of the Diocese of Albany*, 859 N. E. 2d at 463.

[49] *Catholic Charities of Sacramento*, 85 P. 3d at 84-87.

[50] *Id.*

[51] 543 U. S. 816 (2004).

[52] The New York case confirms this view. See *Catholic Charities of the Diocese of Albany*, 859 N. E. 2d 459. For discussions of the New York situation, see Edward T. Mechmann, "Illusion of Protection? Free Exercise Rights and Laws Mandating Insurance Coverage of Contraception," 41 *Catholic Lawyer* 145 (2001); Susan J. Stabile, "State Attempts to Define Religion: The Ramifications of Applying Mandatory Prescription Contraceptive Coverage Statutes to Religious Employers," 28 *Harvard Journal of Law & Public Policy* 741 (2005);

coverage mandate is a "neutral law of general applicability,"[53] and therefore would fall outside First Amendment protection altogether. Even if a court found that a mandate failed this test (because of the way it evaluated the relevance of any exemptions, for example), it might still conclude that a law passed the strict scrutiny test.[54] This is a test that sounds demanding but did not prove to be so in the religious freedom area prior to the *Smith* case in 1990. As one commentator described the situation, during this era this test was "strict in theory, but ever-so-gentle in fact...."[55]

Susan J. Stabile, "When Conscience Clashes with State Policy: Catholic Institutions," 46 *Journal of Catholic Legal Studies* 137 (2007); Piero A. Tozzi, "When Conscience Clashes with State Policy: Catholic Institutions: A Response to Susan Stabile," 46 *Journal of Catholic Legal Studies* 161 (2007).

[53] *Catholic Charities of the Diocese of Albany*, 859 N. E. 2d at 463-464.

[54] For additional discussion of this issue, see Inimai M. Chettiar, Comment, "Contraceptive Coverage Laws: Eliminating Gender Discrimination or Infringing on Religious Liberties?," 69 *University of Chicago Law Review* 1867 (2002). See also *Catholic Charities of Sacramento*, 85 P. 3d at 89-94 (finding that the California statute survived strict scrutiny under the California Constitution); *Catholic Charities of the Diocese of Albany*, 859 N. E. 2d at 465-468 (finding that the New York statute survived the balancing test applicable under the New York Constitution).

[55] Ira C. Lupu, "The Trouble with Accommodation," 60 *George Washington Law Review* 743, 756 (1992). See Richard S. Myers, "Curriculum in the Public Schools: The Need for an Emphasis on Parental Control," 24 *Valparaiso University Law Review* 431, 436 (1990); see also Michael J. Frank, Note, "Safeguarding the Consciences of Hospitals and Healthcare Personnel: How the Graduate Medical Education Guidelines Demonstrate a Continued Need for Protective Jurisprudence and Legislation," 41 *St. Louis Law Journal* 311, 328-37 (1996), discussing a case in which the court rejected the religious freedom arguments of a Catholic hospital that had its accreditation withdrawn because it refused to provide abortion or sterilization training for its ob/gyn residents. The Supreme Court's decision in *Gonzales v. O Centro Espirita Beneficente Uniao Do Vegetal*, 546 U. S. 418 (2006) suggests that there may be some renewed vigor to the test applicable in this area. For commentary, see Richard Garnett and Joshua D. Dunlap, "Taking Accommodation Seriously: Religious Freedom and the *O Centro* Case," 2006 *Cato Supreme Court Review* 257 (2006).

Another recent case that confirms this assessment is *Storman's Inc. v. Selecky.*[56] In *Storman's,* the Ninth Circuit refused to enjoin the enforcement of regulations in the state of Washington that required pharmacies to dispense Plan B Contraceptives, the so-called morning after pill. The federal district court had enjoined the regulations because the court thought that the regulations targeted religious practice and therefore fell outside the *Smith* rule.[57] The federal court of appeals reversed this ruling. In so holding, the court of appeals emphasized that the regulations were not focused only on those with a religious objection to filling the prescriptions in question. As the court of appeals explained, under current law it does not matter if those with religious objections are disproportionately affected. In addition, the court did not believe that the legislative history supported the claim that the state regulations were enacted with a single purpose of burdening religious practice.[58]

An important reason why the religious freedom claims are likely to fail is that courts in the United States tend to have a very restricted view of religious liberty, even in those situations when the Constitution provides any protection at all. Religion only receives much protection in areas such as religious belief and worship. But when religion is out in the world–running schools or hospitals or homeless shelters–the courts tend to say that it must be treated just like any other entity. Under this view, there is very little room for religious entities to be faithful to their religious identities when they venture out into the public realm; these entities must bow to the

---

[56] 586 F. 3d 1109 (9th Cir. 2009).

[57] 524 F. Supp. 2d 1245 (W. D. Wash. 2007), rev'd, 586 F. 3d 1109 (9th Cir. 2009).

[58] 596 F. 3d at 1131-1134. The court of appeals noted that there is a dispute in the cases about the extent to which courts are permitted to rely on legislative history in free exercise cases. The court did not believe it was necessary to resolve this issue to decide the case. *Id.*

demands of the secular state.

The opinions of the California courts in the *Catholic Charities* case are good examples. For example, the California Supreme Court was untroubled by the statement of the law's sponsor who noted that the law's narrow exemption was intended to cover only the "religious" activities of employers. As the sponsor explained, "[t]he more secular the activity gets, the less religiously based it is, and the more we believe that they should be required to cover prescription drug benefits for contraception."[59] Although the courts typically will say that they will assume that religious individuals and institutions are sincere in claiming a religious basis for objection to a government mandate, the underlying tone of the opinion is that Catholic Charities is not really engaged in a religious practice at all. This is apparent from the testimony at a legislative hearing dealing with rights of conscience in healthcare. An ACLU official stated: "When, however, religiously affiliated organizations move into secular pursuits–such as providing medical care or social services to the public or running a business–they should no longer be insulated from secular laws that apply to these secular pursuits. In the public world, they should play by public rules."[60] The ACLU has issued an official report on this topic entitled "Religious Refusals and Reproductive Rights," and the choice to characterize claims of conscience with the far less appealing label of "religious

---

[59] Catholic Charities of Sacramento, 85 P. 3d at 87. Justice Brown's dissenting opinion objected because she correctly concluded that "[t]he government is not accidentally or incidentally interfering with religious practice; it is doing so willfully by making a judgment about what is or is not religious." *Id.* at 102 (Brown, J., dissenting).

[60] "Protecting the Rights of Conscience of Healthcare Providers and a Parent's Right to Know: Hearing on H. R. 4691 Before the House Committee on Energy and Commerce, 107th Congress" (2002), statement of Catherine Weiss, Director, ACLU Reproductive Freedom Project, available at http://energycommerce.house.gov/107/hearings/07112002Hearing632/Weiss1088print.htm.

refusals" was surely no accident.[61] This Report says that it supports "protecting the religious practices of insular, sectarian institutions while insisting on compliance with general rules in the public, secular world."[62] This is obviously far from any sort of broad acceptance for hospitals and individuals maintaining a strong sense of their religiously informed identities.

Although this separation between religious and secular sides of life is foreign to the self-understanding of many religious men and women, the courts commonly draw this distinction. We have seen this in areas outside the healthcare context. Thus, landlords have been forced to rent to unmarried couples, even when so doing violates the landlord's religious beliefs.[63] The courts that have ruled against these landlords reflect the view that this kind of "commercial" activity is not really religious, or is at any rate not entitled to the protection afforded to "core" religious activity.[64] The cases

---

[61] "Religious Refusals and Reproductive Rights" (2002), available at http://www.aclu.org/files/FilesPDFs/ACF911.pdf.

[62] *Id.* This ACLU Report was updated in 2007. See "Religious Refusals and Reproductive Rights: Accessing Birth Control at the Pharmacy" (April 17, 2007), available at http://www.aclu.org/reproductive-freedom/religious-refusals-and-reproductive-rights-accessing-birth-control-pharmacy. The 2007 Report takes the same basic approach.

[63] See, e.g., *Smith v. Fair Employment and Housing Commission*, 913 P. 2d 909 (Cal. 1996), cert. denied, 521 U. S. 1129 (1997); *Swanner v. Anchorage Equal Rights Commission*, 874 P. 2d 274 (Alaska), cert. denied, 513 U. S. 979 (1994).

[64] The *Swanner* case is illustrative. There, the Supreme Court of Alaska stated: "*Swanner* has made no showing of a religious belief which requires that he engage in the property-rental business. Additionally, the economic burden, or 'Hobson's choice,' of which he complains, is caused by his choice to enter into a commercial activity that is regulated by anti-discrimination laws. *Swanner* is voluntarily engaging in property management. The law and ordinance regulate unlawful practices in the rental of real property and provide that those who engage in those activities shall not discriminate on the basis of marital status. Voluntary commercial activity does not receive the same status accorded to directly religious activity." *Swanner*, 874 P. 2d at 283 (citation omitted).

candidly state that if these landlords do not want to follow the prevailing secular wisdom that they can just get out of the business of being a landlord.[65] The net result is that religious institutions and individuals are being forced to abandon their distinctive missions– either "secularize" their operations or get out of the healthcare field altogether.

C. *Other Legal Bases for Protection of Conscience*

It seems clear that there is no solid basis for claiming that the U.S. Constitution, as currently interpreted, provides significant protection for those with a religious objection to being forced to comply with legislative mandates. There are, however, still some religious freedom arguments that can be made. In certain situations, with respect to federal laws, there are certain statutory protections for religious freedom. In 1993, Congress passed The Religious Freedom Restoration Act as an effort to "overrule" the *Smith* decision.[66] In 1997 the Supreme Court invalidated RFRA as applied to state and local laws,[67] but RFRA still provides a basis to argue for a religious exemption when faced with a federal mandate,[68] although such claims still may not succeed in a court of law.[69] With respect to state and local laws, there may be other possible bases to

---

[65] *Smith*, 913 P. 2d at 925, 928-929.

[66] *City of Boerne v. Flores*, 521 U. S. 507, 512-516 (1997)(describing the Religious Freedom Restoration Act).

[67] *City of Boerne v. Flores*, 521 U. S. 507 (1997).

[68] See *Gonzales v. O Centro Espirita Beneficente Uniao Do Vegetal*, 546 U. S. 418 (2006). In the *O Centro* case, the Court made it clear the RFRA applied to federal statutes. See Lund, *supra* note 37, at 632 n. 26, citing the prior cases that have so held and briefly discussing the controversy about this.

[69] See generally Ira C. Lupu, "The Failure of RFRA," 20 *University of Arkansas Little Rock Law Journal* 575, 585-597 (1998). Professor Lupu's study concluded that "at least insofar as the litigation record demonstrates, RFRA resulted in surprisingly little protection for religion." *Id.* at 597.

argue for a religious exemption. State constitutions sometimes provide broader protection for religious freedom than the federal Constitution, and some states have passed state legislative counterparts to the Religious Freedom Restoration Act.

The other protection for religious conscience arises on a case-by-case basis pursuant to other statutes. In certain contexts, Congress or individual states have provided protections for those with conscientious objection to compliance with legislative mandates. So, for example, in the United States there is fairly strong protection for doctors and nurses who do not wish to perform or participate in abortions.[70]

These case-by-case exemptions have very serious limitations.[71] They tend to only apply with respect to certain procedures and the procedures covered may be interpreted narrowly (so that the morning after pill may not be considered to cause an abortion if the pill acts prior to implantation). These exemptions only cover certain medical personnel. Sometimes these exemptions are limited to institutions and do not even potentially extend to individuals (a Catholic doctor who employs five or six people, for example). These exemptions rarely deal with the serious issues involved in funding of healthcare, which, as the California and New York cases involving contraceptive mandates demonstrate, is more and more

---

[70] See "Protecting the Rights of Conscience of Healthcare Providers and a Parent's Right to Know: Hearing on H. R. 4691 Before the House Committee on Energy and Commerce, 107th Congress" (2002), statement of Lynn Wardle[hereinafter Wardle Testimony], available at http://energycommerce.house.gov/107/hearings/07112002Hearings632/Wardle1089print.htm; Katherine A. White, Note, "Crisis of Conscience: Reconciling Religious Healthcare Providers' Beliefs and Patients' Rights," 51 *Stanford Law Review* 1703, 1705-1711 (1999). But, it is important to note that this strong protection is largely a matter of legislative grace. See Richard S. Myers, "Current Legal Issues Regarding Rights to Conscience in Healthcare," *Josephinum Journal of Theology* 16/2 (2009): 400.

[71] Wardle Testimony, *supra* note 70.

becoming the focal point of the debate. With the exception of the states such as Illinois and Mississippi, which have comprehensive statutes protecting the right of conscience in healthcare, there is no comprehensive protection in the United States. Even in these states, the protection for conscience is not secure because the protection for conscience can be overridden, as we have seen in Illinois with the Governor's actions with respect to requiring pharmacists to dispense Plan B contraceptives.[72]

In sum, the law on conscientious objection is not at all satisfactory. There are some bright spots in narrow areas, but there is no comprehensive protection for religious freedom in healthcare. There is a pressing need for a more comprehensive strategy. One solution would be for a federal law that would provide legal protection for those with a conscientious objection to being forced to comply with a governmental mandate. This has been a non-starter. Even narrower conscience protections are often resisted because they allegedly interfere with the provision of mainstream medical care. These efforts to seek protection for those with a conscientious objection to these mandates are important. In the current legal environment, these efforts to preserve the religious vision of healthcare by invoking the democratic process to protect religious liberty are about all that is available, given the narrow scope of the constitutional law in this area. There arc, perhaps paradoxically, some risks to invoking this religious vision, at least in the way this tends to be articulated.

IV. Risks to Claims for Protecting Religious Conscience

The argument in favor of conscience is often made in terms of the need to promote a genuine pluralism in healthcare–a vision that would protect Catholic or Jewish or Mormon visions of healthcare. I have a lot of sympathy for this view, but I have concerns about

---

[72] See Kromhout, *supra* note 35, at 268-73.

this as well. In many legal or policy discussions on these issues, a "religious" reason for acting is taken as inappropriate.[73] Such a vision is considered to be nonrational[74] or "irrational superstitious nonsense,"[75] in the words of the one of the leading constitutional scholars in the United States. Certainly such a view cannot be the fit subject of public action.

There are many Supreme Court opinions that refer disparagingly to religiously informed moral judgments. Justice Stevens, for example, has expressed the view that the preamble to the Missouri abortion statute, which stated that "the life of each human being begins at conception" and that "unborn children have protectable interests in life, health, and well-being," violated the Establishment Clause.[76] That conclusion was based on the view "that the preamble, an unequivocal endorsement of a religious tenet of some but by no means all Christian faiths, serves no identifiable secular purpose."[77]

His opinion in the *Boy Scouts* case is similar. Justice Stevens

---

[73] See Richard S. Myers, "The Privatization of Religion and Catholic Justices," 47 *Journal of Catholic Legal Studies* 157, 163-65 (2008); Myers, *supra* note 17, at 73; Richard S. Myers, "The United States Supreme Court and the Privatization of Religion," *Catholic Social Science Review* 6 (2001): 228-30. See also Robert P. George, *The Clash of Orthodoxies: Law, Religion, and Morality in Crisis* (Wilmington DE: ISI, 2001).

[74] See Steven G. Gey, "Why is Religion Special? Reconsidering the Accommodation of Religion Under the Religion Clauses of the First Amendment," 52 *University of Pittsburgh Law Review* 75 (1990). In this article, Professor Gey stated: "religion is an alternative system of nonrational and unprovable beliefs. As such, religion is fundamentally incompatible with the critical rationality on which democracy depends." *Id.* at 176.

[75] Suzaanna Sherry, "Outlaw Blues," 87 *Michigan Law Review* 1418, 1427 (1989).

[76] *Webster v. Reproductive Health Services*, 492 U. S. 490, 566 (1989)(Stevens, J, concurring in part and dissenting in part).

[77] *Id.* at 566-567 (footnote omitted)(Stevens, J., concurring in part and dissenting in part).

referred to the Boy Scouts' views about homosexuality as "atavistic opinions...[whose] roots have been nourished by sectarian doctrine."[78] According to this opinion, it was not appropriate for the Court to permit the Boy Scouts to rely on such "prejudices;" "the light of reason" required that these prejudices be eradicated.[79]

The *Lawrence* opinion is to the same effect. The Court, in a majority opinion by Justice Kennedy, again referred to moral disapproval of homosexual conduct as evidencing unreflective animosity.[80] Justice Kennedy noted that the condemnation of homosexual conduct had "been shaped by religious beliefs, conceptions of right and acceptable behavior, and respect for the traditional family." "These views" were swept aside in favor of the extreme individual autonomy view expressed in *Casey*: "'Our obligation is to define the liberty of all, not to mandate our own moral code.'"[81]

This way of thinking is increasingly common,[82] and potentially threatening to invoking "religious pluralism" in this effort to seek an exemption for conscientious objectors to healthcare mandates. It is risky to have issues such as abortion or contraception viewed as if they were "religious" issues.

---

[78] *Boy Scouts of America v. Dale*, 530 U. S. 640, 698 (2000)(Stevens, J., dissenting).

[79] *Id.* at 700 (Stevens, J., dissenting). See Richard S. Myers, "The Supreme Court and the Privatization of Religion," 41 *Catholic University Law Review* 19, 60 n. 232 (1991), noting that Justice Stevens seems to be hostile to religion). See also Robert F. Nagel, "Justice Stevens' Religion Problem," *First Things* (June/July 2003), at 9.

[80] *Lawrence*, 539 U. S. at 575, 578. See also *Goodrich v. Department of Public Health*, 798 N. E. 2d 941 (Mass. 2003).

[81] *Lawrence*, 539 U. S. at 571, quoting *Planned Parenthood v. Casey*, 505 U. S. 833, 850 (1992).

[82] See Richard S. Myers, "The Privatization of Religion and Catholic Justices," 47 *Journal of Catholic Legal Studies* 157 (2008).

We saw this working itself out in the *Catholic Charities* case in California. There, the California court did not think that the contraceptive mandate impermissibly inhibited religion. The California Supreme Court was not even sure that Catholic Charities' religious beliefs were implicated at all. Catholic Charities had explained that paying its workers a just wage included, as a matter of justice and charity, coverage for prescription drugs. The Court could not seem to comprehend how "justice and charity" could be considered "religious."[83] In any event, these beliefs were entitled to little weight because Catholic Charities had entered "the general labor market."[84] We see here a very disturbing approach on the part of the court–simultaneously concluding that Catholic Charities is not really engaged in something "religious" when it provides social services, while also claiming that Catholic Charities' "religious" views on contraception are entitled to little weight.

These views are quite commonplace, and that is why I am concerned when people who are sympathetic to the rights of conscience describe issues such as abortion, euthanasia, human cloning, and stem cell research as "profoundly religious issues."[85] I understand why the religious vision of healthcare is invoked, but there are real risks because such views may be considered as idiosyncratic, nonrational, irrational, not publicly accessible, or what have you. (I want to make it clear that I do not accept any of these characterizations.[86]) On the disputed issues in play, we are not talking about "theological" issues at all, such as the nature of the Trinity or the Eucharist. We are talking about moral questions, and

---

[83] *Catholic Charities of Sacramento,* 85 P. 3d at 92.

[84] *Id.* at 93.

[85] Edmund D. Pellegrino, "The Physician's Conscience, Conscience Clauses, and Religious Belief: A Catholic Perspective," 30 *Fordham Urban Law Journal* 221, 224 (2002).

[86] See Myers, *supra* note 82; Myers, *supra* note 79.

for many Catholics and others that means drawing on a rich tradition of natural law. But to the extent religious people persist in describing their moral vision of healthcare as "religious" they risk having this vision privatized and marginalized. It will only be protected when it does not matter very much. The moral vision will not be permitted to influence public business. Religion may be protected if practiced in one's home or in a house of worship, but that will be it.

While the appeal to religious pluralism taps into the attractiveness many find in this "republic of choice," it risks being marginalized in the face of the onslaught of the secular vision of healthcare, which is becoming increasingly aggressive in mandating its vision of the world. As a matter of first principle, then, an appeal to choice and in particular to religious choice has grave risks. The most desirable strategy is to promote a vision of healthcare that furthers a public morality with the substantive vision that promotes the truth about the dignity of the human person. On matters about which we are confident (that it is wrong to sexually abuse minors, for example), we are perfectly willing to limit choice. We should also be willing to do so on life and death issues in healthcare, where neutrality is really not possible. On these matters, it is imperative that we work to restore norms such as that it is wrong to intentionally take the life of an innocent human person. This is necessary, I believe, even though many hold this "moral" position because of the influence of deep theological commitments. Such moral positions, though, are the fit subjects of public action, and in some areas–the prohibition against taking the life of an innocent human person–ought to be mandatory.

V. Conclusion

An appeal to religious choice has serious risks. The task ought to be to build up a public morality on these issues, so as to eliminate the clash between legislative mandates and traditional moral teachings;

unfortunately, claiming a "religious" basis for acting may jeopardize this broader cultural effort. Building up the culture on these issues will also make the claim for conscientious objection, when that proves necessary to pursue, more likely to succeed, because the claims for conscience are more likely to succeed the more support for the underlying moral position there is in the broader society. So, the conscience claims in the area of abortion are more successful than those in the area of contraception, where the opposition to contraception is held by so few and is not even comprehensible to most people.

But, we are not just considering this from a position of first principles. We also ought to take account of the current cultural realities. The moral vision of healthcare that would have been held in common by most religions in the United States a hundred years ago does not exist on a widespread basis any longer. We need to work to advance our moral vision, and it is altogether fitting and proper that we do so.[87] But in the interim, we also need to pursue a second-best approach. The individuals and groups who dissent from the public orthodoxy in areas such as abortion need to have the ability to preserve their distinctive witness. This requires protection for conscience–not as the best or most desirable strategy but because in the face of the increasing demands of the secular vision of healthcare–that is all that we are going to be permitted in the foreseeable future.

The choice is to pursue this second-best strategy of conscience–or go out of the vocation of healthcare altogether. The choice is really that stark.

---

[87] Cf. Abraham Lincoln, "Address Delivered at the Dedication of the Cemetery at Gettysburg," reprinted in *Collected Works of Abraham Lincoln*, vol. 7, ed. Roy P. Basler (New Brunswick NJ: Rutgers University Press, 1953), p. 23.

“Partial-Birth Abortion” Is Not Abortion: *Carhart II*’s Fundamental Misapplication of *Roe*

Samuel W. Calhoun

ABSTRACT: In explaining his constitutional objection to Wisconsin’s partial-birth abortion ban, Judge Richard Posner contrasts killing during “normal labor” with partial-birth abortion. The former can be constitutionally prohibited, but the latter cannot. Why the distinction? For Posner, the former involves “killing a live baby that is half-born,” whereas the latter does not. This article will show that Judge Posner is correct to assert that killing a baby in the midst of the birth process is not constitutionally protected. But Judge Posner is wrong to say that partial-birth abortion does not kill “a live baby that is half-born.” This article will demonstrate that the partial-birth procedure in fact does kill a baby during its birth. Ban-proponents are correct in their long-standing argument that the partial-birth procedure is not really an abortion. Consequently, *Roe*, properly understood, is inapplicable to partial-birth abortion bans. Courts, however, including the U.S. Supreme Court in *Carhart II*, have nonetheless routinely used the analytical framework of *Roe* and *Casey* to evaluate bans. This common mistake undermines current partial-birth abortion jurisprudence. The rational basis test, not *Roe/Casey*, is the proper evaluative tool. Using the correct standard could have significant consequences for future challenges to the federal ban and to the bans of the various states.

THE 2007 U.S. SUPREME COURT decision in *Gonzales v. Carhart* [*Carhart II*][1] would seem to end the long fight over partial-birth abortion. Ever since the 1992 disclosure of the details of the

[1] 550 U.S. 124 (2007). *Carhart II* will hereinafter be used to refer to the *Gonzales* decision, which upheld the Federal Partial-Birth Abortion Ban.

partial-birth procedure, which Congress later described as "gruesome and inhumane,"[2] the majority of Americans, both pro-choice and pro-life, have favored prohibiting it.[3] While ban proponents experienced widespread success in enacting partial-birth abortion bans,[4] almost all were stricken as unconstitutional under *Roe v. Wade,*[5] as modified by *Planned Parenthood of Southeastern Pennsylvania v. Casey.*[6] The defining moment was the Supreme Court's 2000 decision in *Stenberg v. Carhart* [*Carhart I*],[7] which disallowed Nebraska's ban on partial-birth abortion. *Carhart II*, however, upheld a Federal Ban,[8]

---

[2] Congressional Finding 14(L), in notes following 18 U.S.C. § 1531 (Supp. V 2000). This same descriptive phrase was used earlier by the first court to rule on the enforceablity of a state partial-birth abortion ban. *Evans v. Kelly*, 977 F. Supp. 1283, 1319 n.38 (E.D. Mich. 1997). An earlier decision barred enforcement of an Ohio statute that no doubt was motivated by the partial-birth controversy, but was so drafted that it cannot accurately be called a partial-birth abortion ban. See *Women's Medical Professional Corp. v. Voinovich*, 911 F. Supp. 1051, 1063 (S.D. Ohio 1995), aff'd, 130 F.3d 187 (6th Cir. 1997); James Bopp, Jr. & Curtis R. Cook, "Partial-Birth Abortion: The Final Frontier of Abortion Jurisprudence," 14 *Issues in Law & Medicine* 3, 5 n.4 (1998).

[3] Gallup polls show that support for bans rose from fifty-seven percent to seventy percent between 1996 and 2003. Kenneth L. Woodward, "What's In A Name? *The New York Times* on 'Partial-Birth' Abortion," 19 *Notre Dame Journal of Legal Ethics & Public Policy* 427, 433 n.13 (2005). Polls showed that a majority of self-identified pro-choice respondents also favored bans. *Id.*

[4] By 2000, at least thirty states had banned the procedure. See *Stenberg v. Carhart*, 530 U.S. 914, 979 (2000) (Kennedy, J., dissenting). For the history of the Federal Ban, see *infra* note 8.

[5] 410 U.S. 113 (1973).

[6] 505 U.S. 833 (1992). *Roe* as modified by *Casey* will hereinafter be referred to as *Roe/Casey*.

[7] 530 U.S. 914 (2000). *Carhart I* will hereinafter be used to refer to the *Stenberg* decision.

[8] Federal partial-birth abortion bans were passed "by wide margins" in 1996 and 1997, but both were vetoed by President Clinton. *Id.* at 994 n.11 (Thomas, J.,

thus prohibiting the partial-birth procedure nationwide.[9] Why, then, isn't it time to move on to other issues in the continuing national controversy over abortion?

Some indeed are shifting their emphasis. Advocacy groups have wondered what *Carhart II* portends for other abortion restrictions.[10] Some scholars have pondered its implications for other legal issues.[11] But many still focus upon *Carhart II* itself. While the decision does not lack supporters,[12] its more numerous critics have argued, among other

---

dissenting). The third Congressional ban, signed by President Bush as the Partial Birth Abortion Ban Act of 2003, passed the House by 281-142, Sheryl Gay Stolberg, "Bill Banning"Abortion Procedure Advances," *The New York Times*, Oct. 3, 2003, at A24, and the Senate by 64-34. Sheryl Gay Stolberg, "Senate Approves Bill to Prohibit Type of Abortion," *The New York Times*, Oct. 22, 2003, at A1. The law is codified at 18 U.S.C. § 1531 (Supp. V 2000) (hereinafter referred to as the Federal Ban).

[9] The approved Federal Ban also shows the states how to craft bans to survive constitutional challenge.

[10] See, e.g., Fundraising Letter, Americans United for Life (June 7, 2007) (on file with author) (stating that *Carhart II* "paves the way for states to pass significant new restrictions on abortion").

[11] See, e.g., Randy Beck, "*Gonzales, Casey*, and the Viability Rule," 103 *Northwestern University Law Review* 249 (2009) (arguing that *Carhart II* erodes the significance of viability in abortion jurisprudence); Steven G. Calabresi, "Substantive Due Process after *Gonzales v. Carhart*," 106 *Michigan Law Review* 1517 (2008) (discussing the decision's impact on substantive due process jurisprudence); David H. Gans, "Severability as Judicial Lawmaking," 76 *George Washington Law Review* 639, 641 (2008) (citing the decision as evidence of the increasing significance of severability doctrine to Supreme Court jurisprudence); B. Jessie Hill, "The Constitutional Right to Make Medical Treatment Decisions: A Tale of Two Doctrines," 86 *Texas Law Review* 277 (2007) (arguing that the decision is a step toward reconciling pre-existing different approaches to the right to make medical treatment choices).

[12] See, e.g., Barry A. Bostrom, "*Gonzales v. Carhart*," 23 *Issues in Law & Medicine* 89 (2007); Richard S. Myers, "The Supreme Court and Abortion: The Implications of *Gonzales v. Carhart* (2007)," in *Life and Learning XVII* (2007) (Proceedings of the Seventeenth University for Life Conference).

things, (1) that *Carhart II* is inconsistent with *Carhart I*;[13] (2) that the Court granted undue deference to the Congressional Findings of Fact underlying the Federal Ban;[14] and (3) that a particular aspect of the Court's rationale–the "regret" factor[15]–is not only based on faulty evidence,[16] but also is demeaning to women.[17]

Beyond this scholarly output, there is additional evidence that *Carhart II* did not completely resolve the issue of partial-birth abortion bans. The Court explicitly contemplated possible as-applied challenges to the Federal Ban.[18] Moreover, federal appellate decisions subsequent

---

[13] See, e.g., Michael J. Gerhardt, "Constitutional Humility," 76 *University of Cincinnati Law Review* 23, 40 n.118 (2007); Martha C. Nussbaum, "Foreward: Constitutions and Capabilities: 'Perception' Against Lofty Formalism," 121 *Harvard Law Review* 4, 84 (2007) (explaining that *Carhart II*'s reading of *Carhart I* was "bizarrely narrow").

[14] See, e.g., "The Supreme Court, 2006 Term–Leading Cases," 121 *Harvard Law Review* 185, 265-75 (2007).

[15] In arguing that Congress could reasonably determine that the partial-birth procedure "implicates...ethical and moral concerns that justify a special prohibition," the Court stated that it was "unexceptional to conclude some women come to regret their choice to abort the infant life they once created and sustained." *Carhart II*, 550 U.S. at 158-59. Any such regret would be "more anguished and sorrow[ful]" when "a mother...learns...that she allowed a doctor to pierce the skull and vacuum the fast-developing brain of her unborn child." *Id.* at 159-60.

[16] See, e.g., Nussbaum, *supra* note 13, at 86; Ronald Turner, "*Gonzales v. Carhart* and the Court's 'Women's Regret' Rationale," 43 *Wake Forest Law Review* 1 passim (2008) (implied throughout rather than explicitly stated). Contra Teresa Stanton Collett, "Judicial Modesty and Abortion," 59 *South Carolina Law Review* 701, 731-32 (2008).

[17] See, e.g., Nussbaum, *supra* note 13, at 85-87; Reva B. Siegel, "The Right's Reasons: Constitutional Conflict and the Spread of Women-Protective Antiabortion Argument," 57 *Duke Law Journal* 1641 (2008); Reva B. Siegel, "Sex Equality Arguments for Reproductive Rights: Their Critical Basis and Evolving Constitutional Expression," 56 *Emory Law Journal* 815, 837 (2007).

[18] *Carhart II* involved a facial challenge to the Federal Ban. The Court suggested that an as-applied challenge might be successful under appropriate circumstances. *Carhart*

to *Carhart II* already reveal disputes about whether state attempts to prohibit the partial-birth procedure are enough like the Federal Ban to survive constitutional challenge.[19]

All of this post-*Carhart II* ferment ignores the most striking aspect of the decision: the Supreme Court committed a fundamental classification error. Despite the procedure's name, partial-birth abortion is not an "abortion" as that term was understood by the *Roe* Court.[20] The Texas statute at issue in *Roe* defined "abortion" as destroying "'the life of the fetus or embyro...in the woman's womb.'"[21] *Roe* is replete with language limiting its application to the duration of a pregnancy–a state's regulatory interests become compelling at some

---

II, 550 U.S. at 167-68.

[19] Virginia's partial-birth infanticide ban was initially invalidated, but then upheld on appeal. See *infra* notes 240-44 and accompanying text. Michigan failed in its attempts to prohibit the procedure by creating a protected legal status for partially delivered fetuses. See *infra* notes 245-48 and accompanying text.

[20] Since the partial-birth abortion procedure had not been devised at the time of *Roe*, see *infra* note 40 and accompanying text, it is apparent that the *Roe* majority did not actually have it in mind when discussing the concept of abortion. The argument here is that the procedure is also not encompassed by *Roe*'s rationale. Consequently, the term "partial-birth abortion" is a misnomer. The erroneous name in itself has helped defeat the argument that *Roe* is inapplicable to the procedure. One court, for example, referred to the fact that the legislature in question had defined partial-birth abortion as "'an abortion'" that encompassed certain specified conduct. *Planned Parenthood of Central N.J. v. Farmer*, 220 F.3d 127, 144 (3d Cir. 2000). Another court emphasized that the ban in question "was intended to be codified under an abortion section–evidencing the state's efforts to restrict abortion access." *Causeway Med. Suite v. Foster*, 43 F. Supp. 2d 604, 613 (E.D. La. 1999), aff'd, 221 F.3d 811 (5th Cir. 2000). This Article will demonstrate that the word "abortion" following "partial-birth" should not be allowed to mask the reality that the procedure kills a child during its birth. See *infra* note 27 and accompanying text.

[21] 410 U.S. 113, 117 n.1 (1973). The Texas "abortion" definition also included causing "'a premature birth,'" *id.*, but the Court never focused on this fact. In any event, the act of causing a premature birth would not be covered by the Federal Ban, which requires an "overt act, other than completion of delivery, that kills the partially delivered living fetus." 18 U.S.C. § 1531(b)(1)(B) (Supp. V 2000).

"point during pregnancy";[22] a state cannot criminalize abortion "without regard to pregnancy stage";[23] a state can regulate more "as the period of pregnancy lengthens."[24] At "live birth," all such constraints on a state's regulatory freedom disappear, as the fetus then becomes a person "in the whole sense."[25] The Court thus thought of "abortion" only as an act that terminates a pregnancy at some point prior to live birth.[26] Consequently, to kill a fetus during its live birth is not an abortion under *Roe.*[27]

Partial-birth abortion kills a fetus during its live birth.[28] "'[B]irth'

---

[22] 410 U.S. at 163.

[23] *Id.* at 164.

[24] *Id.* at 165.

[25] *Id.* at 162.

[26] In *Webster v. Reproductive Health Services*, the plurality opinion characterized *Roe* as establishing "a constitutional framework for judging state regulation of abortion during the entire term of pregnancy." 492 U.S. 490, 520 (1989). The framework sought to balance state interests in protecting the fetus "against the claims of a woman to decide for herself whether or not to abort a fetus she was carrying." *Id.* Once live birth begins, the "term of pregnancy" is essentially over. *Id.* Moreover, the woman is no longer "carrying" the fetus in the conventional sense of that term. *Id.*

[27] See *infra* notes 92-141 and accompanying text. Thus the term, "partial-birth abortion," is an ironic misnomer. The description, "partial-birth," undoubtedly gives ban proponents a rhetorical edge. So much so that *Newsweek* Contributing Editor Kenneth Woodward argues that *The New York Times*, because of its well-known support of abortion rights, has studiously avoided using what it regards "as a toxic term." Woodward, *supra* note 3, at 436-37, 441-42. But whatever rhetorical advantage opponents of the procedure gain by the phrase, "partial-birth" is offset by the disadvantages of calling the procedure an "abortion." This label no doubt indirectly, and sometimes directly, see *supra* note 20, supports the erroneous perspective that the partial-birth procedure is an abortion properly subject to *Roe*.

[28] The Court in *Carhart II* agrees with this characterization. See *infra* note 91 and accompanying text. "Fetus" is what biologists call an unborn human being beginning at about eight weeks gestational age. Lennart Nilsson & Lars Hamberger, *A Child Is Born* (1990), p. 91. At this developmental stage, "all the organs are already in place.

is the 'passage of the offspring from the uterus to the outside world.'"[29] An intended step of the partial-birth procedure is forcibly to begin pulling a fully formed, living, and intact fetus into the outside world.[30]

Everything to be found in a fully grown human being has already been formed." *Id.* Also, "the growing organism, small as it is, looks human even if quite unlike its parents." Roberts Rugh & Labdrum B. Shettles, *From Conception to Birth: The Drama of Life's Beginnings* (1971), p. 39. "Fetus" thus is the technical term used for an unborn human baby at or beyond a particular gestational age. I will therefore use the terms "fetus" and "baby"/"child" interchangeably. This usage is supported by *Carhart II*, in which the Court speaks most often of the "fetus," 550 U.S. 124 passim (2007), but refers also to "the unborn child," *id.* at 134, 160, "the infant life," *id.* at 159, and "'the baby,'" *id.* at 138-39. Although using "fetus" and "baby"/"child" synonymously is also consistent with the Latin word, "fetus," which "simply means 'offspring' or 'unborn young,'" David K. DeWolf, Book Review/Essay, 26 *Gonzaga Law Review* 257, 259 n.10 (1991) (quoting *American Heritage Dictionary* 260 (1983)), some find it objectionable as revealing "hostility to the right *Roe* and *Casey* secured." *Carhart II*, 550 U.S at 186-87 (Ginsburg, J., dissenting).

[29] *National Abortion Federation v. Gonzales*, 437 F.3d 278, 311 n.14 (2d Cir. 2006) (Straub, J., dissenting) (quoting *Dorland's Illustrated Medical Dictionary* 207 (27th ed. 2000)), vacated, 224 Fed. Appx. 88 (2d Cir. 2007). See also *Taber's Cyclopedic Medical Dictionary* 251 (20th ed. 2001) ("[t]he act of being born; passage of a child from the uterus").

[30] The steps of the partial-birth procedure were plainly described by Dr. Martin Haskell in a 1992 presentation at a National Abortion Federation meeting. This description not only played an important role in igniting the partial-birth abortion controversy, see *infra* note 40 and accompanying text, but also has been relied upon in partial-birth abortion decisions as accurately describing the procedure. See, e.g., *Carhart II*, 550 U.S. at 138-39; *Carhart v. Ashcroft*, 331 F. Supp. 2d 805, 825-27 (D. Neb. 2004), aff'd, 413 F.3d 791 (8th Cir. 2005), rev'd, *Carhart II*, 550 U.S. 124 (2007). Haskell spoke of grasping a "lower [fetal] extremity" with "a large grasping forcep" and pulling it "into the vagina." Dr. Martin Haskell, "Dilation and Extraction for Late Second Trimester Abortions," presented at the National Abortion Federation Risk Management Seminar (Sept. 13, 1992) (hereinafter "Haskell Presentation"). The surgeon then uses "his fingers to deliver the opposite lower extremity, then the torso, the shoulders and the upper extremities." *Id.* The accompanying textual sentence makes four assertions about the state of the fetus during the partial-birth process: (1) fully formed; (2) living; (3) intact; and (4) partially in the outside world. It is incontestable that fetuses subjected to the partial-birth procedure are fully formed. According to Dr. Haskell, the procedure is used "in patients 20-26 weeks in

The procedure thus initiates a live birth process.[31] Before the fetus has fully emerged, but when either its head or half its lower body is outside the woman's body,[32] its skull is collapsed.[33] Because the partial-birth

---

pregnancy." Haskell Presentation, *supra*. "Even at 20 weeks, doctors say, a developing fetus appears remarkably full-formed, right down to the fingerprints." Roy Rivenburg, "Partial Truths," *Los Angeles Times*, Apr. 2, 1997 (Life & Style), at 1. This can be corroborated by consulting any book on fetal development. See, e.g., Alexander Tsiaras, *From Conception to Birth: A Life Unfolds* (2002). As to whether the fetus is living, in one sense there is no reason for dispute. If the fetus is not living at the time of the partial-birth procedure, the ban does not apply. The Federal Ban is triggered only if "a living fetus" is delivered to a certain point and then killed by an "overt act, other than the completion of delivery." 18 U.S.C. § 1531(b)(1)(A)-(B) (Supp. V 2000). For a discussion of whether the fetus is in fact "alive" during this process, see *infra* note 34 and accompanying text. Regarding intactness, Dr. Haskell describes a two-day process to dilate the cervix prior to the partial-birth procedure. Haskell Presentation, *supra*. This accomplishes sufficient dilation for the fetus's body to be extracted intact, but usually is inadequate to allow the fetus's skull "to pass through." *Id.* See Rivenburg, *supra* (the doctor "pulls out the body except for the head, which is too large to pass without injuring the woman"). For information on the extent to which the doctor brings the fetus outside the woman's body, see *infra* note 32 and accompanying text.

[31] The Court in *Carhart II* explicitly stated that partial-birth abortion involves "birth"–the procedure's effect is to kill "a fetus...just inches before completion of the birth process." 550 U.S. at 157. The Court later found that Congress was reasonable to conclude that the partial-birth procedure "'perverts a process during which life is brought into the world.'" *Id.* at 160.

[32] The Federal Ban only applies if "in the case of a head-first presentation, the entire fetal head is outside the body of the mother, or, in the case of a breech presentation, any part of the fetal trunk past the navel is outside the body of the mother." 18 U.S.C. §1531(b)(1)(A) (Supp. V 2000). Breech presentations [feet first] are the most common. Thus, "[i]n the usual...[partial-birth procedure,] the fetus' head lodges in the cervix [see *infra* note 207], and dilation is insufficient to allow it to pass." *Carhart II*, 550 U.S. at 138; see *id.* at 150. For evidence that in this situation the required degree of separation from the mother commonly occurs, see *infra* note 208 and accompanying text.

[33] Professor Cynthia Gorney quotes the following as a "fairly accurate [technical] summation" of the partial-birth procedure: "[T]he abortionist uses forceps to pull a living baby feet-first through the birth canal until the baby's body is exposed, leaving

procedure kills a fetus during its live birth,[34] it lies outside the constitutional right recognized in *Roe*. Courts have therefore been mistaken to rely upon *Roe* in evaluating legislative bans.

It is important to stress the modesty of the foregoing thesis. I do not argue here that the partially born are constitutional persons under the Fourteenth Amendment.[35] Nor do I argue here that the partially

---

only the head just within the uterus. The abortionist then forces surgical scissors into the base of the baby's skull, creating an incision through which he inserts a suction tube to evacuate the brain tissue from the baby's skull. The evacuation of this tissue causes the skull to collapse, allowing the baby's head to be pulled from the birth canal." Cynthia Gorney, "Gambling With Abortion," *Harper's*, Nov. 2004, at 34. Gorney does not explain why she finds this description only "fairly" accurate. It certainly comports with Dr. Haskell's explanation of the partial-birth procedure: "[T]he surgeon...forces the scissors into the base of the skull...[and] spreads [them] to enlarge the opening. The surgeon removes the scissors and introduces a suction catheter into this hole and evacuates the skull contents." Haskell Presentation, *supra* note 30. Haskell's description, in conjunction with his account of the prior partial delivery of the fetus, see *supra* note 30, makes it clear that the procedure does in fact kill, as Gorney's account portrays and as Congress has found, a "partially-born child." See Gorney, *supra*; Congressional Findings 14(H) & (K), in notes following 18 U.S.C. § 1531 (Supp. V 2000).

[34] Early in the partial-birth controversy, some ban opponents argued that anesthesia given to the woman kills the fetus before its skull is collapsed. These included nationally syndicated columnist Ellen Goodman. Ellen Goodman, "Pro-life Lawmakers Aren't Looking at All the Pictures," *Roanoke Times*, Nov. 14, 1995, at A7. Kate Michelman, then President of the National Abortion Rights Action League, stated that because anesthesia has already killed the fetus, "it is not true that they're born partially. This is a gross distortion, and it's really a disservice to the public to say this." Effects of Anesthesia During a Partial-Birth Abortion: Hearing Before the Subcommittee on the Constitution of the House Comm. on the Judiciary, 104th Cong. 7 (1996) (transcript of Michelman radio statement). In fact, the early fetal demise argument was the "gross distortion." Anesthesiologists "blasted" it as "scientific bunk." Rivenburg, *supra* note 30 (the article later states that the claim has "been debunked"). See Gorney, *supra* note 33, at 41 (characterizing as a "misstep" and "wrong" ban opponents' argument that "the fetus is always dead by the time the doctor begins" the partial-birth procedure).

[35] This argument has appeared from time to time during the partial-birth controversy, e.g., Bopp & Cook, *supra* note 2, at 27-28; *infra* note 60, but evaluating it is beyond

born are a class of humanity otherwise intrinsically entitled to legal protection.[36] My claim is much more limited: because the partial-birth procedure is not an abortion, a legislative body unencumbered by *Roe/Casey* can appropriately choose to ban it.

Part I will show that the "*Roe* is inapplicable" argument appears throughout the fight to ban the partial-birth procedure. The view was communicated to Congress on multiple occasions by prominent legal authorities. It was also asserted numerous times in ban litigation. To overlook this reality is to miss an important aspect of the partial-birth abortion controversy.

Part II will demonstrate that the constitutional right to abortion choice conferred by *Roe* does not encompass partial-birth abortion. *Roe* strongly implied that it does not apply to killing a baby during its birth. The partial-birth process kills a baby while being born.[37] It is therefore wrong to apply *Roe/Casey* to evaluate partial-birth abortion bans. Doing so illegitimately constrains lawmakers' right to prohibit the partial-birth procedure.[38]

Part III will discuss the consequences of recognizing that

---

the scope of this article.

[36] Such an argument might be based, for example, on the "created equal" and "inalienable rights" language of the Declaration of Independence. *The Declaration of Independence* para. 2 (U.S. 1776).

[37] See *infra* note 91 and accompanying text.

[38] Some courts that have rejected the "*Roe* is inapplicable" argument have explicitly recognized judges' duty not to substitute their own policy choices for those of the legislature–a law should be overturned only if it is clearly unconstitutional. See, e.g., *Planned Parenthood of Central N.J. v. Farmer*, 220 F.3d 127, 130-31 (3d Cir. 2000); *Little Rock Family Planning Services v. Jegley*, No. LR-C-97-581, 1998 U.S. Dist. LEXIS 22325, at *38 (E.D. Ark. Nov. 13, 1998), aff'd, 192 F.3d 794 (8th Cir. 1999). The sincerity of judicial efforts to apply the Constitution correctly in the partial-birth abortion context is not in question. Nonetheless, this article posits that to the extent that courts have applied *Roe* to evaluate partial-birth abortion bans, they have inappropriately limited the freedom of the people, acting through their elected representatives, to curtail the partial-birth procedure.

partial-birth abortion is not an abortion under *Roe*. Most importantly, the partial-birth procedure is not entitled to the same constitutional protection accorded to abortion. Partial-birth abortion bans should therefore be scrutinized under a rational basis standard, not the criteria applicable to abortion legislation. Applying the appropriate constitutional test could very well have dispositive impact if the Federal Ban is ever subjected to an as-applied challenge.[39] Applying the proper standard could also have implications for evaluating state partial-birth abortion legislation in the wake of *Carhart II*.

I. History

Partial-birth abortion burst into the public consciousness in the early to mid-1990s.[40] Widespread abhorrence quickly led to legislative bans of the procedure.[41] Legal challenges to the bans followed just as swiftly.[42]

---

[39] See *supra* note 18 and accompanying text.

[40] According to the Supreme Court, the procedure "gained public notoriety when, in 1992, Dr. Martin Haskell gave a presentation describing his method of performing the operation." *Carhart II*, 550 U.S. 124, 138 (2007). See Rivenburg, *supra* note 30 (the debate arose when "[n]ot long after" Haskell "presented...[his] how-to paper[,]...a copy...found its way to the National Right to Life Committee"). Professor Cynthia Gorney gives 1993 as the start of "intense public argument," the year that "a physician's published description [undoubtedly Dr. Haskell's]... was reprinted in right-to-life journals." Cynthia Gorney, *Articles of Faith: A Frontline History of the Abortion Wars* (1998, 2000), p. 522.

[41] See *supra* notes 4, 8 and accompanying text. The extent of public opposition to the partial-birth procedure is demonstrated not only by the proliferation of bans, but also by some states' multiple attempts to pass a ban that would survive constitutional scrutiny. One example is Virginia. Its 1998 ban of "partial-birth abortion" was invalidated in *Richmond Medical Center for Women v. Gilmore*, 55 F. Supp. 2d 441 (E.D. Va. 1999), aff'd, 224 F.3d 337 (4th Cir. 2000). In 2003, Virginia again tried to ban the procedure by criminalizing "partial birth infanticide." *Richmond Medical Center v. Hicks*, 301 F. Supp. 2d 499 (E.D. Va. 2004), aff'd, 409 F.3d 619 (4th Cir. 2005). This statute was also invalidated. *Id.* The State successfully sought certiorari from the Supreme Court, which, due to *Carhart II*, vacated the Fourth Circuit decision and remanded the case. *Herring v. Richmond Medical Center for Women*,

Critics had three principal arguments for the unconstitutionality of a ban[43]: (1) vagueness,[44] (2) imposition of an undue burden on a woman's right to obtain a pre-viability abortion,[45] and (3) lack of a

---

550 U.S. 901 (2007). Virginia initially failed in defending its ban, but on appeal was ultimately successful. *Richmond Medical Center for Women v. Herring*, 527 F.3d 128 (4th Cir. 2008), rev'd on reh'g, *Richmond Medical Center for Women v. Herring*, 570 F.3d 165 (4th Cir. 2009) (en banc). See *infra* notes 240-44 and accompanying text. Michigan's opposition to the partial-birth procedure perhaps surpasses Virginia's. For an account of its dogged efforts to enact a prohibition, including a step requiring the direct involvement of the people of Michigan, see *infra* note 245.

[42] For an early, comprehensive assessment of bans' constitutionality under the *Roe/Casey* standard, see Ann MacLean Massie, "So-Called 'Partial-Birth Abortion' Bans: Bad Medicine? Maybe. Bad Law? Definitely!" 59 *University of Pittsburgh Law Review* 301 (1998). Massie mentions the argument that the partial-birth procedure is not an abortion, *id.* at 363, but does not discuss it.

[43] In addition to claims of unconstitutionality, ban opponents tried in other ways to quell the widespread outcry against the partial-birth procedure. Some used factual distortions. The most notable example was revealed when Ron Fitzsimmons, executive director of the National Coalition of Abortion Providers, admitted "that he lied in earlier statements when he said...[that the procedure] is rare and performed primarily to save the lives or fertility of women bearing severely malformed babies." David Stout, "An Abortion Rights Advocate Says He Lies About Procedure," *The New York Times*, Feb. 26, 1997, at A11. In fact, "[i]n the vast majority of cases, the procedure is performed on a healthy mother with a healthy fetus." *Id.*

[44] See, e.g., *Causeway Medical Suite v. Foster*, 43 F. Supp. 2d 604, 615-19 (E.D. La. 1999), aff'd on other grounds, 221 F.3d 811 (5th Cir. 2000); *Planned Parenthood of Greater Iowa, Inc. v. Miller*, 30 F. Supp. 2d 1157, 1164-66 (S.D. Iowa 1998), aff'd on other grounds, 195 F.3d 386 (8th Cir. 1999); *Evans v. Kelley*, 977 F. Supp. 1283, 1304-11 (E.D. Mich. 1997).

[45] An undue burden "exists if a regulation's 'purpose or effect is to place a substantial obstacle in the path of a woman seeking an abortion before the fetus attains viability.'" *Carhart II*, 550 U.S. at 146 (quoting *Planned Parenthood of Southeastern Pennsylvania v. Casey*, 505 U.S. 833, 878 (1992)). The principal argument that partial-birth abortion bans constitute an undue burden is that they prohibit, in addition to the partial-birth procedure, the more common D&E method of abortion. See *infra* text accompanying notes 152, 197. See, e.g., *Eubanks v. Stengel*, 28 F. Supp. 2d 1024, 1033-35 (W.D. Ky. 1998), aff'd, 224 F.3d 576 (6th Cir. 2000); *Evans*, 977 F. Supp. at 1315-19. The undue burden critique also sometimes is based on the lack of

health exception.[46] Ban proponents contested these three points, but soon introduced a new argument pertinent to the *Roe/Casey*-based attack. They argued that *Roe/Casey* were inapplicable because the proscribed procedure, although labeled as a type of abortion, actually is outside the *Roe* conception of what an abortion entails. The procedure kills a partially born baby, i.e., one in the process of being born. It therefore actually either is or nearly is infanticide.[47]

Determining the precise origin of the "*Roe* is inapplicable" perspective is difficult. Although described in a 1999 federal district court opinion as "a unique new argument in abortion litigation,"[48] the

---

a health exception. See *infra* note 46.

[46] The health exception argument is premised in the requirement that even post-viability abortion regulations must contain a health exception. See *Carhart I*, 530 U.S. at 929-30. Concerning partial-birth abortion bans, the absence of a health exception has sometimes been relied upon as an independent constitutional deficiency, e.g., *Causeway Medical Suite v. Foster*, 43 F. Supp. 2d 604, 613-14 (E.D. La. 1999), aff'd, 221 F.3d 811 (5th Cir. 2000); *Planned Parenthood of Greater Iowa, Inc. v. Miller*, 30 F. Supp. 2d 1157, 1167-68 (S.D. Iowa 1998), aff'd, 195 F.3d 386 (8th Cir. 1999); and sometimes as an element in an undue burden analysis. E.g., *Planned Parenthood of Central N.J. v. Verniero*, 41 F. Supp. 2d 478, 501-03 (D.N.J. 1998), aff'd sub nom. on other grounds, *Planned Parenthood of Central N.J. v. Farmer*, 220 F.3d 127 (3d Cir. 2000). The presence of a health exception was a key factor in perhaps the only decision upholding a state partial-birth abortion ban subsequent to *Carhart I*. See *Women's Medical Professional Corp. v. Taft*, 353 F.3d 436, 444-50 (6th Cir. 2003). *Carhart II* held that the lack of a health exception in the Federal Ban was constitutionally permissible. 550 U.S. at 161-66.

[47] Between 1996 and 1997, the late pro-choice Senator Patrick Moynihan's opinion of the partial-birth procedure changed from the latter to the former. In 1996, he stated that the procedure was "'as close to infanticide as anything I have come upon in our judiciary.'" Barbara Vobejda & David Brown, "Harsh Details Shift Tenor of Abortion Fight; Both Sides Bend Facts On Late-Term Procedure," *The Washington Post*, Sept. 17, 1996, at A01. By 1997, based on Ron Fitzsimmons's confession of how he had lied about the procedure [see *supra* note 43], Moynihan had become convinced that the procedure "is infanticide, and one would be too many." See *Meet the Press* (NBC television broadcast Mar. 3, 1997) (transcript on file with the author).

[48] Foster, 43 F. Supp. 2d at 609.

theory clearly had surfaced by 1998, in court[49] and elsewhere.[50] One advocacy group claims that the "*Roe* is inapplicable" argument originated in its 1997 defense of Arizona's ban.[51] This might well be its first judicial mention,[52] but the theory clearly predates 1997. The approach was asserted at a 1996 House Subcommittee Hearing by Harvard Law Professor Mary Ann Glendon.[53] The earliest mentions of the argument that I have found come from November 1995 by law

---

[49] See, e.g., *Verniero*, 41 F. Supp. 2d at 496-98.

[50] Examples include a professional journal article, see Bopp & Cook, *supra* note 2, at 25-27, and a failed Washington State ballot initiative to ban partial-birth infanticide. See Jill R. Radloff, Note, "Partial-Birth Infanticide: An Alternative Legal and Medical Route to Banning Partial-Birth Procedures," 83 *Minnesota Law Review* 1555, 1556-57 (1999).

[51] See "AFA [American Family Association] Law Center defends Arizona ban with novel argument," *AFA Journal*, Jan. 1998, at 18.

[52] *See Planned Parenthood of S. Arizona v. Woods*, 982 F. Supp. 1369, 1377 (D. Ariz. 1997). In addition to this assertion in a lawsuit, the "*Roe* is inapplicable" argument was made several times at a March 1997 Congressional Hearing. See "Partial-Birth Abortion: The Truth: Joint Hearing Before the Senate Committee on the Judiciary and the Subcommittee on the Constitution of the House Comm. on the Judiciary, "105th Cong. 53, 108 (1997) [hereinafter March 1997 Hearing] (Prepared Statement and testimony, respectively, of Douglas Johnson, representing the National Right to Life Committee); *id.* at 72 (testimony of Helen Alvare, representing the National Conference of Catholic Bishops); *id.* at 161 (Letter from Prof. Douglas Kmiec to Sen. Orin G. Hatch & Rep. Henry J. Hyde (Mar. 10, 1997)). The argument was also submitted as part of Congressional floor debate on partial-birth abortion. See *infra* note 75 and accompanying text.

[53] "Origins and Scope of *Roe v. Wade*: Hearing Before the Subcommittee on the Constitution of the House Committee on the Judiciary," 104th Cong. 47 (1996) [hereinafter April 1996 Hearing] (Prepared Statement of Professor Mary Ann Glendon). The "*Roe* is inapplicable" argument was also suggested by Helen Alvare, representing the National Conference of Catholic Bishops, on a television broadcast. *60 Minutes: Partial-Birth Abortion* (CBS television broadcast June 2, 1996) (the procedure "is not truly abortion as the Supreme Court addressed that issue in *Roe v. Wade*").

professors Doug Kmiec[54] and David Smolin[55] at a Senate Judiciary Committee Hearing.[56]

Professor Kmiec came to the view that *Roe* does not cover the partial-birth procedure largely through thinking about the meaning of the word "abortion."[57] His instincts told him that abortion means the termination of a pregnancy, and a search of numerous medical dictionaries confirmed this initial understanding. Thus, an abortion can occur only during an ongoing pregnancy. But doesn't pregnancy end with the beginning of the birth process? How, then, can the partial-birth procedure be an abortion? To Kmiec, the answer depended on what counts as the beginning of birth. Does it mean only a birth begun in the natural way, by God? Or does it also include a birth begun by man's intervention? He determined that, in this secular age, a man-begun process was also a birth, and thus that *Roe* was inapplicable.

Professor Smolin's submission to the November 1995 Hearing is especially interesting because of his interaction with Congress a few months earlier. In June 1995, at the first Congressional Hearing on a proposed federal ban, he submitted a written statement, thus perhaps becoming the first law professor formally to communicate to Congress

---

[54] "The Partial-Birth Abortion Ban Act of 1995: Hearing Before the Senate Committee on the Judiciary," 104th Cong. 170, 174, 186, 194, 198 (1995) [hereinafter November 1995 Hearing] (testimony of Prof. Douglas Kmiec); *id.* at 231 (Letter from Prof. Douglas Kmiec to Sens. Orrin G. Hatch & Patrick Leahy (Nov. 27, 1995)).

[55] *Id.* at 345-46 (Written Testimony of Prof. David Smolin).

[56] As was true for Professor Mary Ann Glendon, see *supra* note 53 and accompanying text, other law professors eventually accepted this new argument. See *infra* note 75 and accompanying text.

[57] Telephone Interview with Doug Kmiec, Professor of Law, Pepperdine University School of Law (Aug. 5, 2008) (also the source for the other statements in the text accompanying this footnote). Professor Kmiec was also influenced by the fact that *Roe* explicitly failed to address a Texas statute that criminalized killing a baby in the process of being born. *Id.*; see *infra* notes 103-05 and accompanying text.

on the subject.[58] Smolin stated that "[t]he proposed prohibition of this particular method of abortion constitutes, in constitutional terms, a regulation of abortion."[59] Five months later, however, he argued that killing a partially extracted infant "has never been held [to be] within the constitutional right or liberty to abort.... Thus, the entire constitutional regime created by *Roe*...and...*Casey* is...irrelevant to the constitutional analysis of a ban on partial-birth abortions."[60]

Regardless of its exact origin, the "*Roe* is inapplicable" theory has persisted in the battle over partial-birth abortion bans. Since 1999, the argument has on occasion appeared in legislative documents,[61] but has

---

[58] Professor Smolin was scheduled to testify in person, but time constraints made that impossible. "Partial-Birth Abortion: Hearing Before the Subcomm. on the Constitution of the House Judiciary Committee," 104th Cong. 97-102 (1995) [hereinafter June 1995 Hearing].

[59] *Id.* at 98.

[60] November 1995 Hearing, *supra* note 54, at 345. Although Smolin has no specific recollection of why his views changed during this five-month period, Telephone Interview with David Smolin, Professor of Law, Cumberland Law School, Samford University (Aug. 5, 2008), the two statements themselves show how his thinking evolved. In June, Smolin argued that although *Roe* held that the "unborn" are not constitutional persons, a partially born infant might nonetheless have that protected status. June 1995 Hearing, *supra* note 58, at 100. He relied in part upon the fact that Texas's parturition statute, which criminalized killing a baby while being born, was not challenged in *Roe*. *Id.*; see *infra* notes 103-105 and accompanying text. Smolin did not emphasize the significance of this assertion–his discussion of constitutional personhood appears as an interlude in the middle of an argument that a partial-birth abortion ban can survive scrutiny under a *Roe/Casey* analysis. June 1995 Hearing, *supra* note 58, at 100. By November, Smolin had revised his written statement to highlight the constitutional personhood argument. It now came first, as a separate subsection. November 1995 Hearing, *supra* note 54, at 344-45. Smolin's second argument, missing from his June statement, but again relying on the fact that *Roe* "did not rule on the constitutionality of the Texas statute prohibiting the destruction of an unborn child during childbirth," was that the partial-birth procedure does not "trigger[] the abortion liberty." *Id.* at 345. Thus, even if fetuses are not constitutional persons, a partial-birth abortion ban must only satisfy "the rational basis test." *Id.*

[61] See, e.g., Partial-Birth Abortion Ban Act of 2002, Hearing Before the

surfaced most often in judicial proceedings. Numerous federal district and circuit court opinions discuss the theory,[62] and it has been advanced in numerous briefs filed with various courts.[63] Although the approach has in part convinced at least one individual judge,[64] courts have unanimously rejected it.[65] Some have done so by totally ignoring

---

Subcommittee on the Constitution of the House Committee on the Judiciary, 107th Cong. 164-65 (2002) (written testimony of Douglas Johnson).

[62] Many partial-birth abortion ban decisions do not mention the theory, e.g., *Planned Parenthood v. Miller*, 30 F. Supp. 2d 1157 (S.D. Iowa 1998), aff'd, 195 F.3d 386 (8th Cir. 1999); *Eubanks v. Stengel*, 28 F. Supp. 2d 1024 (W.D. Ky. 1998), aff'd, 224 F.3d 576 (6th Cir. 2000). Such decisions also have a significant role in any account of the "*Roe* is inapplicable" perspective–as examples of the flaw currently undermining partial-birth abortion jurisprudence.

[63] See, e.g., *infra* note 90 and accompanying text.

[64] Judge Chester Straub "do[es] not believe that a woman's right to terminate her pregnancy under *Roe*...extends to the destruction of a child that is substantially outside of her body." *National Abortion Federation v. Gonzales*, 437 F.3d 278, 298 (2d Cir. 2006) (Straub, J., dissenting), vacated, 224 Fed. Appx. 88 (2d Cir. 2007). See *id.* at 312. While this acknowledgment would seem to compel the conclusion that *Roe* is inapplicable to the partial-birth procedure, Judge Straub would still apply *Roe*, but in a way that would uphold the Federal Ban. See *id.* at 310-13. A 2003 House Judiciary Committee Report makes the same mistake. The Report first states that "partial-birth abortion should not implicate...[the abortion] right because the pregnancy ended once the birth process began and the right to terminate one's pregnancy by aborting one's unborn child does not include an independent right to assure the death of that child regardless of its location to the mother." H.R. Rep. No. 108-58, at 21-22 (2003). But rather than arguing that *Roe* is thus inapplicable to the partial-birth procedure, the Report says only that "the government [therefore] has a heightened interest in protecting the life of the partially-born child." *Id.* at 22.

[65] An interesting case study is the history of the "*Roe* is inapplicable" argument in Virginia. The State in 1998 had tried unsuccessfully to ban "partial-birth abortion." In the ensuing litigation, the State asserted what the district judge called "the rather unusual view that *Roe*...[is] inapplicable because...the Supreme Court did not announce constitutional protections to abortions where 'the child is partially born.'" *Richmond Medical Center for Women v. Gilmore*, 11 F. Supp. 2d 795, 822 (E.D. Va. 1998). The court "decline[d] the State's invitation to circumvent the requirements of Roe," *id.*, a rejection it reiterated in a later phase of the case. *Richmond Medical*

the argument,[66] but others have openly scoffed. Courts have characterized the theory in various ways: unsupported by precedent[67]; "a conceptual theory that...has no relationship to fact, law or medicine"[68]; a "back door effort to limit...[the abortion] right"[69];

Center for Women v. Gilmore, 55 F. Supp. 2d 441, 480 (E.D. Va. 1999), aff'd, 224 F.3d 337 (4th Cir. 2000) (*per curiam*). In 2003, Virginia tried again to ban the partial-birth procedure, this time making its policy rationale clearer by now seeking to ban "partial birth infanticide." A different federal district judge invalidated the new statute, once more rejecting Virginia's attempt "to establish a line [demarking a State's ability to prohibit abortion] in 'terms of whether a fetus was in the process of being born.'" *Richmond Medical Center for Women v. Hicks*, 301 F. Supp. 2d 499, 515 (E.D. Va. 2004). The Fourth Circuit affirmed, without explicitly referring to the State's argument that *Roe* is inapplicable to the partial birth procedure. See *Richmond Medical Center for Women v. Hicks*, 409 F.3d 619 (4th Cir. 2005), vacated & remanded, 550 U.S. 901 (2007), aff'd sub nom. *Richmond Medical Center for Women v. Herring*, 527 F.3d 128 (4th Cir. 2008), rev'd, 570 F.3d 165 (4th Cir. 2009). The Fourth Circuit ultimately upheld the Virginia ban based upon *Roe/Casey* as applied in *Carhart II*, with no reference to the "*Roe* is inapplicable" argument. See *Richmond Medical Center for Women v. Herring*, 570 F.3d 165 (4th Cir. 2009).

[66] A prime example is the Supreme Court in both *Carhart I* and *Carhart II*. See *infra* notes 89-90 and accompanying text.

[67] *Planned Parenthood of S. Ariz., Inc. v. Woods,* 982 F. Supp. 1369, 1377 (D. Ariz. 1997).

[68] *Causeway Medical Suite v. Foster*, 43 F. Supp. 2d 604, 615 (E.D. La. 1999), aff'd, 221 F.3d 811 (5th Cir. 2000).

[69] *Id.* at 619.

ideological[70]; and "specious."[71] Third Circuit Judge Maryanne Barry had an extraordinarily negative reaction to the argument. In a span of two pages, she characterized it as (1) "based on semantic machinations, irrational line-drawing, and an obvious attempt to inflame public opinion instead of [on] logic or medical evidence"[72]; (2) "a desperate attempt to circumvent over twenty-five years of abortion jurisprudence"[73]; and (3) "an effort to cloud the issues."[74]

This host of derogatory comments suggests that the "*Roe* is inapplicable" argument is frivolous, if not deliberately obfuscating. In fact, courts have been far too dismissive. Part II will demonstrate that sixty-three law professors were correct in stating to Congress that "[t]he destruction of human beings who are partially born is...entirely outside the legal framework established in *Roe v. Wade* and *Planned Parenthood v. Casey*."[75] Courts that have rejected the "*Roe* is

---

[70] *Northland Family Planning Clinic v. Cox*, 487 F.3d 323, 346 (6th Cir. 2007), cert. denied, 128 S. Ct. 873 (2008). In affirming the district court's denial of permissive intervention to Standing Together To Oppose Partial-Birth-Abortion (STTOP), the court characterized STTOP's brief as taking "an ideological approach to the litigation rather than attempting to argue for the...[challenged law's] validity under relevant Supreme Court precedent." *Id.* And what was STTOP's principal argument? That *Roe* does "not address the legal status of...transitional person[s]," i.e., human beings in the process of being born. See Final Reply Brief of Proposed Intervenor/Appellant, 2006 WL 3223977, at 14.

[71] *R.I. Medical Society v. Whitehouse*, 66 F. Supp. 2d 288, 304 (D.R.I. 1999), aff'd, 239 F.3d 104 (1st Cir. 2001).

[72] *Planned Parenthood of Central N.J. v. Farmer*, 220 F.3d 127, 143 (3d Cir. 2000).

[73] *Id.* at 144.

[74] *Id.* Judge Barry also brands as "mischaracterization" a standard, authenticated description of the partial-birth procedure. See *id.* at 140. It thus is ironic that she herself fails to grasp what the procedure actually involves. See *infra* notes 206-09 and accompanying text.

[75] Letter from sixty-three Law Professors to Sen. Orrin Hatch (May 8, 1997), in 143 *Congressional Record* 8807 (1997).

inapplicable" argument have inappropriately limited the people's power to express their corporate repudiation of the partial-birth procedure.

II. MISAPPLYING *ROE*

In evaluating whether *Roe/Casey* protect partial-birth abortion, an initial response might be to decry the very idea of constitutional protection for killing a baby during its birth[76] via what one federal judge has called "a gruesome, brutal, barbaric, and uncivilized medical procedure."[77] This protest would be understandable, but misguided. Judge John Noonan has reminded us that the long-protected life of American slavery shows that moral depravity does not necessarily mean the absence of constitutional status.[78] The proper legal question is whether *Roe*, properly interpreted, encompasses the partial-birth

---

[76] This characterization of partial-birth abortion is not only justified by what the process in fact entails, see *supra* notes 28-34 and accompanying text and *infra* notes 142-86 and accompanying text, but also has been accepted by the Court in *Carhart II*. See *infra* note 91 and accompanying text. For an eloquent denunciation of the idea of constitutional protection for the partial-birth procedure, see *Richmond Medical Center for Women v. Herring*, 570 F.3d 165, 180-83 (4th Cir. 2009) (Wilkinson, J., concurring).

[77] *National Abortion Federation v. Ashcroft*, 330 F. Supp. 2d 436, 479 (S.D.N.Y. 2004), aff'd sub nom. *National Abortion Federation v. Gonzales*, 437 F.3d 278 (2d Cir. 2006), vacated, 224 Fed. Appx. 88 (2d Cir. 2007). Cynthia Gorney writes that "[a] tone of queasy resignation permeates parts of [the district judge's] ruling [invalidating the Federal Ban], as though the judge were still reeling from descriptions of things that appear to be constitutionally protected despite being gruesome and brutal and so forth." Gorney, *supra* note 33, at 45.

[78] See John T. Noonan, Jr., "The Root and Branch of *Roe v. Wade*," 63 *Nebraska Law Review* 668, 668-69 (1984). Slavery was not explicitly mentioned in the Constitution, but its "legitimate presence" in American society was implicitly acknowledged by the "three-fifths clause," the "slave-trade clause," and the "fugitive-slave clause." See Don E. Fehrenbacher, *The Dred Scott Case: Its Significance in American Law and Politics* (1978), pp. 26-27.

procedure within the constitutional right to an abortion.[79]

The theoretical concept that *Roe* has only a limited reach presumably is not controversial. For example, no one would argue that the decision protects a woman's right to kill any of her children under the age of two. Another example of *Roe*'s limited scope is provided by Born-Alive Infants Protection Acts. These Acts, at both the federal[80] and state[81] level, are a legislative response to live-birth abortions.[82]

---

[79] *Roe* itself, of course, is highly controversial, but the question of its correctness, i.e., whether the Constitution, properly interpreted, confers a constitutional right to an abortion, is beyond the scope of this article.

[80] See *infra* note 85.

[81] Making accurate generalizations about state laws protecting infants born alive following an attempted abortion is complicated. Some such laws are officially named "Born-Alive Infant Protection Acts" and were enacted in the early 2000s more or less contemporaneously with the similarly named Federal Act. See, e.g., 5 *Ill. Comp. Stat. Ann.* 70/1-36 (Supp. 2008) (modeled after the Federal Act); *Mich. Comp. Laws Ann.* §333.1071.73 (2008) (not modeled after the Federal Act). Some states, however, protected born-alive infants long before the recent flurry of legislation. Pennsylvania, for example, as part of its 1974 Abortion Control Act, punished as second degree murder one who, "with intent to do so, ...intentionally and wilfully take[s] the life of a premature infant aborted alive." 35 *Pa. Stat. Ann.* § 6604 (1977). In 1978, this statute was repealed with the entire 1974 Act, but was replaced in 1982 by a provision in Pennsylvania's new Abortion Control Act entitled "Infanticide": "The law of this Commonwealth shall not be construed to imply that any human being born alive in the course of or as a result of an abortion or pregnancy termination, no matter what may be that human being's chance of survival, is not a person under the Constitution and laws of this Commonwealth." 18 *Pa. Stat. Ann.* § 3212(a) (2000). For other examples of this early protection for born-alive infants, see *Mont. Code Ann.* § 50-20-108(1) (2007) (entitled "Protection of premature infants born alive"); and *Neb. Rev. Stat.* § 28-331 (1995) (entitled "Care and treatment of child aborted").

[82] The legislation, at least to federal lawmakers, was considered essential "'to establish...a limit to...[the] sweeping right to abortion'" recognized in *Carhart I*. See Roger Bryon, "Children of a Lesser Law: The Failure of the Born-Alive Infants Protection Act and a Plan for Its Redemption," 19 *Regent University Law Review* 275, 278 (2006-07). The Federal Act was also motivated by the decision in *Planned Parenthood of Central New Jersey v. Farmer*, 220 F.3d 127 (3d Cir. 2000), which alarmed lawmakers by stressing a woman's intent in defining "the scope of her right

Some abortion procedures result in infants born alive.[83] Abortionists nonetheless have either directly killed these newborn infants or left them unattended to die.[84] Born-Alive Infants Protection Acts confer legal personhood status on such babies.[85] This legislation is unaffected by *Roe/Casey*.[86]

---

to destroy her offspring." *National Abortion Federation v. Gonzales*, 437 F.3d 278, 311 n.14 (2d Cir. 2006) (Straub, J., dissenting), vacated, 224 Fed. Appx. 88 (2d Cir. 2007). See *infra* note 183.

[83] Liz Jeffries & Rick Edmonds, "The Dreaded Complication," *Philadelphia Inquirer* (Aug. 2, 1981) (Special Reprint Edition). At the time, the Center for Disease Control estimated "400 to 500 abortion live births" each year in the United States. *Id.* The incidence of live births, of course, depends chiefly on the abortion technique used. A D&E abortion [see *infra* note 152 and accompanying text] is "foolproof," i.e., it "never, ever results in live births." *Id.* Prostaglandin instillation, on the other hand, can produce a live birth rate as high as eight percent. Nancy K. Rhoden, "The New Neonatal Dilemma: Live Births From Late Abortions," 72 *Georgetown Law Review* 1451, 1458 (1984). Live births following abortions are a continuing phenomenon. See Shantala Vadeyar, Tracey A. Johnston, Mary Sidebotham & Jean Sands, "Neonatal Death Following Termination of Pregnancy," 112 *BJOG* 1159 (Aug. 2005) (a study of neonatal death following abortion in thirty-one cases over six years in a certain medical region in England).

[84] Jeffries & Edmonds, *supra* note 83. See Bryon, *supra* note 82, at 275-76 (giving real-life examples of born infants "killed or left to die" following abortion attempts). There sometimes is an attempt to provide medical care to fetuses born alive after an attempted abortion. See Magda Denes, *In Necessity and Sorrow: Life and Death in an Abortion Hospital* (1976), p. 39.

[85] For example, the Federal Born-Alive Infants Protection Act defines "'person,' 'human being,' 'child,' and 'individual'" as including "every infant member of the species homo sapiens who is born alive at any stage of development." 1 U.S.C. § 8(a) (2006). "'[B]orn alive'" includes (but is not limited to) an infant who, following "complete expulsion or extraction" from its mother, "breathes or has a beating heart...regardless of whether the expulsion or extraction occurs as a result of natural or induced labor, cesarean section, or induced abortion." *Id.* at § 8(b). Bryon, *supra* note 82, argues that the Federal Act in fact confers very little, if any, actual protection on such infants.

[86] Although the declaration obviously does not bind a court, Michigan's Born Alive Infant Protection Act states: "A woman's right to terminate pregnancy ends when the

The "*Roe* is inapplicable" argument follows naturally from *Roe*'s acknowledged inapplicability to babies born alive. In the partial-birth procedure, the baby is killed before it is completely separated from the woman, but during a birth process–either the baby's entire head or its trunk from above the navel is entirely outside the woman.[87] At this

---

pregnancy is terminated. It is not an infringement on a woman's right to terminate her pregnancy for the state to assert its interest in protecting a newborn whose live birth occurs as the result of an abortion." *Mich. Comp. Laws Ann.* § 333.1072(c) (2008). While I have not found a judicial ruling on the constitutionality of Born-Alive Infant Protection Acts, there is substantial legal authority that *Roe* is inapplicable once live birth occurs. The decision most on point is *Showery v. State*, 690 S.W.2d 689 (Tex. Ct. App. 1985), which upheld a murder conviction for a doctor who suffocated a fetus after it was removed alive from its mother's body following an abortion attempt. The court held that *Roe* was irrelevant because "[s]eparation from the mother is a rite of passage beyond the shadow of conflict with her fundamental rights." *Id.* at 693-94. *Nealis v. Baird*, 996 P.2d 438 (Okla. 1999) (upholding a wrongful death action for a non-viable fetus born alive), reached a similar conclusion: "Nothing in *Roe* prohibits the states from affording legal protection to fetuses that are born alive." *Id.* at 454-55. Moreover, Judge Richard Posner has stated that "[o]nce the baby emerges from the mother's body, no possible concern for the mother's life or health justifies killing the baby." *Hope Clinic v. Ryan*, 195 F.3d 857, 882 (7th Cir. 1999) (Posner, J., dissenting) (involving partial-birth abortion bans), rev'd, 249 F.3d 603 (7th Cir. 2001). See *infra* text accompanying note 221. Finally, the history of Pennsylvania's statutory protection for born-alive infants strongly supports the view that *Roe* is inapplicable to such legislation. Both the 1974 and 1982 statutes were part of comprehensive abortion legislation, each entitled "Abortion Control Act." See *supra* note 81. When both of these Acts were challenged as unconstitutional, the born-alive infant protection provisions were not attacked individually, but only as part of the claim that the Acts as a whole were unconstitutional. When the courts in both cases denied these comprehensive claims, Act opponents did not even argue that the born-alive protective provisions were individually invalid. See *American College of Obstetricians & Gynecologists, Pennsylvania Section v. Thornburgh,* 552 F. Supp. 791 (E.D. Pa. 1982) (challenging the 1982 Act), aff'd, 476747 (1986); *Planned Parenthood Ass'n v. Fitzpatrick*, 401 F. Supp. 554 (E.D. Pa. 1975) (challenging the 1974 Act), aff'd sub nom. *Franklin v. Fitzpatrick*, 428 U.S. 901 (1976) (plaintiffs' appeal), aff'd sub nom. *Colautti v. Franklin*, 439 U.S. 379 (1979) (defendants' appeal). Thus, even those eager to challenge abortion restrictions acknowledged *Roe*'s inapplicability to measures protecting humans born alive.

[87] See *supra* note 32 and accompanying text.

stage of partial separation, when the baby clearly is alive, its skull is collapsed.[88] As will now be demonstrated, *Roe* cannot properly be read to protect the right to kill a baby in this manner.

A. *By Its Own Terms Roe Does Not Apply Once the Birth Process Begins*

In view of *Carhart I* and *Carhart II*, it would seem the height of presumption to argue that *Roe* does not apply to the partial-birth procedure. The argument was explicitly discussed in the lower court decisions leading to *Carhart I*.[89] The theory was also articulated in briefs submitted to the Court in both cases.[90] Nonetheless, the Court in both decisions totally ignored the "*Roe* is inapplicable" argument and applied *Roe/Casey* to evaluate partial-birth abortion bans. While the Court's complete disregard of the theory admittedly seems to be its deathblow, this would be an unduly negative assessment. *Carhart II*

---

[88] See *supra* note 33 and accompanying text.

[89] In the initial phase of the lawsuit, the State argued that *Roe* did not recognize "'a constitutional right to kill a partially born human being.'" *Carhart v. Stenberg*, 972 F. Supp. 507, 529 (D. Neb. 1997) (abortionist's request for preliminary injunction). The court interpreted this argument as an "invitation to ignore *Roe*" and declined to accept it because there was "no precedent...[that] uses the 'partially born human being' category as a construct for constitutional analysis." *Id.* The court declined that invitation for a "second time" in ruling favorably on the abortionist's request for a permanent injunction. *Carhart v. Stenberg*, 11 F. Supp. 2d 1099, 1132 n.48 (D. Neb. 1998). The Eighth Circuit expressed no final opinion on whether "there is a separate legal category for the 'partially born.'" *Carhart v. Stenberg*, 192 F.3d 1142, 1151 (8th Cir. 1999). Even if there were, the category would not be relevant to the present litigation because the court believed "that the word 'born' refers most naturally to a viable fetus." *Id.* This article demonstrates the deficiencies in this argument. See *infra* notes 159-72 and accompanying text.

[90] For *Carhart I*, see Brief of Amici Curiae Louisiana and Mississippi in Support of Petitioners, 2000 WL 228483, at 2-11. For *Carhart II*, see, e.g., Brief of Amici Curiae the American Center for Law and Justice, 78 Members of Congress, and the Committee to Protect the Ban on Partial-Birth Abortion in Support of Petitioner, 2006 WL 1436694, at 9-11.

acknowledges that the partial-birth procedure kills a baby during its birth.[91] All that remains is for the Court to recognize that *Roe* did not extend constitutional protection to a process that kills a baby after its birth has begun.

The *Roe* Court held that the constitutional right of privacy encompasses "the abortion decision,"[92] i.e., "a woman's decision whether or not to terminate her pregnancy."[93] There plainly is no constitutional right to abort once birth occurs. First, once the fetus is born, it enjoys the protection accorded by the Fourteenth Amendment to the life of every "person."[94] Second, while the Court stated that it would "not resolve the difficult question of when life begins," it was responding to the assertion that "life "begins at conception and is present throughout pregnancy."[95] The Court therefore was only expressing its unwillingness to "speculate" as to when life begins

---

[91] This conclusion follows undeniably from several statements in the opinion. The fetus is extracted from the womb by methods "conducive to pulling out its entire body, instead of ripping it apart." *Gonzales v. Carhart*, 550 U.S. 124, at 137 (2007). Doctors thus extract "the fetus intact or largely intact." *Id.* This extraction method is a "delivery" in that it "'assist[s] a woman in childbirth.'" *Id.* at 152 (quoting *Stedman's Medical Dictionary* 470 (27th ed. 2000)). It thus is properly characterized as a "birth process." *Id.* at 157; see *id.* at 160. The fetus, regardless of viability, "is a living organism while within the womb," *id.* at 147–an "unborn child," *id.* at 160; see *id.* at 134, and an "infant life." *Id.* at 159. The doctor then kills the fetus after either its head or "'trunk past the navel is outside the body of the mother.'" *Id.* at 147-48 (quoting 18 U.S.C. § 1531(b)(1)(A) (Supp. IV 2004)). Taken together, these statements acknowledge that the partial-birth procedure kills a baby during its birth. See *id.* at 138-39 (the Court relating a nurse's description of how a doctor stuck "'scissors in the back of...[a "'baby's'"] head'") (quoting H.R. Rep. No. 108-58, at 3 (2003)). For a defense of the Court's characterization, see *supra* notes 28-34 and accompanying text and *infra* notes 142-186 and accompanying text.

[92] *Roe v. Wade*, 410 U.S. 113, 154 (1973).

[93] *Id.* at 153. See *supra* notes 20-27 and accompanying text.

[94] See 410 U.S. at 157-58.

[95] *Id.* at 159.

during a pregnancy.[96] The Court elsewhere stated its belief that at "live birth" both human life[97] and personhood "in the whole sense"[98] unquestionably are present.[99]

But what exactly does "live birth" mean? In particular, what is the status of a fetus in the process of being born? *Roe* is not entirely clear on this point, but it contains important indicators. First, in speaking of both constitutional and ontological personhood, the Court stated that these categories do not include "the unborn."[100] As James Bopp and Dr. Curtis Cook have argued, "[a] baby who is partially delivered cannot properly be termed unborn."[101] In the partial-birth procedure, either the fetus's head or the lower half of its body is outside the woman,[102] i.e., born. Second, the Court quotes, but does not comment upon, a Texas parturition statute, not challenged in the *Roe* litigation, that criminalized killing "'a child in a state of being born and before actual birth.'"[103] Professor Richard Stith argues that this bare reference shows that the Court "explicitly left undecided" the issue of whether the

---

[96] See *id.* But as argued by Judge Michael McConnell, the result in *Roe*, withdrawing legal protection for fetal life, shows that the Court in fact decided the question. Samuel W. Calhoun & Andrea E. Sexton, "Is It Possible to Take Both Fetal Life and Women Seriously? Professor Laurence Tribe and His Reviewers," 49 *Washington & Lee Law Review* 437, 453 n.79 (1992).

[97] 410 U.S. at 150, 161.

[98] *Id.* at 161-62.

[99] See *supra* notes 80-86 and accompanying text (discussing Born-Alive Infant Protection Acts).

[100] 410 U.S. at 158, 162.

[101] Bopp & Cook, *supra* note 2, at 26. Justice Scalia argues that the partial-birth procedure involves "killing a human child–one cannot even accurately say an entirely unborn human child." *Carhart I*, 530 U.S. 914, 953 (2000) (Scalia, J., dissenting).

[102] See *supra* note 32 and accompanying text; see also *infra* notes 206-08 and accompanying text.

[103] 410 U.S. at 118 n.1.

"momentous shift from sub-human to human life [occurs] at the beginning, in the middle, or at the end of the birth process."[104] Since, however, the Court denies personhood only to "the unborn," one can reasonably read its silence about this Texas statute as suggesting "that abortion jurisprudence does not govern state regulation of procedures during extraction of the child."[105] This conclusion is further supported by an exchange that occurred during the oral arguments in *Roe*:

MR. JUSTICE MARSHALL: What does it [the parturition statute] mean?
MR. FLOWERS:[106] I would think that –
JUSTICE STEWART: That it is an offense to kill a child in the process of childbirth?
MR. FLOWERS: Yes, sir. It would be immediately before childbirth, or right in the proximity of the child being born.
JUSTICE MARSHALL: Which is not an abortion.

---

[104] Richard Stith, "Location and Life: How *Stenberg v. Carhart* Undercut *Roe v. Wade*," 9 *William & Mary Journal of Women & Law* 255, 266-67 (2003). Yet Professor Stith himself still argues that to disregard the beginning of the birth process is to act inconsistently with *Roe*'s premise that "[l]ocation–in or out of the womb–...determined whether actual human life existed and whether it was constitutionally protected." *Id.* at 255; see *id.* at 266-67.

[105] Bopp & Cook, *supra* note 2, at 26-27. The U.S. Court of Appeals for the Third Circuit gave two reasons for rejecting this argument based on the Texas statute. First, "[t]he fact that the Supreme Court did not *sua sponte* review a provision no party asked it to review says nothing about its position on that provision or on [the argument that *Roe* is inapplicable to partial-birth abortions]." *Planned Parenthood of Central N.J. v. Farmer*, 220 F.3d 127, 144 (3d Cir. 2000). This is a good point, but the court ignores the important exchange in oral argument concerning the statute. See *infra* notes 106-07 and accompanying text. Second, the court considered any arguments based upon the statute as inapplicable to partial-birth abortion because the statute, "[b]y its own terms...applies explicitly to killing the fetus...during the process of giving birth, not during an abortion procedure." *Farmer*, 220 F.3d at 144. It will be shown that the partial-birth procedure is an instance of "giving birth." See *infra* notes 142-86 and accompanying text.

[106] Robert C. Flowers was an Assistant Attorney General of Texas. *Roe*, 410 U.S. at 115.

MR. FLOWERS: Which is not–would not be an abortion, yes sir. You're correct, sir. It would be homicide.[107]

Based on this dialogue, it is reasonable to conclude that Justice Marshall, who voted with the majority in *Roe*, did not intend to recognize a constitutional right that would bar states from prohibiting killing a child once delivery has begun.[108] Justice Stewart, also in the *Roe* majority, did not question Justice Marshall's characterization. One can therefore reasonably surmise that he agreed with Justice Marshall's understanding that the right to abortion ends when the birth process begins.

It is noteworthy that *Roe*'s inapplicability to the partial-birth procedure was asserted by numerous law professors during the legislative process leading to the Federal Ban.[109] Those law professors who believed a ban to be unconstitutional had mixed responses. Harvard Professor Laurence Tribe, while never commenting directly on the "*Roe* is inapplicable" theory, demonstrated that he failed to grasp its underlying anatomical facts. Tribe asserts that a ban is irrational

---

[107] Transcript of Oral Re-argument, *Roe v. Wade*, 410 U.S. 113 (1972) (No. 70-18) (emphasis added), available at http://www.oyez.org/cases/1970-1979/1971/1971_70_18/reargument (last visited Jan. 25, 2010)) My thanks to my former student, Mark Trapp, for bringing this enlightening colloquy to my attention. See Mark M. Trapp, "Blackmun's Bane," *Enter Stage Right*, Jan. 27, 2003, available at http://www.enterstageright.com/archive/articles/0103/0103abortion.htm (last visited Jan. 25, 2010).

[108] I am aware of the grounds for criticizing placing undue emphasis on this exchange concerning a statute that was not under review in *Roe*. See *infra* note 129 and accompanying text.

[109] As mentioned, sixty-three professors endorsed the theory in a 1997 letter to Congress, submitted in conjunction with congressional debate on the proposed ban. See *supra* note 75 and accompanying text. In addition, *Roe*'s limited scope was asserted by several different law professors on multiple occasions during congressional hearings on the ban. See *supra* notes 53-55, 60 and accompanying text.

because it "defies plausible justification in terms of anything real."[110] How so? Because the ban draws a distinction based, strangely, on the physical location of the fetus between the uterus and the vagina...as though the fetus that is being aborted were suddenly to acquire...traits of personhood, simply by virtue of having been moved from one point to another within the woman's body prior to completion of the abortion procedure.[111] Tribe unaccountably overlooks the crucial fact of the fetus's partial emergence into the outside world.[112]

In 1996, Georgetown Professor Mark Tushnet was asked directly whether the partial-birth procedure, "in which a child is partially delivered before being killed and the delivery is completed[,] is within the scope of the protections afforded by *Roe v. Wade*[.]"[113] Tushnet testified that his "intuition" led him to conclude that *Roe* applied because the Court "drew the line at birth," and it would be difficult to draw it any earlier.[114] This is a particularly interesting response given that Tushnet was Justice Marshall's law clerk when *Roe* was reargued and decided. As already shown, the Justice himself had no difficulty in drawing a line earlier than birth–to him, the word "abortion" did not encompass killing a child during the process of childbirth.[115]

Professor Louis Seidman, another Marshall clerk at the time of *Roe*, would seemingly agree with the distinction drawn by Justice

---

[110] March 1997 Hearing, *supra* note 52, at 137 (prepared statement of Prof. Laurence H. Tribe).

[111] *Id.* (emphasis added).

[112] See *supra* note 32 and accompanying text. Tribe is not the only one to make this mistake. See *infra* notes 206-08 and accompanying text (emphasizing Judge Richard Posner's error).

[113] April 1996 Hearing, *supra* note 53, at 123 (question from Rep. Canady, Member, House Committee on the Judiciary).

[114] *Id.*

[115] See *supra* notes 106-07 and accompanying text.

Marshall. Seidman, although arguing in 1995 for a ban's unconstitutionality, came close to admitting the validity of the "*Roe* is inapplicable" theory. Professor Seidman's testimony was preceded by that of Professor Douglas Kmiec, who defended the theory.[116] After Senator Fred Thompson repeatedly pressed for Professor Seidman's response to the distinction Kmiec drew between abortions–covered by *Roe/Casey*–and the partial-birth scenario that he asserted fell outside those decisions,[117] Seidman said, "I suppose if Congress wants to pass a law that prohibits stabbing a scissors into the head of a baby where everything is out of the birth canal but a portion of the head, that would be something we could consider."[118] Judge Richard Posner would allow even more extensive protection for the baby. In explaining his constitutional objection to Wisconsin's partial-birth abortion ban, Posner stated:

> We...do not doubt that if in the course of a normal labor the mother asked her obstetrician to kill the baby in the birth canal and he did so, the state could criminalize this act as infanticide. But here...the state has criminalized merely a procedure, and acknowledged the right to abort by an alternative procedure the same fetus whose death by partial birth abortion would subject the doctor to punishment as a murderer. So there is no issue of infanticide, of killing a live baby that is half-born.[119]

Posner thus flatly proclaims that a state can criminalize killing a baby still wholly within the birth canal,[120] i.e., none of it is outside the

---

[116] November 1995 Hearing, *supra* note 54, at 170, 174, 194, 198.

[117] See *id.* at 199-200.

[118] *Id.* at 200.

[119] *Planned Parenthood of Wisconsin v. Doyle*, 162 F.3d 463, 471 (7th Cir. 1998) (citation omitted).

[120] Professor Laurence Tribe presumably would agree: "Nearly everyone, surely, would think it profoundly wrong if 'people with power' chose to treat an admittedly 'unborn' infant, struggling to push itself through the birth canal during the final

mother.[121] His necessary presupposition is that *Roe* does not extend constitutional protection to such an act.

My principal thesis thus far has been threefold: (1) that the abortion right recognized in *Roe* is delimited by the onset of birth; (2) that the partial-birth procedure entails the beginning of birth; and (3) thus that *Roe* does not constrain legislative bans. It might be argued, however, that my syllogism has a glaring weakness– "birth" as used in *Roe* most probably connoted a full-term delivery. Thus, when Justice Marshall indicated that killing a child during childbirth "is not an abortion," he likely had in mind a full-term fetus emerging from the womb in a routine delivery. Judge Posner obviously had such a fetus in mind when he referred to a state's ability to criminalize killing a "baby in the birth canal" during "a normal labor."[122] Consequently, even if one accepts the proposition that *Roe* has a limited scope, the limitation is not nearly broad enough to encompass the typical partial-birth abortion, which occurs far earlier than full-term.[123]

The foregoing argument can be readily overcome by focusing once more on Justice Marshall's suggestion, via his comment on the Texas parturition statute, that *Roe* does not apply to killing a child during childbirth.[124] The Texas statute criminalized killing "'a child in a state of being born and before actual birth, which child would otherwise

---

minutes of its mother's labor, as not yet a person morally entitled to our protection and love." Laurence H. Tribe, *Abortion: The Clash of Absolutes* (1990), p. 120.

[121] Posner speaks of a killing within the birth canal, whereas Seidman refers to killing a baby mostly outside the mother. See *supra* text accompanying note 118. It will be shown that Posner's grasp of the anatomy of the partial-birth procedure is erroneous. See *infra* notes 206-09 and accompanying text.

[122] See *supra* text accompanying note 119.

[123] See *infra* note 134 and accompanying text.

[124] See *supra* text accompanying notes 106-07.

have been born alive.'"[125] The critical phrase is "would otherwise have been born alive." Does it connote a full-term delivery? The clear answer is "no." At the time of Justice Marshall's comment,[126] the only proof Texas required was that, "but for the act of the accused,"[127] the child would have been able to breathe following complete separation from its mother.[128] The common occurrence of premature births plainly shows that breathing ability precedes full-term development. Consequently, Justice Marshall, in indicating that the act prohibited by the Texas parturition statute was not an "abortion," did not contemplate a "full-term baby" constraint on *Roe*'s inapplicability to the birth process.

---

[125] *Roe v. Wade*, 410 U.S. 113, 118 n.1 (1973).

[126] Marshall made his observation on October 11, 1972. See *supra* note 107.

[127] *Hardin v. State*, 106 S.W. 352, 353 (Tex. Crim. App. 1907).

[128] This understanding of "born alive" is extrapolated from Texas homicide law. A successful homicide prosecution required proof that the victim was living after complete expulsion from the mother's body. See *Wallace v. State*, 10 Tex. Ct. App. 255, 270 (1881). Showing "aliveness" in turn required a showing that the baby breathed following its complete separation. See *id.* at 271-74. If this test was met, the child was deemed to be "born alive." Thereafter, "'however frail it may be, and however near extinction from any cause,'" a person who intentionally killed it would be guilty of homicide. See *id.* at 275-76. The parturition statute, which covers killings "before actual birth," obviously eliminates any separation requirement. Instead, the question is whether the child, had it not been killed during its birth, would have been able to breathe following its complete separation. The homicide standard of "'however frail'" shows that in 1972 the parturition statute did not require proof that the baby would have been viable, see *infra* note 131, had it not been killed prior to complete separation, despite what at least one court has stated. *R.I. Medical Society v. Whitehouse*, 66 F. Supp. 2d 288, 304 (D.R.I. 1999), aff'd, 239 F.3d 104 (1st Cir. 2001). This conclusion is bolstered by the fact that Texas, a few years after the oral argument in *Roe*, enacted a definition of "born alive" that plainly excludes a viability requirement: a child is deemed to be born alive, "irrespective of the duration of pregnancy," as long as it breathes or shows other stipulated "evidence of life" after its "complete expulsion or extraction" from its mother." *Tex. Fam. Code Ann.* §12. 05(b) (Vernon 1979) (now codified at *Tex. Fam. Code Ann.* § 151.002(b) (Vernon 2001)).

But isn't it unconvincing to rely so heavily on the specifics of the Texas parturition statute in evaluating Marshall's statement? The statute was not at issue in *Roe*,[129] and one therefore cannot fairly assume that Marshall's brief comment was made in full awareness of its particulars. In addition, there is an indication that the Texas courts themselves believe that *Roe* impacted the constitutionality of the Texas statute. In *Showery v. Texas*,[130] the court stated that "[a] prosecution under [the] statute might necessitate an analysis in terms of viability under *Roe*."[131] This statement does not support the "full-term baby" constraint on *Roe*'s inapplicability to the birth process, but it does suggest that there might be a viability constraint.[132] In fact, *Roe*'s emphasis on viability is a principal reason that many courts have rejected the "*Roe* is inapplicable" approach. A representative assertion is that "*Roe*...categorized fetuses as viable or not viable. No case with which we are familiar uses the 'partially born human being' category as a construct for constitutional analysis."[133]

If there is a viability limitation on *Roe*'s inapplicability to the birth process, the argument that *Roe* does not apply to partial-birth abortion bans is largely defeated, for the partial-birth procedure is mainly used

---

[129] See *supra* note 105.

[130] 690 S.W.2d 689 (Tex. Crim. App. 1985).

[131] *Id.* at 692. A fetus is viable when it is "potentially able to live outside the mother's womb, albeit with artificial aid." *Roe v. Wade*, 410 U.S. 113, 160 (1973).

[132] The court's statement is far from definitive: *Roe* "might" be pertinent. Moreover, the Showery court's statement was dictum, as the case did not involve a prosecution under the parturition statute.

[133] *Carhart v. Stenberg*, 972 F. Supp. 507, 529 (D. Neb. 1997). See, e.g., *R.I. Medical Society v. Whitehouse*, 66 F. Supp. 2d 288, 304 (D.R.I. 1999), aff'd, 239 F.3d 104 (1st Cir. 2001); *Planned Parenthood of Central N.J. v. Verniero*, 41 F. Supp. 2d 478, 497 (D.N.J. 1998), aff'd sub nom. *Planned Parenthood of Central N.J. v. Farmer*, 220 F.3d 127 (3d Cir. 2000).

for pre-viable fetuses.[134] *Roe* itself, however, refutes a viability constraint. As already noted, the Court denied personhood only to the "unborn," a word that can reasonably be read to exclude any partially delivered baby, regardless of stage of development.[135] Moreover, to impose a viability constraint is to misperceive the role of viability in *Roe*'s analytical framework. Viability marks the point during a pregnancy at which the state interest in potential life becomes compelling, therefore justifying prohibition of abortion.[136] But the beginning of the birth process means that the pregnancy is essentially over.[137] The "potential life" is now manifest as the baby emerges alive from the woman's body. To acknowledge this reality in no way conflicts with the Court's unwillingness to speculate about when life begins in an ongoing pregnancy.[138] Viability is thus not a prerequisite for the power to legislate constitutionally about the birth process.

There is a final argument that *Roe* did not intend to encompass non-viable, partially born children within the abortion right. As noted, Judge Posner assumes that a state can constitutionally prohibit as infanticide the killing of a baby during "normal labor."[139] But he argues that partial-birth abortion bans are unconstitutional because they do not

---

[134] See Woodward, *supra* note 3, at 439 (discussing an investigative report by David Brown of *The Washington Post*).

[135] See *supra* notes 100-01 and accompanying text.

[136] See *Roe*, 410 U.S. at 162-63. However, *Roe* prevents the states from according meaningful protection even to viable fetuses. See *infra* notes 219, 227 and accompanying text.

[137] At one point, the *Roe* Court refers to viability as an "interim point" preceding "live birth." 410 U.S. at 160. This does not mean that "live birth" can only occur after viability. The Court no doubt was referring to a pregnancy of normal length, in which viability does precede birth. To say that live birth can never precede viability would be to contradict medical reality. See *infra* notes 159-72 and accompanying text.

[138] See *supra* notes 95-96 and accompanying text.

[139] See *supra* notes 119-21 and accompanying text.

constitute "killing a live baby that is half-born."[140] Posner's characterization of the partial-birth procedure can be evaluated mpirically. If the procedure does in fact kill "a live baby that is half-born"–a test that does not mention viability–Posner's logic compels the conclusion that partial-birth abortion bans, just like the infanticide laws he endorses, are not subject to *Roe*. The Supreme Court in *Carhart II* acknowledges that the partial-birth procedure does kill a baby during its birth.[141] The next section will demonstrate that the Court is correct. *Roe* therefore does not constrain partial-birth abortion bans.

B. *Partial-Birth Abortion Kills a Baby During Its Birth*

Does the reference to "birth" in "partial-birth abortion" ring true? Ban opponents have strenuously said "no," branding the term as disingenuous,[142] propagandistic,[143] and "inflammatory."[144] Professor Cynthia Gorney has written that "[t]here is no textbook reference to any...medical state called 'partial birth.'"[145] Even if one assumes she is correct–which is doubtful today given the prominence of the partial-birth abortion controversy–this would not mean there is no actual physical state of being partially born. To my knowledge, there is no word that means "a person in the process of going through a door

---

[140] See *supra* text accompanying note 119.

[141] See *supra* note 91 and accompanying text.

[142] Alisa Solomon, "Fetal Distraction: In the Fight over Abortion, Women's Rights Seem to Have Disappeared," *The Village Voice*, Jan. 27, 1998, at 49.

[143] See *60 Minutes: Partial-Birth Abortion*, *supra* note 53 (comment of Dr. Warren Hern).

[144] "In Depth: Late-Term Abortions" (*America's Talking* television broadcast June 22, 1995) (comment of Vicki Saporta, Executive Director, National Abortion Federation) (on file with author).

[145] Gorney, *supra* note 33, at 33.

from the inside of a house to the outdoors." This does not mean there are no people who are partially outdoors as they emerge from doorways.

The simplest way to resolve this dispute over use of the term, "birth" is to ask if the phrase "partial birth" describes what actually happens in the partial-birth abortion procedure. It does. As pointed out by Justice Clarence Thomas, "the fetus is all but born when the physician causes its death."[146] The fetus dies while being born, i.e., being removed from the woman's body.[147] Its life is terminated when it "has already emerged partly into what we would call in layperson's terms the outside world."[148] Hence, it was partially born at the time of its death.[149]

As noted, Judge Richard Posner asserts that the partial-birth procedure does not involve "killing a live baby that is half-born."[150] His explanation, however, is curious at best–that a state cannot constitutionally prohibit killing the same fetus "by an alternative procedure."[151] Posner here is referring to the fact that partial-birth abortion bans do not apply to standard D&E abortions, in which a fetus is dismembered and removed from the uterus in pieces,[152] rather than

---

[146] *Carhart I*, 530 U.S. 914, 986 n.5 (2000) (Thomas, J., dissenting). Thomas's "all but born" characterization is clearly correct, given that either the fetus's head or over half its lower body is outside the woman's body before it is killed. See *supra* note 32 and accompanying text.

[147] See *supra* note 29 and accompanying text.

[148] November 1995 Hearing, *supra* note 54, at 150 (statement of Helen Alvare). And "partly" means far more than minimally. See *supra* note 146.

[149] "'Partial-birth' as a label emphasizes the fact the delivery of a fetus/baby takes place, but only up to a point...." Woodward, *supra* note 3, at 433.

[150] See *supra* text accompanying note 119.

[151] See *supra* text accompanying note 119.

[152] See *Carhart II*, 550 U.S. 124, 135-37 (2007).

being extracted intact, as in the partial-birth procedure. But does Posner's point matter at all in evaluating what actually occurs during the partial-birth procedure? The fetus either is or is not alive and half-born when killed. The fact that it could be killed in some other way is irrelevant.[153]

But there are other possible objections to characterizing the partial-birth procedure as involving an actual partial birth.[154] Admittedly, the initial picture the word "birth" suggests is a full-term, natural birth.[155] That said, few, presumably, would conclude that "partial-birth" is an inapt description because the procedure takes place far earlier than at full-term[156] and depends upon artificial means.

---

[153] Despite the weakness of Posner's argument, one court characterizes it as adequately addressing the concern that striking a partial-birth abortion ban "will condone infanticide." See *Planned Parenthood of Central N.J. v. Verniero*, 41 F. Supp. 2d 478, 498 (D.N.J. 1998), aff'd sub nom. *Planned Parenthood of Central N.J. v. Farmer*, 220 F.3d 127 (3d Cir. 2000). For an extended discussion of the rationality of banning the partial-birth procedure, despite the inability to prohibit standard D&Es, see *infra* notes 193-233 and accompanying text.

[154] For the argument that the Federal Born-Alive Infants Protection Act precludes the concept of "partial birth," see *infra* note 163.

[155] In fact, some have criticized the term "partial-birth" for the very reason that "birth" most naturally connotes a full-term baby. See Bopp & Cook, *supra* note 2, at 22. Some ban opponents have further alleged that ban advocates deliberately cultivated the misimpression that the partial-birth procedure normally involves near-term fetuses, see March 1997 Hearing, *supra* note 52, at 86-90 (statements of Kate Michelman), a charge denied by ban proponents. See *id.* at 87-88 (statements of Helen Alvare and Douglas Johnson). There undeniably were some instances when ban advocates gave incorrect information. See Vobejda & Brown, *supra* note 47 (relating Newt Gingrich's assertion that the procedure is used to abort "'child[ren] in the eighth or ninth month'"). In fact, the procedure is mainly used for fetuses of "less than 24 weeks gestation." *Id.* It should be noted, however, that Dr. Martin Haskell stated that he knew of a surgeon who used it "up to 32 weeks or more." Haskell Presentation, *supra* note 30.

[156] See *supra* note 134 and accompanying text.

Deliveries prior to full-term are habitually called premature births,[157] and deliveries that are induced, assisted by forceps, or occur via Caesarian section all constitute births.[158] But there are two more serious arguments: the partial-birth procedure is not a partial "birth" because (1) it involves a fetus who likely is pre-viable; and (2) it aims for a dead, not a live, baby. Neither of these characteristics negates a partial "birth."

1. *Viability Is Not a Prerequisite for Partial Birth*

The U.S. Court of Appeals for the Eighth Circuit, in addressing the "*Roe* is inapplicable" argument, believed there was no need to determine whether there is a "legal category" for the "'partially born,'" to which "the rule of *Roe*...does not apply."[159] This step was unnecessary because the record was insufficient to prove that fetuses subject to the partial-birth procedure were partially born"–the word 'born' refers most naturally to a viable fetus, one that is capable of surviving outside the mother," whereas the case seemed "to be

---

[157] James Bopp and Curtis Cook are thus correct in saying that "full-term" and "birth...are two completely different things, both legally and in common parlance." Bopp & Cook, *supra* note 2, at 22. While premature births are not uncommon, "birth" has also been used to describe some quite unusual deliveries prior to full-term. *The CBS Evening News* of June 6, 2008 contained an intriguing segment entitled "Born Twice." It was the story of Macee McCartney, who had prenatal surgery at twenty-five weeks. To perform the procedure, the doctors temporarily pulled the uterus from her mother's body and then pulled half of Macee's body outside the uterus. The CBS correspondent spoke of Macee's "two birth dates," i.e., the day of her surgery–"the first time she was born"–and her delivery-day ten weeks later. *Evening News* (CBS television broadcast June 6, 2008) (transcript on file with the author). Katie Couric referred to the "baby born not once, but twice." *Id.*

[158] Macee's example, *supra* note 157, also shows that "birth" includes non-standard removal from the mother. It is interesting that CBS used "birth," not partial birth, to describe Macee's half-delivered state.

[159] *Carhart v. Stenberg*, 192 F.3d 1142, 1151 (8th Cir. 1999), aff'd, 530 U.S. 914 (2000).

exclusively about non-viable fetuses."[160]

Assuming that "born" does "most naturally" refer to a viable fetus,[161] does non-viability mean there can be no partial birth? In answering this question, it is instructive first to consider viability's pertinence to full-birth status. The National Right to Life Committee's Douglas Johnson gives this view:

> The fetus's location is what matters...if it's all the way out of the woman's body and it's alive, it's been born, no matter how developed it is.... "Let's say you have a baby born at twenty-two and three-quarters weeks," ...[and] "[y]ou have two neo-natologists standing over the incubator, arguing about whether they should do this or that, whether it's futile, whether this baby has a chance. Suddenly somebody rushes in from the corridor and strikes the baby on the head with a hammer. Does anybody dispute that a homicide just occurred? No. One neo-natologist may say a certain intervention is futile here. Another may say, 'No, we should do this or that thing.' But they're both going to grab that guy and call the cops."[162]

Johnson's argument rings true. Viability is clearly irrelevant to birth status for fetuses killed after complete separation from the woman. This is now a legal reality under federal law, even if the separation occurred during an abortion procedure. Under the Federal Born-Alive Infants Protection Act, fully separated infants can fit the definition of

---

[160] *Id.* See *R.I. Medical Society v. Whitehouse*, 66 F. Supp. 2d 288, 304 (D.R.I. 1999) (suggesting that non-viability in itself precludes a birth process), aff'd, 239 F.3d 104 (1st Cir. 2001). This article's earlier discussion of viability evaluated and rejected the argument that *Roe*'s implied inapplicability to the birth process encompassed only viable fetuses. See *supra* notes 130-38 and accompanying text. The present discussion of viability evaluates the empirical question of whether the concept of "partial birth" includes only viable fetuses.

[161] See *supra* text accompanying note 155.

[162] Gorney, *supra* note 33, at 44. In this hypothetical, the baby's gestational age when born suggests its possible viability. It is unclear whether Johnson would state the same outcome if the baby were clearly non-viable. Regardless, other legal developments demonstrate that lack of viability should be irrelevant to a fully separated baby's entitlement to legal protection. See *infra* notes 163-68 and accompanying text.

"born alive,"[163] regardless of their stage of development.[164] Viability has also been found to be irrelevant in other contexts. Some states issue birth certificates for babies born alive regardless of viability.[165] Most states allow actions for non-fatal prenatal injuries regardless of when

---

[163] See *supra* note 85. One court has used this complete separation requirement to suggest that partially separated infants cannot be "born alive." See *National Abortion Federation v. Gonzales*, 437 F.3d 278, 288 (2d Cir. 2006), vacated, 224 F. App.x 88 (2d Cir. 2007). The court's argument reflects a complete misreading of the statute. The Federal Act includes only fully separated infants within its statutory definition of "born alive," but also says that it shall not "be construed to...deny...or contract any legal status or legal right applicable to any member of the species homo sapiens at any point prior to being 'born alive.'" 1 U.S.C. § 8(c) (2006). The law thus "affirms the existence and dignity of postnatal life without denying the same of prenatal life." Stith, *supra* note 104, at 275. See *National Abortion Federation v. Gonzales*, 437 F.3d 278, 312 (2d Cir. 2006) (Straub, J., dissenting), vacated, 224 F. App.x. 88 (2d Cir. 2007).

[164] See *supra* note 85. Viability is also irrelevant under most State Born-Alive Infant Protection Acts. See, e.g., 5 *Ill. Comp. Stat.* 70/1.36 (Supp. 2008); *Mich. Comp. Laws* §333.1071(2)(b) (2008). Some states require viability, e.g., *Mont. Code Ann.* §50-20-108(1) (2007) (the statute is not named a "Born-Alive Infant Protection Act," but instead is entitled "Protection of premature infants born alive"), but this is a minority view. See H.R. Rep. No. 107-186, at 7, 13 (2001) (stating that thirty States follow a definition of "live birth" that does not contain a viability prerequisite and applies in a failed abortion context).

[165] E.g., Fla. Stat. §§ 382.002(10), 382.013 (2007); 410 Ill. Comp. Stat. 535/1(5), 535/12(1) (2005). The authors of a 2005 British study, which examined the incidence of completely expelled or extracted living fetuses following abortion attempts, presumably would question this practice. The study documents eighteen examples of pre-viable fetuses that met the criteria of "live birth" according to the World Health Organization definition. Vadeyar et. al., *supra* note 83, at 1159-60. The authors said, "it is clear that there is significant underreporting." *Id.* at 1161. The law required that "all live births and neonatal deaths must be registered." *Id.* at 1159-60. Nonetheless, the authors questioned "what purpose it serves to register as a live birth a fetus that is clearly not capable of being born alive and surviving...because the gestational age is below the clinical limit of viability. This...misleadingly increases the perinatal mortality rate." *Id.* at 1161. It is difficult to imagine a more striking example of an effort to mask the reality of live birth.

during pregnancy they were inflicted.[166] Viability is also not a requirement for wrongful death actions brought in connection with babies who died after being born alive.[167] Criminal convictions have also been upheld for causing the death of a live-born baby, regardless of viability.[168]

Stage of development should also be irrelevant to partial-birth status for partially delivered fetuses. Non-viability does not mean that a partially extracted fetus has not been partially born. The key inquiry

---

[166] Paul Benjamin Linton, "*Planned Parenthood v. Casey*: The Flight from Reason in the Supreme Court," 13 *St. Louis University Public Law Review* 15, 47-49 (1993).

[167] *Nealis v. Baird,* 996 P.2d 438, 455 (Okla. 1999): "Reason dictates that a child, once born alive, must be recognized as a person regardless of its ability to sustain life for any particular period of time thereafter." *Hudak v. Georgy*, 634 A.2d 600, 603 (Pa. 1993): "[T]oday we are reaffirming the unremarkable proposition that an infant born alive is, without qualification, a person." The *Hudak* court states that "no jurisdiction...[requires] that a child must be viable at the time of [live] birth in order to maintain an action in wrongful death." *Id.* at 602.

[168] See *Showery v. State*, 690 S.W.2d 689 (Tex. App. 1985) (upholding the murder conviction of a doctor who suffocated a fetus after it was removed alive from its mother's body following an abortion attempt). But cf. *People v. Chavez*, 176 P.2d 92, 94-95 (Cal. Dist. Ct. App. 1947) (stating that a showing of viability is required, but, in finding the evidence sufficient to prove that the "child was born alive and became a human being," only mentions "that the baby was born alive and that it breathed and had heart action"). In the non-abortion context, there is also increasing legal recognition of the irrelevance of viability. The Federal Unborn Victims of Violence Act (Laci and Conner's Law) "provides that if a child *in utero* is injured or killed during the commission of certain federal crimes of violence against its mother, then the assailant has committed an offense against two victims: the mother and the unborn child." Luke M. Milligan, "A Theory of Stability: John Rawls, Fetal Homicide, and Substantive Due Process," 87 *Brigham Young University Law Review* 1177, 1183 (2007) (describing 18 U.S.C. § 1841 (Supp. V 2005)). The Act applies regardless of the unborn child's stage of development. *Id.* at 1183 n.19. Thirty-six states have also "incorporated the double-victim approach into their penal codes[,]" *id.* at 1184, and twenty-four of these "provide that unborn children become legally separate entities upon their conception." *Id.* at 1185 & n.25.

is not viability, but whether the fetus is alive.[169] The Supreme Court in *Carhart II* stated that viability is irrelevant to whether a fetus is alive within the womb: "[B]y common understanding and scientific terminology, a fetus is a living organism while within the womb, whether or not it is viable outside the womb."[170] Viability is also irrelevant to whether fetuses are alive when doctors begin to drag them from the womb during the partial-birth process. As previously shown, the evidence plainly establishes that these fetuses are living up until the time their skulls are collapsed.[171] Since they are "all but" outside the woman when this occurs,[172] they are in fact partially born. To say otherwise is to deny physical reality.

---

[169] Because the Federal Ban applies even to non-viable fetuses, one court severely criticized Congress for its "misleading and inaccurate language" suggesting that the partial-birth procedure kills a baby during its birth. *Planned Parenthood Federation of America v. Ashcroft*, 320 F. Supp. 2d 957, 1029-30 (N.D. Cal. 2004), aff'd sub nom. *Planned Parenthood Federation of America, Inc. v. Gonzales*, 435 F.3d 1163 (9th Cir. 2006), rev'd, *Gonzales v. Carhart II*, 550 U.S. 124 (2007). To the court, "a 'live' fetus is not the same as a 'viable' fetus." *Id.* at 1030. No one can dispute this point. But it is also indisputable that a non-viable fetus can still be alive. "While a fetus typically is not viable until at least 24 weeks lmp [last menstrual period], it can be 'living'...as early as seven weeks lmp, well before the end of even the first trimester." *Planned Parenthood Federation of America, Inc. v. Gonzales*, 435 F.3d 1163, 1183-84 (9th Cir. 2006), rev'd, *Gonzales v. Carhart II*, 550 U.S. 124 (2007). Why then is it inaccurate to refer to a living, non-viable fetus, largely outside the woman's body, as partially born?

[170] *Carhart II*, 550 U.S. at 147. In upholding South Dakota's informed consent-to-abortion statute, the Eighth Circuit endorsed the "truthfulness" of a required disclosure describing the fetus as "'a whole, separate, unique, living human being,'" with "'human being'" defined as "'an individual living member of the species of Homo sapiens.'" *Planned Parenthood Minn., N.D., S.D. v. Rounds*, 530 F.3d 724, 735-36 (8th Cir. 2008). As stated by Professor Randy Beck, "[n]o one can reasonably doubt that a developing fetus constitutes a living biological organism distinct from its mother long before the point of viability." Beck, *supra* note 11, at 274.

[171] See *supra* notes 33-34 and accompanying text.

[172] See *supra* note 146 and accompanying text.

2. *Intent to Kill Does Not Negate Partial Birth*

The U.S. Court of Appeals for the Third Circuit, in rejecting the argument that *Roe* is inapplicable to partial-birth abortion bans because a fetus "is in the process of being 'born' at the time of its demise," stated that "[a] woman seeking an abortion is plainly not seeking to give birth."[173] The court saw no need to conduct an independent evaluation as to whether the partial-birth procedure initiates a birth process. In fact, even to suggest that a partial birth occurs was to engage in "semantic machinations, irrational line-drawing, and an obvious attempt to inflame public opinion."[174] The woman's intent to kill indelibly marked the procedure as an abortion.

In refusing to view the partial-birth procedure as an actual partial birth, the Court in *Causeway Medical Suite v. Foster*[175] also stressed the woman's intent–"to terminate her pregnancy"[176]–but in addition relied upon the physician's objective in initiating the alleged "'process of birth.'"[177] "'[B]irth'" is induced "artificially" in order to complete a "particular abortion procedure."[178] This marks the procedure as an abortion, not "the killing of a child during delivery."[179]

To say that intent to kill precludes characterizing the partial-birth procedure as killing a partially born child is to saythat "[t]here [are] no objective facts" about birth and the entity being killed.[180] Once the

---

[173] *Planned Parenthood of Central N.J. v. Farmer*, 220 F.3d 127, 143 (3d Cir. 2000).

[174] See *id.*

[175] 43 F. Supp. 2d 604 (E.D. La. 1999), aff'd, 221 F.3d 811 (5th Cir. 2000).

[176] *Id.* at 612.

[177] *Id.* at 618.

[178] *Id.*

[179] See *id.*

[180] Hadley Arkes, *Natural Rights and the Right to Choose* (2002), p. 276. Professor

"fateful choice" to abort is made, "there [is] no child to be killed, no birth to take place."[181] But intent to kill does not alter what has actually occurred in the real world–the partial emergence of a living baby from the woman's body. This physical reality should override anyone's intent.

Lawmakers have already embraced this principle in the different context of Born-Alive Infant Protection Acts. These laws, previously discussed, recognize that birth has in fact occurred when a fetus is completely separated from the woman, even when the separation results from induced abortion.[182] The Acts thus subordinate the woman and doctor's common intent to kill to undeniable physical reality–the existence of a born, living baby.[183]

Arkes does not refer explicitly to the doctor's intent to kill. He focuses on Judge Barry's opinion in the Farmer decision, which spoke only of the woman's intent. See *supra* notes 173-74 and accompanying text. Arkes thinks that "[i]f there was ever a decision that embodied the very vices it was decrying, this must surely have been it." Arkes, *supra*. Why? Because Judge Barry eschews "objective facts" in favor of "perceptions, ... 'semantics' and 'line-drawing'." *Id.*

[181] Arkes, *supra* note 180, at 276.

[182] See, e.g., *supra* notes 81, 85, 164.

[183] The Federal Born-Alive Infants Protection Act was in part motivated by the "logical implications" of the Farmer decision [*supra* notes 173-74 and accompanying text], i.e., once a child is marked for abortion, it is wholly irrelevant whether that child emerges from the womb as a live baby. That child may still be treated as though he or she did not exist, and would not have any rights under the law.... [T]here would, then, be no basis upon which the government may prohibit an abortionist from completely delivering an infant before killing it or allowing it to die. The 'right to abortion,' under this logic, means nothing less than the right to a dead baby, no matter where the killing takes place. H.R. Rep. No. 107-186, at 2 (2001). Some might criticize this perspective on Farmer as an alarmist interpretation of what the opinion actually sa*id.* Admittedly, there is nothing in Judge Barry's discussion of the significance of intention explicitly indicating that she would give the mother's intention to kill dispositive weight in assessing the legal status of a fully separated child. Still, this possible expansion of intention's impact has troubled others besides the House Committee. See *National Abortion Federation v. Gonzales*, 437 F.3d 278,

Intention to kill also does not change the physical reality of a partially born baby. As noted, Judge Posner believes that a state could criminally punish a doctor who, at the request of the mother, kills a baby in the birth canal.[184] The intent of the mother and the doctor to kill is no obstacle. Posner denies the partially born state of a baby killed during the partial-birth procedure,[185] but his rationale has been shown to be unpersuasive.[186] No one's intention to destroy should be allowed to mask the actual existence of these partially born babies.

This part has shown that partial-birth abortion is not entitled to the *Roe/Casey* level of constitutional protection. Given that the procedure brutally kills a baby during its birth,[187] diminishing partial-birth abortion's constitutional status in itself would be a worthwhile accomplishment,[188] even if no practical consequences followed. But Part III will demonstrate that "demoting" partial-birth abortion in fact

---

311 n.14 (2d Cir. 2006) (Straub, J., dissenting) ("If the intent of the mother controls the scope of her right to destroy her offspring, there is no reason why she should not be able to destroy the child after it has completely been separated from her body."), vacated, 224 F. App.x 88 (2d Cir. 2007); Arkes, *supra* note 180, at 276. At least one abortionist has clearly indicated that he feels obligated to kill a fully separated living fetus "because 'my ultimate job on any given patient is to terminate that pregnancy, which means that I don't want a live birth.'" *Richmond Medical Center for Women v. Herring*, 527 F.3d 128, 152 (4th Cir. 2008) (Niemeyer, J., dissenting). Born-Alive Infant Protection Acts eliminate any uncertainty by according legal protection to living, fully separated babies, regardless of anyone's original intention to kill.

[184] See *supra* text accompanying note 119.

[185] See *supra* text accompanying note 119.

[186] See *supra* notes 151-153 and accompanying text.

[187] See *supra* note 91 and accompanying text.

[188] As previously stated, moral repulsiveness alone does not mean lack of constitutional protection. See *supra* notes 76-78 and accompanying text. But a morally repellant practice should receive only the protection that is clearly mandated. Partial-birth abortion is not encompassed by the abortion right recognized in *Roe/Casey*.

could have a significant impact.

III. Consequences of Diminishing Partial-Birth Abortion's Constitutional Status

If partial-birth abortion does not qualify for protection under *Roe/Casey*, are there any constraints on majority will with respect to the procedure? This part demonstrates that any legislation is still subject to "rational basis" review and that partial-birth abortion bans readily satisfy this standard. The part then comments on some of the implications of using the correct evaluative standard in both the federal and state contexts.

A. *Evaluating Partial-Birth Abortion Bans Under the Rational Basis Standard*

The normal standard for evaluating legislative enactments is the rational basis test. *Williamson v. Lee Optical*,[189] a Supreme Court decision in the business realm, contains a classic explanation of this standard: "It is enough that there is an evil at hand for correction, and that it might be thought that the particular legislative measure was a rational way to correct it."[190] But the test applies beyond a commercial setting. In *Washington v. Glucksberg*,[191] which upheld Washington's assisted-suicide ban, the Court stated that to survive constitutional scrutiny a law must only be "rationally related to legitimate governmental interests."[192]

---

[189] 348 U.S. 483 (1955).

[190] *Id.* at 488. See also *Ferguson v. Skrupa*, 372 U.S. 726, 730 n.7 (1963), quoting *Sproles v. Binford*, 286 U.S. 374, 388-89 (1932): "When the subject lies within the police power of the state, debatable questions as to reasonableness are not for the courts but for the Legislature, which is entitled to form its own judgment...."

[191] 521 U.S. 702 (1997).

[192] *Id.* at 728. This was the proper test because the Court had first determined that

Do partial-birth abortion bans satisfy the rational basis standard? Are they reasonably related to furthering legitimate governmental interests? Justice Clarence Thomas has written that there is a clear governmental interest in "prohibiting a procedure that approaches infanticide, and thereby dehumanizes the fetus and trivializes human life."[193] This quote reveals a legitimate governmental interest–promoting the value of human life–and a step rationally related to its promotion–banning an act "that approaches infanticide."[194] But does this phrase accurately describe the partial-birth procedure? Here is what one nurse observed:

> The baby's little fingers were clasping and unclasping, and his little feet were kicking. Then the doctor stuck the scissors in the back of his head, and the baby's arms jerked out, like a startle reaction, like a flinch, like a baby does when he thinks he is going to fall. The doctor opened up the scissors, stuck a high-powered suction tube into the opening, and sucked the baby's brains out. Now the baby went completely limp.[195]

While these facts seem to speak for themselves as to the accuracy of

---

assisted suicide is not a fundamental right. *Id.* Part II of this article has established that the same is true of partial-birth abortion.

[193] *Carhart I*, 530 U.S. 915, 1006 (2000) (Thomas, J., dissenting).

[194] *Id.* In prohibiting an act "that approaches infanticide," Congress intervened to curtail any movement down a slippery slope toward actual infanticide. See *Carhart II*, 550 U.S. 124, 158 (2007). The Court in *Glucksberg*, in concluding that Washington's assisted suicide ban was "rationally related to legitimate government interests," 521 U.S. at 728, relied in part on the state's "fear that permitting assisted suicide [would] start it down the path to voluntary and perhaps even involuntary euthanasia." *Id.* at 732. In addition, Congress could reasonably "think that partial-birth abortion...'undermines the public's perception of the appropriate role of a physician during the delivery process, and perverts a process during which life is brought into the world.'" *Carhart II,* 550 U.S. at 160. Thus, a ban is rationally related to the legitimate governmental interest of "'protecting the integrity and ethics of the medical profession.'" *Id.* at 157 (quoting *Glucksberg*, 521 U.S. at 731).

[195] *Carhart I,* 530 U.S. at 1007 (Thomas, J., dissenting). The Court in *Carhart II* also relied on this description of the partial-birth procedure. 550 U.S. at 139.

Justice Thomas's description–and to bans' resulting rationality[196]–some have argued that partial-birth abortion bans are irrational because they do not prohibit the more common D&E method of killing a second trimester fetus–pulling it "from a woman's body in dismembered pieces."[197] Justices Stevens and Ginsberg have especially advanced this argument[198] and, in doing so, have heavily relied upon an opinion of Judge Posner.[199] Posner's reasoning therefore warrants a closer look.

Posner's opinion was a dissent to a Seventh Circuit decision upholding partial-birth abortion bans in Illinois and Wisconsin.[200] He used an example of the abortion of a hydrocephalic baby to demonstrate the bans' irrationality:

> If the physician performing the abortion crushes the fetus's skull in the uterus, killing the fetus while the fetus is still entirely within the uterus, he is not guilty of violating either of the statutes.... But if before crushing the fetus's skull the physician turns the

---

[196] "The question whether...[there is] a legitimate interest in banning the procedure does not require additional authority.... In a civilized society, the answer is too obvious, and the contrary arguments too offensive, to merit further discussion." *Carhart I*, 530 U.S. at 1007-08 (Thomas, J., dissenting).

[197] Gorney, *supra* note 33, at 33.

[198] See *Carhart II*, 550 U.S. at 181-82, 191 (Ginsburg, J., dissenting); *Carhart I,* 530 U.S. at 946-47 (Stevens, J., concurring); *id.* at 951-52 (Ginsburg, J., concurring). Their perspective has led to the further allegation that Congress's only purpose in enacting the Ban was to "chip away" at *Roe*. See *Carhart II*, 550 U.S. at 191 (Ginsburg, J., dissenting). See also Caroline Burnett, "Comment, The Unconstitutional Purpose Behind the Federal Partial-Birth Abortion Act of 2003," 42 *U.S.F. Law Review* 227 (2007). Similarly, it is asserted that state legislators have supported state bans only to "chip away at the private choice shielded by *Roe*." *Carhart I*, 530 U.S. at 952 (Ginsburg, J., concurring). Judge Posner is credited for originating this "chipping away" characterization of legislative motives. *Id.* It will be shown that this view is untenable.

[199] See *Carhart II*, 550 U.S. at 191 (Ginsburg, J., dissenting); *Carhart I*, 530 U.S. at 946 (Stevens, J., concurring); *id.* at 951-52 (Ginsburg, J., concurring).

[200] *Hope Clinic v. Ryan,* 195 F.3d 857 (7th Cir. 1999), rev'd, 249 F.3d 603 (7th Cir. 2001) (reversed due to *Carhart I*).

fetus around so that its feet are protruding into the vagina, he has committed a felony.[201]

Posner believes that to "any rational person, it makes no difference whether, when the skull is crushed, the fetus is entirely within the uterus or its feet are outside the uterus."[202] How can "the position of the feet"[203] have any moral significance?[204]

Posner's argument fails in part because his facts are wrong. He incorrectly thinks that the partial-birth procedure kills the fetus when it is still entirely within the woman, i.e., its feet are "protruding into the vagina."[205] Posner's misperception is made irrefutably clear in an earlier decision in the same lawsuit, in which he states that "death [occurs] while the body of the fetus [is] in the vagina."[206] There is overwhelming evidence contradicting Posner's conclusion. In part due to instruments used to reduce the distance between the cervix[207] and the outer vaginal opening, pulling the fetus into the vagina generally results in its body being in part, if not largely, outside the woman before it is killed.[208]

---

[201] *Id.* at 879 (Posner, J., dissenting).

[202] *Id.*

[203] *Id.*

[204] Posner says there is "[n]o reason of policy or morality that would allow the one [but] would forbid the other." *Id.* See *Planned Parenthood of Wisconsin v. Doyle*, 162 F.3d 463, 470 (7th Cir. 1998) (another Posner opinion in which he wonders "how a rational legislature could sense a moral difference between" the two different abortion methods).

[205] *Hope Clinic*, 195 F.3d at 879 (Posner, J., dissenting).

[206] *Planned Parenthood of Wisconsin v. Doyle*, 162 F.3d 463, 466 (7th Cir. 1998).

[207] The cervix is the lower "neck of the uterus" through which a fetus moves into the vagina. See *Taber's Cyclopedic Medical Dictionary* 382 (20th ed. 2001), p. 832.

[208] One doctor uses a ring forceps to pull the cervix toward the outer vaginal opening. *Carhart v. Ashcroft*, 331 F. Supp. 2d 805, 874-75 (D. Neb. 2004), aff'd sub nom.

Posner's blindness to what the partial-birth procedure actually entails[209] is richly ironic, for later in his opinion he criticizes public support for partial-birth abortion bans as based "on sheer ignorance of the medical realities of late-term abortion."[210] In purporting to instruct

---

Carhart v. Gonzales, 413 F.3d 791 (8th Cir. 2005), rev'd, 550 U.S. 124 (2007). Sometimes the cervix is pulled "to the level of the entrance to the vagina." *Id.* at 875. This in turn means that when the fetal head lodges at the cervix, "the fetal body past the level of the navel may be outside the woman's body." *Id.* at 874. For similar testimony by other doctors, see *id.* at 853, 860, 866, 869, 871, 877, and 881. Based on this evidence, the court concluded "that the cervix of the woman will frequently be at or very near the vaginal opening and sometimes even protruding outside the woman's body. Hence delivery of the fetal body, including the trunk past the navel, 'outside the body' customarily would be anticipated before the surgery begins." *Id.* at 1034 n.160. See also *Northland Family Planning Clinic, Inc. v. Cox,* 487 F.3d 323, 335 n.4 (6th Cir. 2007) (stating that a tenaculum is used to "shorten[], if not eliminate[], the distance between the cervix" and the outer opening of the vagina), cert. denied, 128 S. Ct. 873 (2008); *infra* note 214 (Justice Kennedy's acceptance of testimony that fetal death occurs when all but the fetus's head is outside the woman's body). The Federal Ban, of course, does not even apply unless either the fetus's head or half its lower body "is outside the body of the mother." See *supra* note 32 and accompanying text. This is also true of State bans that use the same limiting language, such as Virginia's recently upheld Partial-Birth Infanticide Ban. See *Richmond Medical Center for Women v. Herring*, 570 F.3d 165, 169 & n.1 (4th Cir. 2009). The statutes that Judge Posner criticized, however, did not make ban application conditional on some described part of the fetus being outside the woman at the time of fetal death. The Illinois and Wisconsin statutes spoke only of "partially vaginally deliver[ing] a living human fetus or infant." See *Hope Clinic v. Ryan*, 195 F.3d 857, 862-63 (7th Cir. 1999), rev'd, 249 F.3d 603 (7th Cir. 2001) (reversed due to *Carhart I*). Nonetheless, the evidence shows that "partially vaginally deliver[ing]" a fetus necessarily involves dragging the fetus partially, if not largely, outside the woman's body.

[209] Posner is not alone in his mistake. As noted, Professor Laurence Tribe misunderstands the procedure, *supra* notes 110-12 and accompanying text, as does Judge Maryanne Barry, *supra* note 74. She thinks that a partial-birth abortion ban is "nonsensical" because it bases "the demarcation line between abortion and infanticide...on where in the woman's body the fetus expires during an abortion." *Planned Parenthood of Central N.J. v. Farmer*, 220 F.3d 127, 144 (3d Cir. 2000).

[210] *Hope Clinic v. Ryan,* 195 F.3d 857, 880 (7th Cir. 1999) (Posner, J., dissenting), rev'd, 249 F.3d 603 (7th Cir. 2001).

the "uninformed," he once more misstates the facts by asserting "that the only difference between [the partial-birth procedure] and the methods of late-term abortion that are conceded all round to be constitutionally privileged is which way the fetus's feet are pointing."[211]

While Posner persistently misstates the facts, Justices Stevens and Ginsberg are unwilling to confront them directly. In their concurring opinions in *Carhart I*, they do not even mention that the partial-birth procedure kills a fetus who is partially, if not largely, outside the woman's body. Similarly, in their dissent in *Carhart II*, they only refer (unfavorably) to any line between "'abortion and infanticide' based not on whether a fetus can survive outside the womb, but on where a fetus is anatomically located when a particular medical procedure is performed."[212] "[W]here a fetus is anatomically located" is a phrase well-calculated to mask the reality lying behind the nurse's observation[213]–moving fingers and kicking feet were visible because they had already emerged from the woman.[214]

Because Judge Posner and Justices Stevens and Ginsberg never directly engage the reality of the partial-birth procedure, it is hard to take seriously their assertions of the ban's irrationality. Professor Cynthia Gorney, however, does not dissemble, but graphically

---

[211] *Id.*

[212] 550 U.S. at 186.

[213] See *supra* text accompanying note 195.

[214] "Witnesses to the procedure relate that the fingers and feet of the fetus are moving prior to the piercing of the skull; when the scissors are inserted in the back of the head, the fetus's body, wholly outside the woman's body and alive, reacts as though startled and goes limp." *Carhart I,* 530 U.S. 914, 963 (2000) (Kennedy, J., dissenting) (emphasis added) (statement obviously refers to the nurse's testimony, see *supra* text accompanying note 195). The Federal Ban, of course, in instances of feet-first deliveries like the one observed by the nurse, does not even apply unless the fetus's body from above the navel is outside the woman. See *supra* note 32 and accompanying text.

describes the partial-birth procedure, including the fact that "'the baby's body is exposed'" when it is killed,[215] i.e., its body is largely outside the woman. Despite her clear-eyed recognition of this crucial fact, Gorney too argues that a ban, because it does not prohibit the classic D&E technique, "makes clear ethical sense only to people who don't spend much time thinking about abortion."[216] "[I]sn't it ethically repugnant to press the case that one method of ending fetal life is worse than another? Isn't this like arguing about whether murder by gunshot is societally preferable to murder by strangulation?"[217]

Professor Gorney's question deserves a straightforward answer. Before I do so, however, it is important to emphasize the precise legal issue under discussion–whether partial-birth abortion bans are rationally grounded. The question thus is not whether one agrees or disagrees with Gorney's critique. Nor is the question whether ban supporters can convince everyone else to endorse bans. Rather, all that

---

[215] Gorney, *supra* note 33, at 34.

[216] *Id.* at 33.

[217] *Id.* at 44. Gorney specifically addresses these two questions to "the dedicated right-to-life person," *id.*, but her article in effect poses them more generally–via her assertion that because "pulling a fetus from a woman's body in dismembered pieces is legal, medically acceptable, and safe," it makes no "ethical sense" to criminalize the partial-birth procedure. See *id.* at 33. Although it will be shown that this argument is deeply misguided, it has broad support. See, e.g., Nussbaum, *supra* note 13, at 84 (*Carhart II*'s "allusions to the state's respect for fetal life spin like an idle wheel, given that the holding does not actually protect fetal lives, in that it permits a range of alternative techniques for late-term abortion") (footnote omitted); *supra* text accompanying notes 110-111 (Professor Laurence Tribe's similar argument). Cf. Jack M. Balkin, "How New Genetic Technologies Will Transform *Roe v. Wade*," 56 *Emory Law Journal* 843, 849 & n.27 (2007) (in view of alternative permissible ways to kill the fetus, *Carhart II* can be criticized for emphasizing the state interest in potential life); Susan Frelich Appleton, "Gender, Abortion, and Travel After *Roe*'s End," 51 *St. Louis University Law Journal*. 655, 661-62 (2007) (legal alternatives of killing the fetus demonstrate that partial-birth abortion bans serve only the state's "ideological or symbolic interests").

ban proponents must do is make a rational case for their position.[218] This task is readily accomplished, as one of Gorney's own illustrations makes clear.

Gorney points out that a woman twenty-eight weeks pregnant who wants an abortion to better fit her prom dress can legally get one under *Roe*.[219] Does this mean that it makes no "ethical sense" to punish as

---

[218] Consider Justice Kennedy's response in *Carhart I* to Justices Ginsberg's and Stevens's assertion that Nebraska's partial-birth abortion ban was irrational because it did not prohibit D&E abortion: "The issue is not whether members of the judiciary can see a difference between the two procedures. It is whether Nebraska can.... [The partial-birth procedure's] stronger resemblance to infanticide means Nebraska could conclude...[it] presents a greater risk of disrespect for life and a consequent greater risk to the [medical] profession and society, which depend for their sustenance upon reciprocal recognition of dignity and respect. The Court is without authority to second-guess this conclusion."

530 U.S. at 962-63 (Kennedy, J., dissenting).

[219] Gorney, *supra* note 33, at 40. This observation succinctly captures *Roe*'s impact on state attempts to limit either the permissible reasons for abortion or the point during pregnancy at which abortion is no longer allowed–*Roe* slammed the door on all such regulatory efforts. Gorney thus acknowledges the validity of abortion opponents' summary of the *Roe* standard: "'[L]egal at any time, for any reason, all the way through the ninth month of pregnancy.'" See *id.* at 39-40. This permissiveness is mandatory due to the broad nature of the health exception that limits a state's power to prohibit even post-viability abortions. *Id.* at 39. See *infra* text accompanying note 227. Gorney's accuracy in describing *Roe* is commendable. Incorrect depictions are legion, in particular those stating that *Roe* only prohibited state restrictions on early abortions. Most surprisingly, even Justice O'Connor has made this mistake. Sandra Day O'Connor, *The Majesty of the Law* (2003), p. 45: *Roe* "struck down as unconstitutional limitations by states on abortions in the first three months of pregnancy." For additional examples, see Jack M. Balkin, "*Roe v. Wade*: An Engine of Controversy" in *What Roe v. Wade Should Have Said,* ed. Jack M. Balkin (2005), p.4 n.4: (describing a 2003 ABC News-Washington Post poll that characterized *Roe* "as giving women the ability to get abortions if they want one at any time during the first trimester"); Gregg Easterbrook, "Abortion and Brain Waves," *The New Republic*, Jan. 31, 2000, at 21, 24 (*Roe* "all but ban[ned]" abortion in the third trimester); and Manny Fernandez, "Abortion Protest Draws Thousands," *The Washington Post*, Jan. 23, 2004, at B1 (*Roe* "prevented states from restricting abortion in the first trimester of pregnancy"). For other examples of accurate

infanticide the killing of babies of that age who have been born prematurely? Of course not. Prohibiting the killing of born infants is essential in any civilized society. Gorney shares this view,[220] despite her awareness that society, due to *Roe*, cannot effectively prohibit the killing of the same baby within the womb.

If protecting babies born prematurely is rational, then so are partial-birth abortion bans. The partial-birth technique kills a baby in the midst of a birth process, just inches from being fully born. Bans are thus supported by the same moral reasoning underlying laws punishing infanticide. Interestingly, Posner provides unintended corroboration in the two opinions already cited. In his heralded 1999 dissent, he defends laws against infanticide because it, unlike feticide, occurs after birth. "Once the baby emerges from the mother's body," Posner opined, killing it can no longer be justified.[221] But there is a right to kill "as long as the baby remains within the mother's body."[222] In the partial-birth process the baby is killed–despite Posner's apparent unawareness

---

descriptions of *Roe*, see David Brown, "Late Term Abortions; Who Gets Them and Why," *The Washington Post*, Sept. 17, 1996, at Z12 ("Contrary to a widely held public impression, third-trimester abortion is not outlawed in the United States.... [L]ife-threatening conditions need not exist in order for a woman to get a third-trimester abortion."), and Roy Rivenburg, *supra* note 30, at E8: "If a woman can find a doctor who says her emotional health is disturbed by a pregnancy, she can get an abortion at any stage of pregnancy."

[220] Professor Gorney has referred to infanticide as an "unquestionable wrong." See Gorney, *supra* note 40, at 346. While this does not necessarily connote her support of laws against the practice, elsewhere she has implicitly assumed the legitimacy of laws against "child-killing." See Cynthia Gorney, "Reversing *Roe*: Is Mainstream Right-to-Life Ready for an Abortion Ban?" in *The New Yorker*, June 26, 2006, at 46, 52.

[221] *Hope Clinic v. Ryan*, 195 F.3d 857, 882 (7th Cir. 1999) (Posner, J., dissenting), rev'd, 249 F.3d 603 (7th Cir. 2001).

[222] *Id.*

of the fact–when it no longer "remains within the mother's body."[223] Why then is it irrational to prohibit the procedure? In his 1998 opinion, Posner "do[es] not doubt" that a state could criminalize the "killing [of] a live baby that is half-born."[224] It has been shown that this is precisely what the partial-birth procedure entails.

Nor are bans rendered irrational by their failure to prohibit classic D&E.[225] Judge Posner, a chief proponent of this view, contradicts himself by acknowledging that a state can appropriately criminalize "as infanticide" the killing of a baby in the birth canal during "the course

---

[223] See *supra* notes 206-08 and accompanying text.

[224] *Planned Parenthood of Wisconsin v. Doyle,* 162 F.3d 463, 471 (7th Cir. 1998). See *supra* notes 119-121 and accompanying text.

[225] In the *Carhart II* oral arguments, Justice Ginsburg rejected as "beside the point" the Solicitor General's ban defense based on concerns about infanticide. Transcript of Oral Argument at 16, *Gonzales v. Carhart*, 550 U.S. 124 (2007) (No. 05-380). Why? Because bans do not prohibit the killing of the same fetus "inside the womb." *Id.* at 4. In response, the Solicitor General asked Justice Ginsberg to consider a "lawful post-viability abortion": "There is a problem with the mother's health, there is a problem with her life so it's a lawful post-viability abortion. I don't think that anybody thinks that the law is or should be indifferent to whether in that case fetal demise takes place *in utero or* outside the mother's womb. The one is abortion, the other is murder" (*id.* at 16). This reply admittedly was somewhat opaque. Its intended, compelling point was that the freedom to kill a child in the womb does not bestow unlimited power to kill it regardless of its location. See *supra* notes 219-20 and accompanying text. But the Solicitor General, in addition to making post-viability abortions sound more restricted than they are, see *supra* note 219 and accompanying text, failed to clarify what "outside the mother's womb" scenario he had in mind–presumably a premature birth. In any event, Justice Ginsburg either missed or deliberately ignored the point the Solicitor General was trying to make. She replied that "if this case were limited to post-viability abortions it would be a different matter." Transcript, *supra* at 17. This comment is completely non-responsive. If bans applied only post-viability, women still could freely have their viable babies killed *in utero*. See *supra* note 219 and accompanying text. Would post-viability bans therefore be irrational? It thus is clear that Justice Ginsberg in no meaningful sense "corrected" the Solicitor General's emphasis on infanticide prevention, as has been claimed. See Burnett, *supra* note 198, at 261.

of a normal labor."[226] But, as Professor Gorney has correctly stated, *Roe* allows the abortion of even a full-term baby: "If the doctor attests that she needs it...the state is not supposed to interfere, no matter how advanced her pregnancy is."[227] Why then, if partial-birth abortion bans are irrational due to their failure to cover D&E, isn't Posner's defense of such infanticide laws also irrational due to their failure to ban full-term abortions? Both laws criminalize killing a baby while it is emerging from its mother, but neither prohibits killing that same baby before it begins to emerge. Consequently, either both laws are irrational or neither is. I obviously endorse the latter option.[228] The emergence of a child from the mother's body has a broader significance than Posner is able to acknowledge. Once the birth process begins–whatever its nature–the child is a proper subject of governmental protection untrammeled by *Roe*.[229]

The gap in ban coverage admittedly leaves most second trimester fetuses unprotected. But any effort to criminalize D&E would plainly

---

[226] See *supra* notes 119-20 and accompanying text.

[227] Gorney, *supra* note 33, at 39. See *supra* note 219 and accompanying text.

[228] Additional support for the rationality of partial-birth abortion bans comes from information on how English physicians are advised to handle the problem of fetuses born alive following abortion attempts. Under English law, such a fetus, if viable, "becomes a child and a deliberate act that causes the death of a child is murder, even if that deliberate act precedes the birth." Vadeyar, et. al., *supra* note 83, at 1159. The authors therefore state "that if an abortion is taking place at a gestational age at which the fetus is capable of remaining alive it is imperative that feticide is performed prior to delivery." *Id.* Does the fact that a fetus can legally be killed before delivery discredit the law designed to protect it after its birth? The obvious answer is "no." Similarly, laws protecting fetuses in the delivery process make "ethical sense," contrary to Professor Gorney's assertion, *supra* text accompanying note 216, even though those same fetuses could be legally killed moments before. (For the argument that it is irrelevant that most fetuses killed via the partial-birth procedure are not viable, see *supra* notes 159-72 and accompanying text.)

[229] But cf. *infra* notes 251-67 and accompanying text (discussing how the protection *Roe* affords to dismemberment D&Es impacts partial-birth abortion bans).

be stricken under the *Roe/Casey* standard. Ban proponents can hardly be branded as "irrational" for failing to prohibit what cannot be constitutionally prohibited.[230] They acted prudently by attacking what was constitutionally open to attack, whether under the theory defended in this Article–that the partial-birth procedure is not encompassed by the abortion right–or on the grounds that *Roe/Casey* permit partial-birth abortion bans.

It is hardly novel for lawmakers to combat incrementally what they believe to be evil. Abraham Lincoln first fought slavery by attempting to restrict its expansion, which he believed the Constitution allowed.[231] He delayed assaulting the institution of slavery itself until changed circumstances made that constitutionally permissible.[232] Legal change may someday permit legislatures so inclined to accord more protection to fetal life. Until that day comes, defending the lives of fetuses who have begun the birth process is a cause to be praised, not belittled as irrational.[233]

---

[230] Similarly, opponents of pornography are not irrational for failing to seek to criminalize the private possession of pornography, since such an effort would inevitably fall to constitutional challenge. See *Stanley v. Georgia*, 394 U.S. 557 (1969). But they also are acting rationally in enacting constitutionally permissible prohibitions of the private possession of child pornography. See *Osborne v. Ohio*, 495 U.S. 103 (1990); *New York v. Ferber*, 458 U.S. 747 (1982).

[231] See Abraham Lincoln, First Inaugural Address (Mar. 4, 1861), in *The Collected Works of Abraham Lincoln*, vol. 4 (Roy P. Basler ed., 1953), p. 262.

[232] The Emancipation Proclamation, for example, was not issued until Lincoln felt it could be justified "[a]s a military measure" to deprive the enemy of property. See David Herbert Donald, *Lincoln* (1995), p. 456.

[233] Ban opponents are not the only ones who have criticized bans' emphasis upon fetal location. At least one pro-life advocate has expressed concern about stressing physical location in defending the value of human life. To Richard Stith, "location cannot make an ontological difference." Stith, *supra* note 104, at 263. In terms of their "real worth," it does not matter whether humans are within the womb, partially outside the womb, or wholly outside the womb. See *id.* at 261, 272. Rather, "human nature, membership in our species," is what actually underlies "human dignity." *Id.*

B. *Implications for Federal and State Bans*

1. *Federal Ban*

Carhart II left the door open for an as-applied challenge to the Federal Ban due to its lack of a health exception.[234] But it can be argued that under a rational basis standard a health exception is unnecessary. Lawmakers acted to prohibit partial-birth abortion because it closely approaches infanticide. Surely no one thinks that a law prohibiting infanticide must have a health exception. There is no reason to treat partial-birth abortion bans differently. In fact, differential treatment–requiring a health exception–would be especially inappropriate because bans are inapplicable if the fetus is killed prior to its partial delivery.[235] Thus, by killing the child while it is still in the womb,[236] any perceived health benefits that intact deliveries offer women arguably can still be realized without thwarting the purpose of deterring infanticide.[237]

---

at 272. From this perspective, partial-birth abortion bans are problematic because they are grounded on a morally irrelevant factor–physical location. But in this regard aren't partial-birth abortion bans like Born-Alive Infant Protection Acts? Physical location–complete separation–is what puts the latter beyond *Roe*'s scope. See *supra* notes 80-86 and accompanying text. They thus erect "a barrier to stop the right to choose from expanding beyond birth." Stith, *supra* note 104, at 275. But, as Professor Stith recognizes, the laws do not interfere "with the right to life expanding into pregnancy." *Id.* Partial-birth abortion bans are no different. They move the barrier to choice back a little further–to the birth process–but they do not preclude the argument that wholly intrauterine life should be protected as well. Any attempt, however, to further protect prenatal life is currently stymied by *Roe*. But see *infra* note 272.

[234] See *supra* note 18 and accompanying text.

[235] See *Carhart II,* 550 U.S. 124, 147-48, 164 (2007).

[236] Common methods include injecting "the fetus with a toxic agent such as potassium chloride or digoxin." *Evans v. Kelley*, 977 F. Supp. 1283, 1318 (E.D. Mich. 1997).

[237] Justice Ginsberg rejects this assertion due to the health risks associated with killing the fetus via injection. *Carhart II*, 550 U.S. at 180 n.6. The weakness in this argument is the apparent routineness with which prior fetal demise is induced. Dr. Leroy

2. *State Bans*

The potential impact of a rational basis analysis on state partial-birth abortion laws is a complicated subject, and it is beyond the scope of this Article fully to explore it. Rather, the types of issues that might arise[238] will be indicated by briefly considering two state bans–in Virginia and Michigan–whose constitutionality has been assessed subsequent to *Carhart II.* The key inquiry in both cases was whether the challenged bans[239] conformed closely enough to the Federal Ban to be upheld.

Virginia's ban was initially stricken by a Fourth Circuit panel because, unlike the Federal Ban, it was interpreted to apply to doctors intending to perform dismemberment D&Es, but who instead accidentally bring an intact fetus substantially outside the woman.[240]

Carhart, for example, almost always does so for fetuses of at least eighteen weeks gestational age. *Carhart v. Ashcroft*, 331 F. Supp. 2d 805, 854, 907-08 (D. Neb. 2004), aff'd sub nom., *Carhart v. Gonzales*, 413 F.3d 791 (8th Cir. 2005), rev'd, 550 U.S. 124 (2007). Further, *The Los Angeles Times* reported that of the 3,000 to 5,000 yearly partial-birth procedures known to one abortion proponent in 1995, every single one was preceded by killing "the fetus in the womb–by injecting it with poison or cutting the umbilical cord." Rivenburg, *supra* note 30 at E8. This high incidence of killing the fetus beforehand must mean that doctors have determined that doing so is not particularly risky.

[238] The lack of a health exception could also be grounds for challenging state bans, if, for example, a state decided that its constitution provides more protection to the abortion right than that conferred by the U.S. Constitution. The potential impact of a rational basis analysis on the asserted requirement of a health exception has already been discussed. See *supra* notes 234-37 and accompanying text.

[239] Michigan's statute was not worded as a ban of the partial-birth procedure, see *infra* notes 245-46 and accompanying text, but that plainly was its purpose.

[240] *Richmond Medical Center for Women v. Herring*, 527 F.3d 128, 137-39 (4th Cir. 2008), rev'd en banc, 570 F.3d 165 (4th Cir. 2009). The Federal Ban does not apply to such situations because it requires that a doctor have had the intent to initiate an intact procedure: "If the doctor intends to remove the fetus in parts from the outset, the doctor will not have the requisite intent to incur criminal liability." *Carhart II,* 550 U.S. at 151.

Since regular D&E is the most common second-trimester abortion technique, subjecting doctors who perform it to the risk of prosecution was held to impose an undue burden on the woman's abortion right.[241] The Fourth Circuit, en banc, reversed and upheld the statute.[242] The court acknowledged that the Virginia ban differs from the Federal Ban by covering doctors who intend a D&E, but unintentionally cause an intact partial delivery.[243] Nonetheless, the ban was constitutional because it has other features that "clearly delineate[] the rare circumstances in which a doctor [would] incur liability, thus enabling a doctor to perform a standard D&E without fear that accidental [substantial] emergence of the fetus" would in itself result in criminal prosecution.[244]

Michigan's statute did not even mention the partial-birth procedure. Instead, "it creates a protected legal status for a partially-delivered fetus that it terms a 'perinate.'"[245] A perinate is "'a

---

[241] See *Richmond Medical Center for Women*, 527 F.3d at 145-46.

[242] *Richmond Medical Center for Women v. Herring*, 570 F.3d 165 (4th Cir. 2009) (en banc).

[243] *Id.* at 176.

[244] *Id.* at 179. Consider, for example, a doctor who intends to procure a dismemberment D&E, but instead faces a substantially delivered fetus whose head is "lodged in the cervix." *Id.* at 178. The court believed that this situation would "almost always endanger the mother's life." *Id.* The Virginia ban's life-of-the-mother exception would allow the doctor to "complete the D & E procedure...[with] an unequivocal affirmative defense to any criminal liability under the Virginia Act." *Id.*

[245] *Northland Family Planning Clinic, Inc. v. Cox*, 487 F.3d 323, 327 (6th Cir. 2007), cert. denied, 128 S. Ct. 873 (2008). The statute in dispute, the Legal Birth Definition Act, *Mich. Comp. Laws Ann.* §§ 333.1081-85 (West Supp. 2008), was Michigan's third attempt to prohibit the partial-birth procedure. Its first effort, a partial-birth abortion ban, was struck down in *Evans v. Kelley*, 977 F. Supp. 1283 (E.D. Mich. 1997). Its second effort, entitled the Infant Protection Act, was invalidated in *WomanCare of Southfield v. Granholm*, 143 F. Supp. 2d 827 (E.D. Mich. 2000). The third attempt, entitled the Legal Birth Definition Act, was passed in 2003, but vetoed by the Governor. See Betsy DeVos, "Voters Rebuke Partial-Birth Abortion Veto,"

live human being at any point after which any anatomical part of the human being is known to have passed beyond the...[outer vaginal opening] until the point of complete expulsion or extraction from the mother's body.'"[246] The Sixth Circuit invalidated the statute because it lacked those "anatomical landmarks," i.e., the entire head or the body from above the navel downward, that ensure the Federal Ban does not apply to D&E's.[247] Because the challenged statute prohibited standard D&E abortions, it imposed an unconstitutional undue burden on the abortion right.[248]

How might the introduction of a rational basis analysis have impacted the resolution of these two cases? Concerning the issue raised in the Virginia litigation, a constitutional challenge to bans applicable to doctors who do not from the outset intend to procure an intact, partial delivery would seemingly more likely fail under a rational basis approach than under the *Carhart II* analysis, premised in *Roe/Casey*.

The Grand Rapids Press, June 24, 2004, at A15, available at 2004 WLNR 17813169. It was passed again in 2004, having been proposed by an initiative petition, a process that insulated the measure from the Governor's veto power. *Id.* The petition drive garnered over 460,000 signatures. *Id.* This third effort also ultimately failed. See *Northland Family Planning Clinic, Inc., v. Cox*, 394 F. Supp. 2d 978 (E.D. Mich. 2005), aff'd, 487 F.3d 323 (6th Cir. 2007), cert. denied, 128 S. Ct. 873 (2008). Undeterred, Michigan lawmakers in 2008 passed another partial-birth abortion ban, but it was vetoed by Governor Jennifer Granholm. See Chris Christoff, "Gov. Granholm Vetoes Abortion Bill, Mandatory Helmet Bill," *Detroit Free Press*, June 13, 2008, available at 2008 WLNR 11198631. An override attempt was contemplated. *Id.* At present, another ban, introduced in 2009 and tracking the language of the Federal Ban, is under consideration by the Michigan legislature. Partial Birth Abortion Ban Act., S.B. 147, 148; H.B. 4212, 4213 (2009).

[246] *Northland Family Planning Clinic*, 487 F.3d at 327.

[247] *Id.* at 336-37. The statute is triggered when "'any anatomical part'" passes outside the woman. *Id.* at 327. "'Anatomical part' means any portion of the anatomy of a human being that has not been severed from the body, but not including the umbilical cord or placenta." *Mich. Comp. Laws Ann.* § 333.1085(a) (West Supp. 2008).

[248] See *Northland Family Planning Clinic*, 487 F.3d at 336-37.

After all, an abortionist's intent surely is irrelevant to the legislative goal of preventing infanticide. If an intact, living fetus is partially born, killing it constitutes infanticide no matter what abortion technique was initially intended. The recent Fourth Circuit decision, though, shows that such an expanded ban can be upheld even under *Carhart II*.[249] As stated by Judge Wilkinson's concurring opinion, "[t]he state's interest in protecting life recognized in [*Carhart II*] does not vanish when the intact delivery of the child is unintentional.... The state may prohibit a deliberate and unconscionable act against the intact, partially born child, regardless of how the child got there."[250] Consequently, a rational basis approach is not an absolute prerequisite for according constitutional legitimacy to broader bans.

But a potential constitutional obstacle remains–the possible negative impact of more expansive bans on the availability of dismemberment D&Es.[251] These standard D&Es do not involve partial births,[252] and thus would still be subject to *Casey*'s undue burden standard. One could defend a broader ban's constitutionality by following the lead of the Fourth Circuit in ultimately upholding Virginia's ban–emphasize other statutory safeguards that would protect doctors from liability in such instances.[253] This approach convinced the six judges in the majority, but not the five dissenting judges, who thought that the alleged protections for doctors performing dismemberment D&Es were inadequate.[254] A rational basis approach

---

[249] See *supra* notes 242-44 and accompanying text.

[250] *Richmond Medical Center for Women v. Herring*, 570 F.3d 165, 181 (4th Cir. 2009) (Wilkinson, J., concurring) (en banc).

[251] The Fourth Circuit panel initially struck down the Virginia ban for precisely this reason. See *supra* notes 240-41 and accompanying text.

[252] But see the discussion in *infra* notes 260-61 and accompanying text.

[253] See *supra* note 244 and accompanying text.

[254] The dissenters believed that the majority's interpretation of the life-of-the-mother

would provide a way to avoid this debate about the effectiveness of Virginia's particular statutory safeguards. As noted, partial-birth abortion bans already provide a safe harbor for abortionists who do not want to risk prosecution–kill the fetus before taking action that could lead to its intact extraction. An injection to stop the fetal heart makes a ban violation impossible.[255] Subjecting an abortionist to this choice arguably is justified by the legitimate governmental purpose of deterring infanticide.[256] Nor is injection barred by concern for health risks to the woman. While there is some risk,[257] it is counterbalanced by the health advantages of avoiding a dismemberment D&E.[258] Injection is also a more humane way to kill the fetus.[259]

---

exception was flawed because it would also permit even intentional partial-birth extractions to proceed without liability for the doctor. 570 F.3d at 193-94 (Michael, J., dissenting).

[255] See *supra* text accompanying note 235.

[256] Critics would undoubtedly brand this suggestion as "irrational" because if the injection alternative kills the fetus, how can one reasonably claim that it furthers a state interest against infanticide? This critique, like the similar criticism based on bans' inapplicability to D&E abortion, gives insufficient weight to a fetus's location at the time of its death. See *supra* notes 219-33 and accompanying text.

[257] See *supra* note 237.

[258] The decisions are replete with assertions that D&Es pose greater health risks to women than the partial-birth procedure. These reputed safety disadvantages were the principal factual basis for the view that partial-birth abortion bans must include a health exception. See, e.g., *Carhart v. Gonzales*, 413 F.3d 791, 801-02 (8th Cir. 2005), rev'd, 550 U.S. 124 (2007); *Planned Parenthood Federation of America v. Ashcroft*, 320 F. Supp. 2d 957, 1000-01 (N.D. Cal. 2004), aff'd sub nom. *Planned Parenthood Federation of America v. Gonzales*, 435 F.3d 1163 (9th Cir. 2006), rev'd sub nom. *Gonzales v. Carhart*, 550 U.S. 124 (2007).

[259] One motivation behind the Federal Ban was concern over fetal pain: "[D]uring a partial-birth abortion procedure, the child will fully experience the pain associated with piercing his or her skull and sucking out his or her brain." Congressional Finding 14(M), in notes following 18 U.S.C. § 1531 (Supp. V 2000). Many of the ban cases contain discussions of the fetus's capacity to feel pain. The conclusions expressed

Concerning the Michigan statute, this Article has earlier stressed that the anatomical landmarks it lacks ensure that the partial-birth procedure does entail, contrary to Judge Posner's assertion, killing a "half-born" baby.[260] But if the *Roe* abortion right is delimited by the onset of birth,[261] should a state be permitted to extend legal protection to babies emerging from the mother's body, but not yet "half-born"? A living, intact baby begins the birth process whenever any part of its body, however small, emerges from its mother. This is so even when caused by an abortionist's pulling an extremity outside the womb for the purpose of initiating a dismemberment D&E.[262] Despite this factual

---

vary. One federal district judge accepted as a fact "unrebutted...credible evidence that...[the partial-birth procedure] subject[s] fetuses to severe pain." *National Abortion Federation v. Ashcroft*, 330 F. Supp. 2d 436, 479 (S.D.N.Y. 2004), aff'd sub nom. *National Abortion Federation v. Gonzales*, 437 F.3d 278 (2d Cir. 2006), vacated, 224 Fed. Appx. 88 (2d Cir. 2007). Another judge found that "[t]he issue of whether fetuses feel pain is unsettled in the scientific community." *Planned Parenthood Federation of America v. Ashcroft*, 320 F. Supp. 2d 957, 1002 (N.D. Cal. 2004), aff'd sub nom. *Planned Parenthood Federation of America, Inc. v. Gonzales*, 435 F.3d 1163 (9th Cir. 2006), rev'd sub nom. *Gonzales v. Carhart*, 550 U.S. 124 (2007). In any event, the court said the issue is irrelevant, for if a fetus does feel pain, it would experience "no less and in fact [what] might be greater [pain]" in a D&E abortion. *Id.* A third judge assumes that a non-viable fetus is able to feel pain "at some point during its gestation," but believes the issue to be only "marginally" legally relevant, if at all, in part because all methods of killing the fetus would be painful. *Carhart v. Ashcroft*, 331 F. Supp. 2d 805, 1029 (D. Neb. 2004), aff'd sub nom. *Carhart v. Gonzales*, 413 F.3d 791 (8th Cir. 2005), rev'd, 550 U.S. 124 (2007). While the court suggests that it is impossible to differentiate levels of pain between death by being "torn apart" in a D&E abortion versus death by heart stoppage due to injection, see *id.*, this conclusion is plainly counterintuitive.

[260] See *supra* notes 207-08 and accompanying text.

[261] See *supra* notes 87-121 and accompanying text.

[262] Justice Thomas, in *Carhart I,* argued that standard D&Es do not involve birth because the concept of "'delivery'" does not encompass removing "the child from the uterus piece by piece." *Carhart I*, 530 U.S. 914, 990 (2000) (Thomas, J., dissenting). The dismemberment that D&Es entail, however, usually does not occur completely within the womb. See *infra* note 263. Thus, a baby typically is still living and intact

reality, a legislature can only protect what the Court allows to be protected. A triggering standard of "'"any anatomical part"'" reveals a contradiction in the impact of *Roe*, even if properly interpreted. A partial-birth prohibition at this earliest stage of delivery should be allowed due to *Roe*'s "onset of birth" limitation, but any such ban would impermissibly infringe upon the right to a D&E abortion.[263]

One solution to this dilemma[264] would be to rewrite the Michigan statute to track the Federal Ban, thus presumably ensuring constitutional validity. But this obviously sacrifices the principle that any partially born baby is a proper subject of state protection.[265] An

---

when its first limb is torn off.

[263] A D&E abortion typically does not tear the fetus apart completely inside the womb. Rather, the doctor pulls a fetal body part, e.g., a leg, out of the womb and often outside the woman altogether before wrenching it off. The disarticulation is possible due to the resistance caused when the rest of the fetus's body lodges at the cervix. Thus, in a D&E abortion, there will often be times when an intact fetus is partially drawn outside the woman before it is killed. See, e.g., *Carhart v. Ashcroft*, 331 F. Supp. 2d 805, 860, 866, 871, 877-78 (D. Neb. 2004), aff'd sub nom. *Carhart v. Gonzales*, 413 F.3d 791 (8th Cir. 2005), rev'd, 550 U.S. 124 (2007). Applying a partial-birth abortion ban to this situation would obviously subject doctors who perform D&E's to the risk of a ban violation. Cf. *Planned Parenthood of Central N.J. v. Verniero*, 41 F. Supp. 2d 478, 497 & n.11 (expressing concern that interpreting *Roe* as inapplicable to partially born fetuses "could potentially exclude all conventional abortion procedures from constitutional protection"), aff'd sub nom. *Planned Parenthood of Central N.J. v. Farmer*, 220 F.3d 127 (3d Cir. 2000). This result could be avoided by retaining the previously criticized intention requirement. See *supra* text accompanying note 249.

[264] It might be argued that the very existence of this dilemma demonstrates that the interpretation of *Roe* defended in this Article is incorrect. After all, is it plausible that the Court would have written a self-contradictory opinion? The problem with this critique is that rejecting the "*Roe* is inapplicable" perspective does not avoid the issue of self-contradiction. If *Roe* is interpreted as still applying once the birth process begins, then what is one to make of all the evidence suggesting that this is not what the *Roe* Court intended? See *supra* notes 92-141 and accompanying text.

[265] It would also sacrifice the argument that the intention of the doctor should be irrelevant to the legal protection offered to partially born babies. See *supra* text

alternative is to argue that the present Michigan statute satisfies the rational basis test. After all, there is no meaningful moral distinction based on how much of a baby is outside the woman.[266] Doctors' freedom to perform D&E's can be preserved by the practice of killing the fetus before beginning any D&E procedure.[267]

CONCLUSION

With respect to what he calls "live-birth abortion," Justice Scalia thinks it "is quite simply absurd" to believe "that the Constitution of the United States...prohibits...banning this visibly brutal means of eliminating our half-born posterity."[268] Scalia is correct, but for reasons beyond those given in his opinion.[269] As has long been argued, the partial-birth procedure is not encompassed by the abortion right conferred by *Roe*.[270] Consequently, current partial-birth jurisprudence

---

accompanying note 249.

[266] It can also be argued that there is no meaningful moral distinction based on whether any of the baby is outside the woman. See *supra* note 233. But some part of a living, intact fetus must be outside of the woman to trigger the "*Roe* is inapplicable" argument.

[267] See *supra* notes 255-56 and accompanying text. As previously discussed, this alternative arguably does not impermissibly put women's health at risk, see *supra* notes 257-58 and accompanying text, and also is supported by humanitarian concern for the fetus. See *supra* note 259 and accompanying text.

[268] See *supra* notes 255-56 and accompanying text. As previously discussed, this alternative arguably does not impermissibly put women's health at risk, see *supra* notes 257-58 and accompanying text, and also is supported by humanitarian concern for the fetus. See *supra* note 259 and accompanying text.

[269] Justice Scalia believed that *Casey* did not support the Court's decision to invalidate Nebraska's ban. See *Carhart I*, 530 U.S. at 953-54 (Scalia, J., dissenting). Whether Justice Scalia was correct as to how *Casey* should be applied to state partial-birth abortion bans is beyond the scope of this article, which instead argues that such statutes are not subject to *Casey*.

[270] This article attempts to establish this proposition beyond challenge. At the very

applies the wrong test. State bans and the Federal Ban are properly subject only to rational basis review.

Prominent ban critics, including Judge Posner and Justices Stevens and Ginsberg, assert that bans are irrational because they do not prohibit D&E abortion. To them, the right to kill by one method bestows an unrestrained right to kill. But D&E is protected by *Roe*, whereas the partial-birth procedure is not.[271] Lawmakers thus have much more freedom to act against the latter.[272] Because they can reasonably conclude that killing a child during its birth verges on infanticide, banning the partial-birth procedure plainly satisfies the rational basis test.[273]

---

least, it is hoped that the article demonstrates that the "*Roe* is inapplicable" argument has substantial merit and that courts have been wrong to respond to it dismissively or derisively. See *supra* notes 65-74 and accompanying text.

[271] The principal point of this article is that *Roe*, properly interpreted, does not apply to killing a baby during its birth. There is, of course, an alternative argument for the constitutionality of partial-birth abortion bans. As *Carhart II* demonstrates, bans can be written in a way that satisfies the *Roe/Casey* standard.

[272] For an argument that *Carhart II* opens the door to banning dismemberment D&Es, see Stephen G. Gilles, As Justice Kennedy Sa*id*. See *First Things* (Jan. 2008), at p. 18, available at http://www.firstthings.com/article/2007/12/002-as-justice-kennedy-said. Evaluating this contention is beyond the scope of this article.

[273] This article is a revised and expanded version of a talk I presented at the 2008 UFL Conference. The author thanks Stephen Calhoun, Teresa Collett, Stephen Gilles, Allan Ides, Doug Kmiec, Ann Massie, Rick Schlauch, David Smolin, Richard Stith, and Robin Wilson for their help. Thanks also to Bridget Fay and Sam Huang for their valuable research assistance. The author also appreciates the financial assistance provided by the Frances Lewis Law Center, Washington and Lee University School of Law.

Constitutional Personhood of the Unborn Child

Robert C. Cetrulo

ABSTRACT: The fatal flaw of *Roe v. Wade*, the 1973 Supreme Court decision legalizing abortion, is that the Court failed to recognize the constitutional personhood of the unborn child within the meaning of the due process and equal protection clauses of the Fourteenth Amendment. The court's majority opinion blatantly ignored the uncontroverted evidence of the personhood of the unborn in medicine, in law, and in literature already extant prior to the adoption of "personhood" protection in the Fourteenth Amendment. Accordingly, from the standpoint of language and logical analysis, the legal separation of "human beings" from "persons" is artificial and arbitrary.

THE THRESHOLD AND FATAL FLAW of *Roe v. Wade*,[1] the 1973 Supreme Court decision legalizing abortion, is that the Court failed to recognize the constitutional personhood of the unborn child within the meaning of clauses within the Fourteenth Amendment to the U.S. Constitution governing due process and equal protection of the law.

Common law has long recognized the primacy of three canons for judicial interpretation of these documents: (1) Words are to be given their "plain meaning." (2) If there exists any ambiguity in the words, we must look to the "original understanding" of their usage at the time when the documentation was drawn. (3) Consideration is to be given to the entire document.

PLAIN MEANING

Without question the first rule of any intelligent discourse or

---

[1] 93 S.Ct. 705 (1973).

disputation is that one must define one's terms. The art of reasoning unquestionably proceeds from that which is known (conceded by all) to that which is unknown (or disputed) in order to arrive at further knowledge. I would submit that the very process of "thinking" demands "words," for they are the vehicles for expressing our thoughts. As someone once put it, "words are the clothes that ideas wear."

Our opponents would concede that all "persons" are "human beings," but they would deny the reverse of that proposition, namely, that all "human beings" are "persons." Approaching this question from the most neutral starting-point possible, one would be compelled to inquire thus: "What is a human being?" Notice that the focus of this question is the broadest one possible, the neutral and impersonal pronoun "what."

I submit that the most common answer that one could receive to this question–and indeed the most logical answer–would be that a human being is one who is a being (i.e., one who is in existence) and one who is a member of the human species. With this answer the inquiry has logically and inescapably progressed to the personal pronoun "who."

Under this process of analysis, which is certainly neither an *a priori* sort of reasoning from some preconceived conclusion or assumption nor the sort of reasoning that we lawyers call "a leading question" (that is, a question suggesting the desired answer), we nonetheless end up inescapably at the conclusion that the "who" of the human being is a "person." Accordingly, from the standpoint of language and logical analysis, the legal separation of "human being" from "person" is artificial and arbitrary, and certainly not rooted in language, logic, or common understanding, nor in medicine, law, or history, as will be shown below.

St. Thomas More, that great English lawyer and Chancellor of England, was once challenged by his son-in-law Roper concerning the crown-promulgated oath that mandated, under penalty of treason, total recognition of King Henry VIII's re-marriage: "We don't need to know the wording–we know what it will mean!" More's incisive response was "It will mean what the words say."[2]

Since every "person" must first be a "human being," let us explore the humanity and the individuality of the unborn child in science, law, and history.

(1) "Biologically, at no stage can we subscribe to the view that the foetus is a mere appendage of the mother. Genetically, mother and baby are separate individuals from conception."[3]

(2) "It is scientifically correct to say that an individual human life begins at conception, when the egg and sperm join to form the zygote, and that this developing human always is a member of our species in all stages of its life. There is not one medical text in use in one medical school in this country that teaches to the contrary."[4]

(3) "Life has a very, very long history, but each individual has a very neat beginning, the moment of its conception."[5]

(4) "The work of Edwards and his associates in England with test-tube babies has repeatedly proved that human life begins when, after the ovum is fertilized, the new combined cell mass begins to divide."[6]

(5) "Human" carries the dictionary definition of "belonging to or relating to man...."[7]

CAN A "HUMAN BEING" FAIL TO BE A "PERSON"?

---

[2] Robert Bolt, *A Man for All Seasons* (New York NY: Vintage, 1990).

[3] A. W. Liley, M.D., widely referred to as "the father of fetology."

[4] Micheline Mathews-Roth, M.D., principal research associate of the Harvard University Medical School.

[5] Jerome Lejeune, M.D., professor of fundamental genetics at the University of Descartes (Paris, France).

[6] Jasper Williams, M.D., past president of the National Medical Association.

[7] *Webster's Collegiate Dictionary*, 5th ed., 1948 (my high school dictionary).

Adolf Hitler apparently thought so, and now, for the first time in American jurisprudence, the *Roe* court sought to teach this gigantic oxymoron.[8]

Eminent sources from philosophy and common sense have taught to the contrary. The great Roman philosopher, Boethius, some fifteen hundred years ago, defined "person" as "an individual substance of a rational nature,"[9] and the twentieth-century children's writer, Dr. Seuss, reminded us that "a person's a person, no matter how small."[10]

Contrary to Mr. Justice Blackmun's assertion in *Roe* that "the unborn have never been recognized in the law as persons in the whole sense," there is a wealth of legal authority to the contrary, both predating and postdating *Roe*. The leading U.S. legal encyclopedia, for instance, states:

Biologically speaking, the life of a human being begins at the moment of conception in the mother's womb, and *as a general rule of construction in the law, a legal personality is imputed to an unborn child for all purposes which would be beneficial to the infant after its birth*.... A child unborn at the time of the death of its parent has also been considered a "child" of the decedent in determining beneficiaries of an award in a wrongful death action or in a workman's compensation case.[11]

A quick overview of the law regarding the personhood of the unborn child can be seen in the authoritative legal work on torts (civil wrongs):

Medical authority has long recognized that an unborn child is in existence from the moment of conception.... All writers who have discussed the problem have joined in

---

[8] The U.S. Supreme Court decision *Dred Scott v. Sanford* (1857) regarded slavery is not applicable here since it pre-dated the document under consideration in this paper, the Fourteenth Amendment to the U.S. Constitution, which was not ratified until 1871.

[9] Boethius, *De duabus naturis*, sec. 3.

[10] *Horton Hears a Who* (New York NY: Random House, 1954).

[11] 42 Am. Jur. 2d, "Infants," sec. 2.

condemning the total no-duty rule and *agree that the unborn child in the path of an automobile is as much a person in the street as its mother*, and should be equally protected under the law.... *Most courts have allowed recovery, even though the injury occurred during the early weeks of pregnancy, when the child was neither viable nor quick.* Viability, of course, does not affect the question of the legal existence of the unborn, and therefore of the defendant's duty, and it is a most unsatisfactory criterion, since it is a relative matter, depending on the health of the mother and child and many other matters in addition to the state of development.[12]

Kentucky joined this progressive majority in 1955, when I was a freshman in law school: "The most cogent reason, we believe, for holding that a viable unborn child is an entity within the meaning of the general word 'person' is because, biologically speaking, such a child is, in fact, *a presently existing person*, a living human being."[13] In 1974 the Michigan Supreme Court rejected the "live birth" requirement and upheld the "personhood" of the unborn child:

If the mother can die and the fetus live, or the fetus die and the mother live, how can it be said that there is only one life? ...The phenomenon of birth is not the beginning of life; it is merely a change in the form of life. The principal feature of that change is the fact of respiration.... A baby fully born and conceded by all to be "alive" is no more able to survive unaided than the infant *en ventre sa mere*. In fact, the babe in arms is less self-sufficient–more dependent–than his unborn counterpart.... The fact of life is not to be denied. Neither is the wisdom of the public policy which regards *unborn persons* as being entitled to the protection of law.[14]

According to Professor Prosser, the viability requirement is being rejected overwhelmingly.[15] In Texas, for instance, recovery was

---

[12] *Prosser and Keaton on Torts*, 2nd ed., sec. 36 (1955).

[13] *Mitchell v. Couch*, 285 S.W.2d 901 (1955). A subsequent case in point was successfully practiced by the author. *Cooper v. Cox*, KY, 510 S.W.2d 530 (1974).

[14] *O'Neill v. Morse*, 188 N.W.2d 785 (Mich., 1971).

[15] *Prosser and Keaton on Torts*, 5th ed., sec. 55, 1984.

permitted to a two-and-a-half month old unborn child.[16]

The unborn child is entitled to social security benefits for the death of the father that preceded the birth of the child: "Medically speaking, Donna was viable from the instant of conception onward."[17]

The New Jersey Supreme Court, already in 1964, not only recognized the personhood of an unborn child but held that his right to life prevailed over constitutionally protected religious beliefs of his mother, a Jehovah's Witness who rejected a blood transfusion necessary to preserve her life (and, of course, his as well): "We are satisfied that the unborn child is entitled to the law's protection and that an appropriate order should be made to insure blood transfusions to the mother in the event that they are necessary in the opinion of the physician in charge at the time."[18]

A very interesting pre-*Roe* decision, totally ignored by Justice Blackmun in *Roe*, rejected the attack by pro-abortionists on the constitutionality of Ohio's restrictive abortion law. The three-judge federal court not only upheld the Ohio restrictive abortion statute but pointed out that, independent of the statute, it was the duty of the law to protect the right to life of unborn children: "Once human life has commenced, the constitutional protections found in the Fifth and Fourteenth Amendments impose upon the state the duty of safeguarding it."[19]

Even the United Nations has recognized pre-natal rights: "The child, by reason of his physical and mental immaturity, needs special safeguards and care, including appropriate legal protection, *before as*

---

[16] *Delgado v. Yandel*, 468 S.W.2d 475 (Tex.Civ.App.).

[17] *Wagner v. Finch*, 413 F.2d 267 (C.A. 5, 1969).

[18] *Raleigh Fitkin-Paul Morgan Memorial Hospital v. Anderson*, 42 N.J. 421, 201 A.2d 537, cert. denied, 377 U.S. 985 (1964).

[19] *Steinberg v. Brown*, 321 F.Supp. 741 (D.C. Ohio, 1970).

well as after birth."[20]

Non-citizen aliens have been afforded the protection of the due process and equal protection of the law clauses of the U.S. Constitution: "The term 'person,' used in the Fifth Amendment, is broad enough to include *any and every human being.*"[21] The same constitutional rights of personhood under the Fourteenth Amendment were afforded by the Supreme Court to fleshless corporations, again long before *Roe.*[22]

Original Understanding

Assuming that the word "person" is ambiguous, which we deny, the second rule of document interpretation would come into play, i.e., we must look to the "original understanding" of the usage of the word at the time when the document was drawn. The Fourteenth Amendment was ratified in 1868. As of 1868, what was the state of medical knowledge concerning the unborn child? What was the state of recognition of its legal rights? How was "personhood" used in common parlance, as described in the dictionaries of the day?

The motivation for the passage of the nineteenth-century anti-abortion statutes throughout the United States from 1857 to 1871 was the then-recent realization by the American Medical Association of the discovery of the precise process of fertilization/conception. As a result the AMA passed resolutions condemning abortion as "unwarrantable destruction of human life" and described "the independence and actual existence of the child before birth as a living being.... We had to deal with human life. In a matter of less importance, we could entertain no compromise. An honest judge on the bench would call things by their

---

[20] United Nations Declaration of the Rights of the Child.

[21] *Wong Wing v. United States*, 163 U.S. 228 (1895).

[22] *Santa Clara County v. Southern Pacific R.R.Co.,* 6 S.Ct. 1132 (1886); *Times Mirror Co. v. Superior Court of California*, 314 U.S. 252 (1941).

proper names. We could do no less."[23]

In the 1828 edition of *Webster's, An American Dictionary of the English Language*, "person" is defined as "an individual human being consisting of body and soul. We apply the word to living beings only, possessed of a rational value; the body when dead is not called a *person*. It is applied alike to man, woman, or child." The 1865 version of the same dictionary defined "person" as "the corporeal manifestation of a soul; the outward experience, expression, etc., body..., an individual of a human race." "Human being" is defined by *Webster* in 1828 as "belonging to man or mankind; pertaining or relating to the race of man," and in the 1865 version "human" is defined as "belonging to man or mankind; having the qualities or attributes of a man; pertaining or relating to the race of man." "Man" is then defined by Webster in 1828 as "mankind; the human race; the whole species of human beings; beings distinguished from all other animals by the powers of reason and speech, as well as by their shape and dignified aspect." In 1865 *Webster* defined "man" as "an individual of the human race; a human being, *a person*." It is obvious that all of these definitions show an understanding of the word "person" to include all human beings, with no reference to the incident of birth.

Lest one should argue the narrow Lockean concept of consciousness, speech, etc., as essential, it should be pointed out that this approach would exclude the child two months out of the womb, the retarded or insane adult, the Alzheimer patient, and so on, and would lead to acceptance of the "subhuman" categorization popularized by Adolf Hitler, which should be an embarrassment to anyone attempting to defend it today.

This same inclusive understanding of "person" as including all members of the human race found expression also in the statements of

---

[23] See R. Sauer, "Attitudes to Abortion in America, 1800-1973," *Populations Study* 28 (1974): 53-59; J. Mohr, *Abortion in America, the Origin and Evolution of National Policy* (New York NY: Oxford Univ. Press, 1978).

the prime sponsor of the Fourteenth Amendment, U.S. Congressman John Bingham of Ohio, who stated that the reach of the Amendment was intended to be "universal" and to apply to "any human being."[24] Fourteenth Amendment rights were intended not only to "pertain to American citizenship but also to common humanity."[25]

That the political climate as of 1868 (as manifested by the people's representatives in the state legislatures) had recognized the unborn child as a human being with legal rights is proven by the fact that as of 1868 "there were at least 36 laws enacted by state or territorial legislatures limiting abortion."[26]

The argument that not all of these state statutes totally prohibited abortion is evidence of non-personhood seems disingenuous when we consider the reality that the personhood rights conferred under the Fourteenth Amendment do not constitute an absolute right to life. In fact, human life may be taken, with "due process of law," e.g., in the self-defense situation, or in the case of capital punishment.

Typical of the widespread and common understanding of the nature of the unborn child as a person is the anti-abortion statutory scheme in Kentucky, which provided criminal penalties for the "death of an unborn child" in a procured abortion and imposed yet a separate and additional penalty if the procured abortion results in the death of the mother.[27]

Consideration of the Entire Document

When one considers the entire Constitution, one finds no express definition of, or limitation on, the concept of "person" such as exists,

---

[24] *Cong. Globe*, 39th Congress, First Session 1089 (1866).

[25] *Cong. Globe*, 40th Congress, First Session 514 (1868).

[26] Dissenting Opinion of Justice Rehnquist in *Roe v. Wade*, supra.

[27] KRS 436.020; KRS 435.040.

for example, regarding citizenship, the right to vote, the age limitations regarding holding of certain offices, and so on, and certainly no limitation upon the "right to life" that is enunciated so strongly in the Declaration of Independence. This point again reinforces the conclusion drawn above, that personhood rights are due to every member of the human race.

Conclusion

The severance of "human being" from "personhood"–dishonestly constructed by the *Roe* Court–is arbitrary, artificial, unscientific, and contrary to history and to traditional constitutional interpretation. The Court has abolished a right that is "of the very essence of a scheme of ordered liberty, ... a principle of justice so rooted in the traditions and conscience of our people as to be ranked as fundamental."[28]

It is a strange society that tells us that the Constitution furnishes legal rights to fleshless corporate entities as "persons" within the meaning of the Fourteenth Amendment but denies those same rights to the live beings–species *homo sapiens*–growing in their mother's wombs.

It is a strange society that says to us that the woman who, on her way to keep a 4 p.m. appointment with her abortionist to kill the unborn child growing in her womb and who suffers a vehicular accident resulting in the injury or death of that child at 3 p.m. may now sue and collect damages for the injury or death of that child.

It is an impotent and clueless society that tells us that the remedy for such atrocity is for the Supreme Court to refer the matter back to the states for their individual decision-making, which would tragically reinforce the hollow and indeed fatal principle that "the State giveth, and the State taketh away"!

Professor Robert M. Byrne published an excellent analysis of *Roe*

---

[28] *Palko v. Connecticut*, 302 U.S. 319 (1937).

in his "An American Tragedy: The Supreme Court on Abortion":

> Three generations of Americans have witnessed decisions by the U.S. Supreme Court which explicitly degrade fellow human beings to something less in law than "persons in the whole sense." One generation was present at *Scott v. Sanford* [denying rights to slaves], another at *Buck v. Bell* [denying rights to retarded people], and now a third at *Roe v. Wade* [denying rights to unborn children]. Are not three generations of error enough? ... First, *Dred Scott*, then *Buck v. Bell*, and now the most tragic of them all, *Roe v. Wade*. Three generations of error are three too many, and the last of them shall be called the worst.[29]

Our Court must not only reverse *Roe*, which has resulted thus far in a surgical slaughter body-count in excess of forty million, the prostitution of our medical and legal professions, and the predictable sequella of the foundational deterioration of the sanctity of all innocent human life, which has indeed occurred and is advancing. It must also acknowledge the personhood of the unborn child, and indeed of every human being, thereby entitling every member of the human family to the constitutional rights of due process and equal protection of the law.

If "what we are" can be reduced by arbitrary definition to "what we can do," then we will have validated "definitional dehumanization," effectively adopted by the Nazis, slavery, and pre-civilization savages. And it promptly will be extended–as is already occurring–beyond the unborn to the newborn, the special born, and the long-born, the retarded, the crippled, the unproductive and countless other categories of "useless eaters." Surely this cannot have been the understanding or intent of the framers of the Fourteenth Amendment. Our continued existence as a free nation is in the balance. The hour is late.

---

[29] *Fordham Law Review* (May 1973).

Political and Cultural Perspectives

Natural Law Liberalism: A Framework for Promoting the Sanctity of Human Life

Christopher Wolfe

ABSTRACT: This essay analyzes the conflict between two major public philosophies that compete to be the public philosophy of the United States: contemporary "antiperfectionist" liberalism and natural law liberalism. After describing contemporary liberal public philosophy, especially by reference to the thought of its most influential figure, John Rawls, the essay comments on some of the inadequacies of Rawlsian public philosophy, particularly with respect to abortion. It then gives an account of the core principles and tendencies of liberalism and shows why natural law theory can and should embrace these core principles and tendencies, even while directing and elevating them. Finally, it applies this "natural law liberalism" to contemporary life issues.

EVERY SOCIETY HAS an implicit "public philosophy"–a set of views about human life and the universe that help to explain its actions in history. The public philosophies of actual historical societies–perhaps especially modern democracies–are inevitably, to a significant extent, mixed-up and incoherent, not only because individual human beings themselves so often hold incoherent views but also because public policies are typically compromises that emerge from conflict among the very divergent views of different individuals and groups. And yet, over time, societies resolve particular issues and add to (or subtract from) the core of agreement about important aspects of the human good that constitutes a public philosophy. The battle to determine the content of the public philosophy will therefore shape many lives.

In this essay I want to describe the conflict between two major public philosophies that compete to be the public philosophy of the United States: contemporary "antiperfectionist" liberalism and natural law liberalism.

There are five parts to my presentation: first, I will describe contemporary liberal public philosophy, especially by reference to the thought of its most influential figure, John Rawls. Second, I will briefly comment on some of the inadequacies of Rawlsian public philosophy, particularly with respect to abortion. Third, I will describe the core principles and tendencies of liberalism. Fourth, I will try to show why natural law theory can and should embrace these core principles and tendencies, while also directing and elevating them. Finally, I will apply this "natural law liberalism" briefly to contemporary life issues.

CONTEMPORARY LIBERAL PUBLIC PHILOSOPHY: THE RAWLS PROJECT

The most influential Anglo-American social philosopher of the second half of the twentieth century was John Rawls, and his influence extended well beyond academia, especially through various public intellectuals who applied his philosophy to current issues. Rawls's political philosophy was by no means the only version of liberal political philosophy but his was clearly the most important one.

Rawls

The key feature of Rawls's political philosophy of interest to us is its commitment to "neutrality" among competing conceptions of the human good and the requirements of "public reason." Like the originators of the liberal tradition, Rawls begins with the problem of differences that portend political conflict. We see this in Hobbes and Locke, with their description of a state of nature in which isolated individuals desire self-preservation above all, but are faced with potential conflicts that threaten it–in Hobbes, this is the famous "war of all against all." Men create civil society and transfer their executive power to enforce their desire for self-preservation to government, but (especially in Locke) on the condition that government confine itself to the duty of protecting life, liberty, and property.

That Rawls shares this starting point is clear from the introduction to the paperback edition of his second major book, *Political Liberalism.*[1] In that introduction he asks the question: "How is it possible that there may exist over time a stable and just society of free and equal citizens profoundly divided by reasonable though incompatible religious, philosophical, and moral doctrines?" Why *this* question? Rawls starts from a view of medieval Christianity and the Reformation. The ancient world never knew "the clash between salvationist, creedal, and expansionist religions" that arose only with the Reformation. The Catholic Church and the Reformers were both dogmatic and intolerant, having no doubts about the nature of the highest good or the basis of moral obligation in divine law. Their problem was this:

> How is society even possible between those of different faiths? ... For many, [toleration was] acquiescence in heresy about first things and [in] the calamity of religious disunity. Even the earlier proponents of toleration saw the division of Christendom as a disaster, though a disaster that had to be accepted in view of the alternative of unending religious civil war.... What is new about this clash is that it introduces into people's conceptions of their good a transcendent element not admitting of compromise. This element forces either mortal conflict moderated only by circumstance and exhaustion, or equal liberty of conscience and freedom of thought.[2]

Modern political liberalism, in contrast to earlier political thought inspired by Christianity, assumes the fact of a pluralism of comprehensive doctrines (religious and nonreligious) and sees this not

---

[1] *Political Liberalism* (New York NY: Columbia Univ. Press, 1993). This article draws on material from my *Natural Law Liberalism* (Cambridge UK: Cambridge Univ, Press, 2006), and more detailed citations can be found there.

[2] *Political Liberalism*, pp. xxiv-xxvi.

as a disaster but as the natural outcome of the activities of human reason under enduring free institutions. Only with the success of liberal constitutionalism did it become clear that social unity and concord was possible without agreement on a general comprehensive doctrine (religious, philosophical, or moral).

Thus, the historical origin of political liberalism (and of liberalism more generally) is the Reformation and its aftermath. For with it the problem of the essential conditions of a viable and just society, among people who are divided by profound doctrinal conflict, moved to (and continues to occupy) center stage.

The liberal response to this problem has generally been to "bracket" fundamental questions that might lead to deadly conflict such as the Reformation Wars. That is, questions like ultimate religious truth are taken off the political stage and are left for individuals to pursue privately. They are placed, in principle, outside the scope of politics. Civil society must be "neutral" with respect to the competing comprehensive views about the human good, tolerating all different religious and philosophical views, at least up to the point where people's comprehensive views compel them to interfere with the freedom of others. If people go beyond that point, then society need not tolerate their actions. This requirement of neutrality must extend beyond religion to all "comprehensive" views, including moral and philosophical views as well as religious views. Political life, in Rawls's view, must be based on principles that are acceptable to people of fundamentally different comprehensive views.

Rawls develops a concept of "public reason" in order to facilitate this goal. According to Rawls, "our exercise of political power is proper and hence justifiable only when it is exercised in accordance with a constitution the essentials of which all citizens may reasonably be expected to endorse in the light of principles and ideals acceptable to them as reasonable and rational. Therefore, the ideal of citizenship imposes a moral duty of civility. Citizens violate the conditions of a peaceful democratic society if they ground their political speech and action on their own comprehensive views rather than on views that they can reasonably expect people of different comprehensive views to understand and accept. (In response to certain obvious criticisms of this approach–one thinks immediately of Martin Luther King, Jr.'s appeal to religious ideals in the fight for racial equality–Rawls qualified his position to allow people to appeal to comprehensive views if and only if they also make arguments consistent with public reason.[3])

Rawlsians and the Sanctity of Human Life: Abortion and Slavery

What are the implications of a "neutralist" contemporary liberalism that employs a Rawlsian notion of "public reason" for key issues regarding the sanctity of human life? Rawls himself did not speak much about practical political issues, but in *Political Liberalism* he explicitly (albeit in a footnote) adopted a "pro-choice" position on the issue of abortion. He began by stating that, in the case of mature adult women, there are three important political values involved: "the due respect for human life, the ordered reproduction of political society over time, including the family in some form, and finally the equality of women as equal citizens." He then argued that "any reasonable balance of these three values will give a woman a duly qualified right to decide whether or not to end her pregnancy during the first trimester. The reason for this is that at this early stage of pregnancy the political value of the equality of women is overriding, and this right is required to give it substance and force." He also suggested that the abortion right might be broader, at least in certain circumstances, apparently arguing for an extension of the abortion right into later stages of pregnancy.[4]

In the face of some trenchant critiques, Rawls backed off this view in the introduction to the paperback edition of *Political Liberalism*,

---

[3] *Political Liberalism*, pp. 247ff.

[4] *Political Liberalism*, pp. 243-44.

admitting the possibility of anti-abortion arguments compatible with public reason.[5] But I think it is fair to say that most Rawlsians would still defend a right to abortion.

This is not surprising, in light of the similarity between Rawls's general goal of putting controversial moral views off-limits to politics and the general political strategy of those who favor abortion rights, which is to argue not for the morality or goodness of abortion but for "bracketing" the issue and leaving it to private choice.

But this attempt to bracket the morality of abortion just will not work. Opponents of abortion rights–defenders of the right to life of the unborn–have frequently responded to the idea of "choice" employed by defenders of abortion rights by drawing a parallel between abortion and slavery. The pro-life argument is that there is no principled distinction, as to the general kind of argument being made, between abortion and slavery. In particular, the issue of the morality of abortion cannot be "bracketed"–put to the side and left to private choice–any more than the issue of the humanity of the black slave can be bracketed. (The latter strategy was the one adopted by Stephen Douglas in his debates with Lincoln, in which he argued that slavery should be a matter for the people of a state to decide in whatever way they pleased.)

Princeton professor Stephen Macedo claims to be following Rawlsian principles in his contention that pro-abortion arguments meet the test of public reason while pro-slavery arguments did not. Macedo's position is that abortion "comes down to a fairly close call between two well-reasoned sets of arguments" and therefore "the best thing for reasonable people to do might be to acknowledge the difficulty of the argument and the burdens of reason, to respect their opponents, and to compromise with them, to find some middle ground that gives something to each side while the argument goes forward." Macedo explicitly rejects arguments by John Finnis and Robert George that abortion is not usually even a close call. He specifically denies

---

[5] *Political Liberalism* (2005 expanded paperback edition), Introduction, pp. liv-lv.

George's argument that the development from zygote to adulthood occurs without "substantial change." He more or less simply asserts that it is "unreasonable to deny that there are reasonable grounds for ascribing substantial moral weight to the development of basic neural or brain functions–the development of some sort of sensory capacity, consciousness, or sentience–and perhaps viability."[6]

Macedo misunderstands George's argument in at least one important respect and fails to come to grips with it in another. First, he seems to understand George's argument about "substantial change" to mean "a lot of change," when in fact George's key argument is that there is no *essential* change; that is, the "something" that the zygote is never at any point becomes, in the course of developing into a mature human being, some other kind of thing (some other substance) than it was as a zygote. It changes in many ways–as in the example of developing basic neural or brain functions or becoming viable outside the womb–but those changes never at any time involve a change from its being one thing to another, different thing, as occurs, for example, when the sperm and the egg unite and those two things become one new essentially or substantially different thing. The ball is still in Macedo's court: what is the substantial or essential change that occurs after conception, such that before that point, the thing was not the same human being it is after that point, and possessed of the same fundamental rights? The fact of the matter is, as George and Patrick Lee have argued, that each of us once *was* a zygote, while none of us ever was a sperm or an egg.[7]

Macedo does not *argue* that it is "unreasonable to deny that there

---

[6] For citations here, and throughout this section, see Robert P. George and Christopher Wolfe, "Natural Law and Public Reason" in *Natural Law and Public Reason*, ed. Christopher Wolfe and Robert P. George (Washington, D.C.: Georgetown Univ. Press, 2000).

[7] Robert George and Patrick Lee, "Acorns and Embryos," *The New Atlantis* (Fall 2004/Winter 2005). Available at: http://www.thenewatlantis.com/publications/acorns-and-embryos.

are reasonable grounds for ascribing substantial moral weight" to certain developments (neural or brain functions, viability)–he just asserts it. George's principle is simple and straightforward: the "thing" in the womb is a human being, from conception onward. As a human being, it shares with other human beings certain fundamental rights, including a right not to be killed. If there are reasonable grounds for saying that more developed human beings should not be killed, but less developed human beings can be killed, then Macedo ought to give them. But, frankly, I doubt that any argument about the moral quality of a human life that turns, for example, on lung capacity–as the viability argument does–will meet the most minimal standards of reason, or even Rawlsian public reason (however much that specious distinction may appeal to certain persons).

This is not to say, of course, that the proponents of the abortion rights position have no legitimate concerns on their side. And therefore, as Macedo argues, "the best thing may be to try and give something to both sides," to find some middle ground. But *Planned Parenthood v. Casey* (contrary to his suggestion) is not the middle ground since it gives virtually no weight to the innocence and right to life of the unborn child. A proper middle ground would be something more like this: public policy should (1) prohibit abortion, in order to give fair weight to the unborn child's right to life; (2) provide assistance (financial, medical, emotional) to women with difficult pregnancies, in order to minimize the costs of carrying through such pregnancies; (3) promote easier adoption laws, to provide for children whose biological parents are not able or willing to care for them (and to minimize the long-term costs of carrying an unborn child to full term); (4) educate people (especially young people) to the enormous costs (especially human costs) of irresponsible sexual activity and also to the equal responsibility of men for the children whom they help to conceive; and (5) focus penalties for abortion not on pregnant women but on those who provide them with (and profit from) abortions.

Now, some people (including most academics) will probably find this "middle position" frankly outrageous on the grounds that it simply represents the position embraced by the pro-life movement in this country–and on that point they would be right. This experience of outrage may be useful, however, if it gives them some inkling of how their opponents feel when *Casey,* and a variety of other purported "compromises," are described as "middle ground" in this debate.

But let me return to the question of public reason. We have seen Macedo's position on abortion. What is his position on slavery? The question arises, of course, because of some of the striking similarities between the two issues. Macedo says–without explaining why–that "there is something a little slick in drawing quick analogies between slavery and abortion in order to impugn public reason." But there is nothing slick about that analogy at all–it is quite solid. If anti-abortion arguments fail to meet the test of public reason today, would anti-slavery arguments have met the test of public reason in the 1850s? I think the answer is clearly "no."

Macedo's argument is that "projecting myself back to, say, 1857, it seems quite doubtful to me that the merits of the arguments for slavery would have appeared in as reasonable a light as do both sides in today's abortion debate.... I suppose there were some whose defense of slavery, coupled perhaps with opposition to 'wage slavery' in the North, amounted to a reasoned public case, worthy of some sort of respect." He then goes on to deny that this is grounds for principled compromise, citing George's argument that "respect may sometimes be owed to persons who in general exhibit reasonableness and good will, but not to some position they have adopted, which one regards as so deeply misguided and wrong as to be unworthy of respect."

The difference between abortion and slavery, then, is simple. Macedo thinks that both sides of the abortion debate really have reasons, so a "principled compromise" is appropriate, along the lines of *Casey*–which Macedo considers a compromise, though, by its own terms, it reaffirms "the central holding" of *Roe v. Wade*. On the other hand, even decent people who supported the slavery position had no reasons but were merely the victims of circumstances and traditions that were indeed morally perverse, so that public reason would not have required some sort of principled compromise–such as Stephen Douglas's position of leaving slavery to the states, perhaps.

The problem, of course, is that there were lots of Americans–and, yes, even decent ones–who believed strongly that slavery was just and good for everyone concerned, and there are lots of people today who believe that the pro-abortion rights position that Macedo finds reasonable is "so deeply misguided and wrong as to be unworthy of respect," even though people of general reasonableness who happen to hold that position should be respected. Macedo has given us no persuasive reason to believe that there is any morally significant difference between the two cases.

If liberals want to provide a plausible defense of abortion, they cannot reasonably do it on the basis of "choice" (whatever rhetorical success they may have with that approach). They must defend the morality of abortion itself. And that argument will require either (1) a showing that there is some plausible point after conception in which there is a substantial change from something pre- and non-human to something human–which, as I have argued, cannot be shown, or (2) a concession that innocent human beings may sometimes be directly and deliberately killed–an argument that liberals are understandably loath to rely on in public discourse.

Natural Law Liberal Public Philosophy

If contemporary liberalism does not provide an adequate public philosophy, then what would be an alternative public philosophy on which we could rely? In my book *Natural Law Liberalism*, I have argued that the best understanding of liberal public philosophy is one that is rooted in the natural law tradition. I want to give a brief description of liberalism, as I understand it, and then give an explanation for why those committed to natural law should find liberalism attractive, and also an explanation of why liberalism needs to be rooted in the natural law.

Natural Law Liberalism

What is "liberalism"? Liberalism is not a single, seamless political philosophy, but rather a tradition with considerable variation. Still, to call it a tradition, we must be able to identify a solid core. What is that core of liberalism? I will try to describe it as five principles and six "tendencies."[8]

Liberal Principles

The first principle of liberalism is the foundation of human dignity rooted in equality. If human beings are not born equal in all regards, they are at least equal in certain fundamental natural rights, among which are "life, liberty, and the pursuit of happiness." No just political order can simply discount or ignore the well-being of certain members of the political community, reducing them to mere means to the well-being of others. This rules out slavery, serfdom, social castes, and other structural forms of inequality.

Second, political rule requires consent. No one group or class of people is born with a right to rule others. Autocracy, aristocracy, and theocracy are forms of despotism that deprive people of their requisite opportunity to participate in government. How broad that participation should be is controversial, even within the liberal tradition, but the consistent liberal impulse has certainly been to expand it. Consent in liberal theory began as consent to the form of government, which (in principle) might not be democratic. But in general–and increasingly over time–liberals have called for increasing, actual popular participation within the form of government. This rules out any form of absolute government and at least points in the direction of representative democracy.

---

[8] For a more extended discussion, see *Natural Law Liberalism*, chapter 7.

Third, the purpose of government is the protection of rights. These rights begin with certain fundamental natural rights (life, liberty, pursuit of happiness), but then they are elaborated as a series of legal rights. Among these rights, five categories stand out: (1) political rights (especially voting), (2) religious freedom and toleration, (3) freedom of thought and discussion, (4) property rights, and (5) impartial legal procedures and equality before the law. These rights are not absolute–they can and must be limited in certain ways–but, appropriately limited, their protection is the primary purpose of political life.

Fourth, to accomplish its purpose, government must be both strong and limited. As Madison argued, we must establish a government that can control the governed (so that rights will be secure) and that can itself be controlled (so that it will not threaten rights). The government must have adequate powers to defend itself, at home and abroad, and it must have adequate power to enforce its laws, for the achievement of legitimate public purposes. The most effective ways to limit government, without depriving it of its necessary powers, are principles such as representative democracy (especially accountability of rulers through elections), separation of powers, and an independent judiciary.

Fifth, men should be governed by law. The rule of law–government according to general standards that apply to all citizens–is the best way to approximate the aspect of justice that demands that those in like circumstances should be treated alike, and the best guarantee that no undue partiality will be shown some people or classes at the expense of the legitimate concerns of others.

To these five principles–equal human dignity, consent of the governed, individual rights, effective limited government, and the rule of law–might be added other "tendencies" that are perhaps too vague to be called principles but that tend strongly to inform or animate liberal thought.

First, the liberal tradition tends to be a rationalist tradition, a tradition of reason and "enlightenment." Inherited truths are submitted to critical analysis, and freedom of inquiry vis-à-vis political and ecclesiastical authorities is highly valued. Modern science assumes a central place in intellectual life and often becomes a model for philosophy. The emphasis on reason and human equality makes education, as the foundation for equality of opportunity, a prominent liberal ideal.

Second, the liberal tradition tends to be reformist, examining the past and present with a critical eye, proposing changes to improve the condition of men, and experimenting with new social forms and policies. Traditional hierarchies (typically based on blood and inheritance) and inequalities based on the chance of birth, and legally and socially enforced limits on individual efforts, are subject to criticism and revision. The traditions of reason and reform unite in a strong tendency of liberalism to pursue what Francis Bacon called "the relief of man's estate," the general cultivation of human health, material well-being, and comfort.

Third, the liberal tradition tends toward individualism. It is concerned that an improper focus on the glory and well-being of the "community as a whole" will redound primarily to the benefit of the few, the powerful and the well-off, at the expense of the many, the weak, and the poor. It is rooted in equality and therefore tends to exalt the individual, whose choices should be curtailed only to the extent that they interfere with others' rights or with requirements essential to maintain the community necessary to protect the rights of all.

Fourth, liberalism tends to promote either rationalist religion (emphasizing the more limited truths of natural theology rather than the wider range of beliefs characteristic of revealed religions) or secularism. It tends to be skeptical of claims of revelation, or at least of their relevance to political life. This was due historically, in no small measure, to an accidental but nearly universal (and therefore not *obviously* accidental) feature of early modern Europe: the social and political intermingling and alliance of State and Church hierarchies.

Fifth, the liberal tradition tends to be universalistic. Appealing to rational principles that apply to all men, it tends to be cosmopolitan and anti-imperialist, though it has its interventionist and non-interventionist strands.

I also want to add a sixth tendency that I neglected to include in *Natural Law Liberalism*, namely, the spirit of commerce. Early liberalism, especially in its Lockean form, saw the threats to self-preservation coming not only from other men but also from the scarcity of nature. Commerce provided help with both these threats. The scarcity of nature could be overcome–indeed, nature itself could be made to yield more fruits–by expanding the possibilities for accumulating property through division of labor and by removing artificial barriers to commerce (such as mercantilist government regulations and an aristocratic contempt for commercial activity). And the accumulation of property made for stronger governments that could protect against foreign and domestic threats to peace and stability.

Disputes among liberals will often concern exactly how far these principles and tendencies are to be pushed. Liberals generally allow for the fact that they are not always absolute. Most obviously, in some cases rights may conflict with each other, or they may be incompatible with certain fundamental requirements of political and social life. Therefore, religious, property, and speech rights are all essential, but they can be limited in certain ways for the public good. This common-sense recognition makes it more difficult to determine what the "true" liberal position is since there will be significant differences among liberals themselves on the scope of liberal principles.

Nonetheless, there is a solid, identifiable core of liberalism that is seen most easily by comparing it with very different forms of government, e.g., Roman republicanism, medieval feudalism, seventeenth-century French monarchy, Ottoman despotism, traditional Latin American feudal oligarchy, twentieth century totalitarianism (Nazi, Communist, Chinese), or contemporary Islamic fundamentalism. In the sometimes bitter disputes of politics (disputes that may admittedly concern absolutely fundamental principles), people in the United States (and in the West generally) can sometimes forget how much they have in common.

That is one reason why it is worthwhile fighting the tendency to identify "liberalism," despite its rich and varied tradition, simply with certain strands of liberalism that are dominant in the Anglo-American academy today, whether it be the political liberalism of John Rawls, or the avowed comprehensive liberalism of many of his critics. In doing so, we would lose sight of the deeper underlying commonalities among the various forms of contemporary political thought solidly rooted in the liberal tradition that extend far beyond the leading forms of contemporary liberalism. Those other forms include, I want to argue, not only communitarianism, with its obvious affinities for liberalism (obvious, because major communitarians, such as Michael Sandel, are readily identified as moderate political liberals) but also forms of thought usually not at all identified with liberalism–above all, natural law theory.

Now let me turn to the question of how proponents of natural law theory will respond to these core principles and tendencies of liberalism.

Natural Law and The Core Principles of Liberalism

How might a natural law theorist evaluate the core principles of liberalism? I think that they would find themselves in general agreement with what I have described as the core principles of liberalism, and that they can even accept the tendencies of liberalism, properly circumscribed.[9]

Let's look first at the core principles. First, natural law theory is strongly committed to the notion of human dignity, rooted in human equality. This dignity involves a high respect or recognition of worth, some form of inviolability, and the inherent possession of rights. That is, this respect is not based on the accomplishments of the particular

---

[9] For a more extended discussion, see *Natural Law Liberalism*, chapter 9.

person but on the simple fact of being human.

What is the source of human dignity? Each human being possesses dignity due to the distinctive human capacities he or she has, especially reason and free will. In its traditional form, this was also expressed by saying that each person had an immaterial and immortal soul that accounted for these capacities. Human dignity is, therefore, not a human "construct," devised by men to make life go better. It is a reflection of the distinctive features of man's very being that set him apart from other, lower beings. In the final analysis, then, natural law theory will concur with liberals who argue that every human being deserves "equal concern and respect."

Second, natural law theorists can readily accept a certain notion of consent. There are serious reasons to hesitate about fully embracing a theory of consent. Nonetheless, as Yves Simon showed in his classic discussion,[10] consent makes good sense, if it is understood as popular participation in the transmission of political power to those who hold political authority (and this can include the general power to determine the form of government as well as the more specific power to determine the persons who will hold office). In this respect Simon is only harkening back to a tradition at least as old as Aristotle, who notes that collecting the opinions of those who experience the effects of rule (asking the person who is wearing the shoe how it feels) is quite sensible. The idea of requiring consent also draws support from its tendency to contribute to political stability (a notion supported by Tocqueville's discussion of the advantages of democracy[11]). Finally, it has a very strong grounding in the severe objections that can be lodged against any theory that makes political power hereditary or limits the choice of rulers to a particular social class since no such class is particularly trustworthy to hold such power, unchecked by others.

---

[10] Yves Simon, *The Philosophy of Democratic Government* (Chicago IL: Univ. of Chicago Press, 1951), chapter 3.

[11] Alexis de Tocqueville *Democracy in America*, Vol. One, Chapter XIV.

(Classes defined by wealth, education, and or any other criteria cannot be trusted to be better rulers, unconstrained by the requirement of consent.) In this sense, then, natural law theorists see consent as a legitimate and valuable aspect of good government.

Third, rights are central to liberalism but barely appear in classical natural law, which focuses on what is right by nature rather than on the rights we have by nature. Yet modern representatives of the natural law tradition have strongly embraced rights in the twentieth century. This embrace is neither a merely tactical one nor a mistake.

As some scholars have argued, there are some dangers in the adoption of rights-language.[12] But the key question is this: is it *true* that people have "rights"? I think the answer that any proponent of classical natural law has to give is clearly "yes." If it is *wrong* for A to hit B, then B can be said to have a *right* not to be hit by A. If it is a principle of justice that A *ought to* give x to B, then B can be said to have a *right* to x from A.

There are, of course, many questions about the nature and scope of rights and about their precise place in the overall teaching of political morality. But that does not preclude natural law thinkers from embracing rights in their proper perspective, properly related to duties and understood as essential conditions for human beings to seek the good and the true. This discussion of the proper framework for understanding rights is one that can be carried on *within* the contexts of both liberalism and natural law.

Fourth, natural law theorists would embrace the liberal principle of strong, but limited, government. Natural law theory recognizes the essential role that government plays in human life. The purpose of government is to promote, to ensure as far as possible, the common good, understood in a rich and comprehensive way, including man's physical, moral, and intellectual well-being.

---

[12] See, for example, certain works of Ernest Fortin and Robert Kraynak. For citation of their views and a more detailed response, see *Natural Law Liberalism*, chapter 9.

Few people complain that natural law theorists hold too narrow a view of government power. More commonly, the concern is that natural law–because it does not limit the common good to "life, liberty, and property"–does not acknowledge sufficient limits on the power of government. But it does. Natural law theorists do not believe in an all-encompassing government or State. They affirm a clear distinction between the public and private spheres of life, and clear limits on government. The distinction between the private and the public is one to which Christianity, in fact, made a significant contribution. It is not central to classical political philosophy. Moreover, natural law theory has articulated the principle of subsidiarity, according to which higher or more general associations should intervene in the life of lower or more particular associations only when the latter are incapable of performing a task adequately. One implication of this is that public authorities ought not to insert their authority into the private worlds of families or of many voluntary associations, except when this is necessary for the common good.

With respect to institutional arrangements to keep the power of government in check, natural law theory has no trouble accepting liberalism's "characteristic set of political institutions," namely, representative democracy, separation of governmental powers, and an independent judiciary. It looks with favor on political arrangements (such as representative democracy) that promote the participation and therefore the capacities of as many citizens as reasonably possible, because this development of capacities is an important part of the common good, and it looks with favor on arrangements that provide checks on political power (such as separation of powers and a limited form of judicial review), because of its recognition of the potential power of evil as well as good in all human beings.

Moreover, natural law theory insists that government is generally bound by ordinary moral norms, such as those against murder, theft, and lying. Natural law theory thus provides a solid foundation for strong but effectively limited government. Many liberals will take issue with particular ways in which natural law theory does not restrict government–perhaps most importantly, its rejection of John Stuart Mills' "harm principle"–but that will be a discussion that takes place *within* the broad family of liberal political theories.

Fifth, the rule of law has deep roots in the natural right and natural law tradition, going back to Aristotle, who argued that law is free from the passion that is innate in man. Although law cannot be perfect (since it makes universal rules that may not apply in some instances), it is superior to rule by decree.

Natural law theory, then, embraces all five of the core principles of liberalism. Like other liberals, various natural law theorists will have differences of opinion (among themselves and with others) as to the best understanding and application of these principles. Those differences, however, are not an external critique of liberalism, but an internal discussion within liberalism as to the best way to understand and realize liberal principles.

Natural Law and the Tendencies of Liberalism

I think that, for the most part, natural law is compatible with what I have described as the tendencies of liberalism, though–even more than is the case with liberalism's core principles–this depends on a having a certain understanding of and giving a certain direction to those tendencies. For the sake of conserving a bit of time, I will focus here on only four of the tendencies–reason, individualism, rational religion, and commerce.

First, the liberal tradition tends to be a rationalist tradition, a tradition of reason and "enlightenment." Natural law concurs in attributing profound importance to reason. Law is defined as an "ordinance of reason" and natural law is said to be "the rational creature's share of the Eternal Reason." Practical reasoning is what the natural law is all about. At the same time, natural law theorists are prudently sensitive to the actual limitations of reason, both in individual human beings and in societies.

In a certain way, ironically, natural law theorists have more faith in reason than do modern liberals. Modern liberalism has tended to exalt the knowledge arrived at by the empirical methods of what we call "science," i.e., the natural sciences, and it has tended to limit reason to "instrumental rationality," reason as a means to achieve ends that are themselves beyond the scope of reason, ends that are simply posited or the objects of desires or passions.

Natural law theorists resist the truncation of reason, maintaining that "science" comprehends knowledge achieved through different methods, and, in particular, should be understood to include metaphysics and ethics as much as physics and chemistry. They hold that human ends as well as means are discernible by reason. Moreover, they are open, in principle, to the possibility of other sources of knowledge than reason itself, especially divine revelation and rational reflection thereon (in the form of theology).

One of the important things that natural law provides is a foundation for liberalism that rests on a confidence that human beings can and do know the truth about the human good (in its great variety of forms) rather than a scepticism about such knowledge or a despair that human beings can ever agree on it. It grounds liberalism positively in the truth about the human person rather than negatively in various forms of agnosticism–agnosticism about man as much as about God.

Natural law, then, is very much a tradition of reason, and, in fact, helps to protect a fuller understanding of reason and its capacities.

Second, one oft-noted, and frequently criticized, aspect of liberalism is its promotion of individualism. On the positive side, this tendency flows from a recognition of the equal worth of each person. Liberals were rightly critical of the subordination of the individual to the glory and greatness of "the nation" (or, perhaps, more accurately, the rulers) in pre-liberal societies. The general recognition of the equality of each person in society, and the equal concern and respect owed him or her, is one of the great achievements of liberalism.

Natural law has always shared this recognition of the importance of the individual, as a free, self-directing person. Its notion of a common good has never been that the good of the greater number outweighs the good of the lesser number. The common good is not a sum of individual goods, but a good which includes the good of each person in the community.

Moreover, the commitment of natural law to equal regard for each person is also reflected powerfully in the contemporary work of its proponents on behalf of the right to life of each person from conception to natural death. In this regard, it carries on the general trend of liberalism in expanding the protection of rights, extending them to a wider range of human beings.

At the same time, natural law prevents this respect for the individual from sinking into an absolutized version of personal autonomy, which is only one, extreme version of respect for the individual. Liberal democracies like the United States have historically rested on strong families. Tocqueville notes that in America the spirit of political liberty has been strengthened by the spirit of religion and the existence of a strong moral framework. Many of the examples he cites involve sexual morality–the morality that channels the sexual impulse into family life.

Third, liberalism has tended to promote either rationalist religion (emphasizing the more limited truths of natural theology rather than the wider range of beliefs characteristic of revealed religions) or secularism. What is unclear is how much the latter tendency, especially, has reflected certain historical circumstances and how much it is intrinsic to liberalism. Alexis de Tocqueville makes a compelling argument, I think, that the opposition between revealed religion and liberalism is due especially to accidental historical factors. In fact, he says, religion and a healthy polity–especially a healthy liberal democracy–are mutually reinforcing. I would by no means deny that Tocqueville himself is aware of certain tensions between liberal democracy and religion, but at least this much can be said: (1) Tocqueville shows that there are considerable resources in the liberal tradition for a respectful relationship between church and state–that relationship need not be one of hostility, and (2) we should not forget that there will be important tensions between revealed religion and *any* political theory and/or practice.[13]

Natural law is more consistent with the liberal emphasis on rational religion than many think, because it promotes the view that there is a fundamental harmony between faith and reason. Revelation is not viewed as something that simply trumps or displaces reason. The lawgiver-God of classical natural law theory is the source of both reason and revelation, and so there can be no real conflict between the two, but only apparent conflict that arises from either the defects of reason (as when natural scientists go beyond the limits of their method and assert that there is no God–a question on which, as natural scientists, they have no competence) or the misapprehension of revelation (as when believers erroneously attribute a literal reading to certain biblical passages that has led to conflict with truths discovered by the natural sciences, such as heliocentrism).

What natural law theory would object to is any assertion that unaided human reason is, in principle, the only source of knowledge, that divine revelation is somehow intrinsically impossible. Natural law would object to the unreasonableness of such an assertion, and nothing in liberalism itself demands a commitment to it. Moreover, classical natural law recognizes that, while faith is something that transcends reason, the credibility of those who claim to be agents of divine revelation is reasonably subjected to rational examination. If reason cannot "prove" revelation, those who embrace a particular claim of divine revelation still ought to be willing and able to show why it is not unreasonable to do so.

Fourth, natural law can have a deep respect for a proper spirit of commerce, since man's productive activity in the world is a great

---

[13] For a fuller discussion, see Christopher Wolfe, "Tocqueville and the Religious Revival," *This World* 1 (Winter/Spring 1982): 85-96.

occasion for the development of a wide range of human capacities and virtues. Tocqueville describes one of liberal democracy's advantages as the abundant activity, energy, and vitality that it makes possible and stimulates. Michael Novak has shown that work and commercial activity involve a wide range of important human virtues and cannot be reduced to mere self-interest and avarice.[14]

At the same time, natural law will regulate this spirit of commerce in important ways. First, it will prevent what both Montesquieu and Tocqueville noted as a tendency to move from a spirit of commerce (the industry, frugality, and personal discipline needed to build up enterprises and wealth) to a spirit of luxury (absorption in consumeristic indulgence in the fruits of commerce) that undermines the springs of commerce and industry. Second, it will preserve a balance in individuals and society by recognizing and encouraging the pursuit of other human goods than prosperity and comfort, including the arts, literature, education, and charitable works.

This examination of the tendencies of liberalism recognizes that there will be points of tension between natural law and liberal tendencies. At the same time, it suggests that there is also a good deal of similarity, and no outright incompatibility. Natural law proponents will find many liberal tendencies congenial. Other tendencies they will feel the need to cabin and direct in certain ways, in order to make them reasonable and beneficial. In this they are not fundamentally different from other liberals, who have the same experience of willingness to accept some principles quite readily, while accepting other principles only if they are understood in certain ways (as, for example, contemporary egalitarian liberals will feel the need to constrain economic liberties, or communitarian liberals will feel the need to constrain individualism).

In evaluating these tendencies, we have to approach them, I think,

---

[14] Michael Novak *The Spirit of Democratic Capitalism* (New York NY: Simon and Schuster, 1982).

in the same way that Tocqueville approached liberal democracy. He recognized that liberal democracy could take a variety of forms, some of them admirable, some of them base, and that what we must do is work to ensure that the form democracy takes is a good one. Following him, we too must work to ensure that the various tendencies of liberalism take forms that will elevate and ennoble human life rather than debase it.

Another way to say this is that liberalism must be moderated so that when it shapes its citizens–as it inevitably will, even in its milder way–it does so in ways that are more fully compatible with important intellectual and moral goods: with reason and faith, and with the moral virtues that regulate the passions and promote individual and social well-being.

At the same time, natural law, without disturbing its convictions that there is a truth, that human beings can know it, and that their well-being lies in finding and living in accord with it, has to be so formulated as to recognize, in ways that its historical representatives have sometimes failed to do, the intrinsic importance–the necessity–of human freedom and the limits of coercion and law. Many of what traditionalists rightly see as evils in liberal societies are not the evils of liberalism as such, but the failures of human beings with free will. When men are free, they can work for good or for ill. Freedom has its glories and its ignominy. We–individually and in our various levels of community life–need to help people live up to their potential for living good lives, and we can do this, to some extent, by curtailing opportunities for acting badly. But, like God Himself, we must take the risk of respecting human freedom.

Conclusion:
Natural Law Liberalism and the Sanctity of Human Life

What are the implications of natural law liberal public philosophy and questions of the sanctity of human life, especially abortion and euthanasia? I want to emphasize two points.

First, natural law liberalism is rooted in a profound respect for the dignity of the human person. This dignity is not the result of any "achievements" of individuals but is rooted in their very nature as rational creatures with free will. Nor is the stage of development or actualization of those capacities to know and choose the ground for human dignity–it is the very capacity itself. Natural law theory will not sacrifice individuals to a cost-benefit analysis, as utilitarianism can, nor will it confine dignity to individuals who have and can exercise actualized rational capacities, as Kantian and Rawlsian analysis is likely to. Natural law liberalism takes the dignity and equality of all human beings seriously in a way that contemporary liberalism does not.

Second, natural law liberalism's commitment to a broad view of reason–one that is not truncated and reduced to empirical knowledge–provides a moral framework within which scientific advances can be pursued, without rationalizing away the undeniable presence of human life, and without allowing some human beings to be reduced to means for the benefit of others.

Natural law liberalism is often viewed by contemporary liberals as being rooted in–and not much more than camouflage for–revealed religion. Yet, ironically, the battle between liberals and conservatives on life issues today reverses what has seemed to be the ordinary structure of debate between modernists and traditionalists. In the past, it was not uncommon to find religiously-oriented moralists deeply suspicious of modernity and all its works (including modern science) pitted against modern progressives for whom modern science was a comprehensive worldview, something close to a religion. (The Scopes trial is often viewed as the classic instance of such forces squaring off.) On the issue of abortion, however, it is the "moral traditionalists"–the natural law liberals–who have been able to invoke the wonders of neonatal technology and who rely on the relatively straightforward scientific facts about the beginning of an individual human life at the point of conception. The "progressives" find themselves in the position of using scientifically awkward circumlocutions for the incipient human being, such as "blob of tissue" or "products of conception." And it is the moral traditionalists who are insisting on expanding the scope of protection of the weak and the vulnerable, such as the unborn, the deformed, and the very elderly and sick–classic liberal ideals. They resist rationalist and utilitarian arguments that minimize the dignity of human life at certain stages (that is, relatively incipient or "un-actualized" human life, or relatively declining or "de-actualized" human life) by subordinating them to other factors such as the personal, economic, and sexual freedom for women, the importance of scientific experimentation for the benefit of others, and the negative value accorded human lives under conditions said to be "inconsistent with" human dignity.

Natural law liberalism provides a sound public philosophy that puts issues of human life where they should be: not on the margins of political life, as "secondary" issues that "distract" us from the "important" issues of economics and foreign affairs, but rather front and center, as questions that go to the heart of the most fundamental principles of public morality and the common good. And natural law liberalism–far more than economic or military power, important as they are–provides the answers to those fundamental questions that will make our nation worthy of respect and emulation.

Epiphanies and *Humanae Vitae*

Janet E. Smith

ABSTRACT: This essay derives from a casual after-dinner talk delivered at the UFL conference of 2008. It reviews Prof Smith's early participation in the pro-life movement and her decision to promote the truths of *Humanae vitae* as a means of combating abortion. It also includes reflections on some pro-family, pro-life elements of modern films and modern culture and a brief excursus on the concept of "conscious parenthood" as developed by John Paul II in *Love and Responsibility*. The essay argues that tapping into the natural love that people have for children and their desire to be good parents might be another avenue for advancing the pro-life message.

DURING THE FORTIETH anniversary of *Humanae Vitae* I received many invitations to write and talk about it. One invitation that really warmed my heart and amused me was from the editor of a pontifical journal. He asked for an article of about fifteen pages, and then added: "if you think you still have something to say on the topic"! I am not sure that I do, but since I have more or less become the "*Humanae Vitae* lady," my name pops up quickly when people are looking for something about *Humanae Vitae*.

When I was casting around for a focus for this talk, I thought of one of my friends who has written a book about the history of the pro-life movement. When I asked her about the focus of her book, she said that she was actually writing what amounted to an autobiography, for it turned out to be about *her* involvement in the pro-life movement. I teased her that this was a rather narcissistic take on the subject.

Not being a stranger to narcissism myself, I have warmed to the idea of doing a history of a movement and using myself as the focus. In fact, that focus may help keep this after-dinner talk the bit of fluffy relief that all of us yearn for after a long day of closely reasoned scholarly work. Nonetheless, I will spare you an unrelenting exercise in narcissism and add a few other elements. Consequently this talk is going to have a few somewhat loosely connected parts: (1) A review of some moments of my life that provide some insight into the story of *Humanae Vitae* over the last forty years. (2) A suggestion that the pro-life movement would do well to promote a concept developed by Karol Wotyła and incorporated into *Humanae Vitae*–the concept of conscious parenthood. (3) A few cultural signs that indicate some important pro-life shifts in the culture.

When *Humanae Vitae* was issued in 1968 I had just graduated from high school. I had no cognizance of that tumultuous event. Nonetheless, my whole adult life has been lived during the forty years after *Humanae Vitae*, and that is really what drew me to the thought of using various events of my life to tell the story of *Humanae Vitae* forty years later. For some of you this will be a trip down memory lane. For others it will be a history lesson for the decades before your birth.

Often I am asked how I got involved in this work. People find it strange that someone should devote her life to defending *Humanae Vitae*. I am one of those people who find it strange. What I am going to do here is to recount a series of epiphanies that have shaped my thinking about contraception and my choices to do this work.

I grew up in Warren, Pennsylvania, a small conservative Republican town in the western part of the state. My family was considered liberal (if not radical) because my father was a Democrat and an advocate of civil rights. That didn't mean much in our town since there was only one African-American living there, a piano teacher who had followed his wife to live in Warren. But my Dad, a man with a keen sense of justice, spent a lot of dinner hours ranting and raving against racial prejudice and against the Vietnam war. In high school I came to think of myself as something of a radical and tried to choose a radical college, not knowing what it really meant to be a radical. I soon found out. I went to Grinnell College in Iowa, which was about as radical as colleges were at that time, and some of them were really radical. But I must admit that it was an even more trivial reason that led me to choose Grinnell from among the several radical schools I visited. I chose Grinnell because I was very taken with a young man I saw there sporting very long and bushy sideburns!

It was during the summer between graduating from high school and going to college that *Humanae Vitae* came out. As I mentioned, I don't really recall the event. My research years later made me realize what a turning point 1968 was for the Church as well as for the culture. It was the year Robert Kennedy and Martin Luther King were killed, it was the year of race riots in many American cities, and it was a year of widespread protests against the Vietnam War, among other disruptive elements. The culture had already embraced contraception. It had been a largely contraceptive culture for much of the century but when the pill appeared in the late 1950s, contraceptive sex and all the irresponsibility and promiscuity and general grossness that come with a diminished view of the value of sexuality became a way of life. Some few faithful theologians warned that if contraception became widely available, then the approval of masturbation, fornication, divorce, and homosexuality and even euthanasia would quickly follow. (The members of this society are well familiar with the connection between these issues.) The dissent that followed *Humanae Vitae* changed things dramatically in the Catholic Church. One encouraging sign that we have begun to emerge from a Church greatly damaged by the dissent is that fidelity has largely returned to the seminaries and there are signs it is returning to some of the universities as well–something I was not confident I would live long enough to see. Some of us are beginning to face the challenges of old age, but one of the benefits to growing older is that we get the satisfaction of seeing some fruits of the battles we have fought. In 1968 I personally knew nothing about the huge revolution that was underway in both the culture and the Church and did not know what a role *Humanae Vitae* would play in my life.

When at Grinnell I decided that if I was going to be radical I had to do what radicals did. So I went to a few meeting of the SDS (Students of a Democratic Society), one of the more anarchic student groups then in existence. My reactionary path began when some of the SDS members started inveighing against policemen by calling them pigs. A little light went off in my head. I had a little epiphany and thought: "These guys don't know what they are talking about; my grandfather was a policeman and he wasn't a pig." When they spoke about their Marxist commitments and their solidarity with the workers, I had additional reason to doubt their grounding in reality. Many of my relatives were assembly- line workers and would have had no patience with these slackers and their long unwashed hair and unwashed slovenly way of dress.

In 1970, when I was a sophomore at Grinnell, some feminists came to campus to organize support for the liberalization of abortion laws. Iowa was a very liberal and progressive state. Although I was nineteen, I had never heard of abortion. I went to the library to look it up. I was astonished. My immediate reaction was that it was a very bad thing indeed, though I was willing to listen to the arguments of those who advocated abortion. The encyclopedia noted that the key question was when human life begins. It also noted that the Catholic Church was against abortion. At that time I had left the Church for a year and a half or so. I had been raised Catholic. I never went to Catholic schools, but I had received fairly good catechetical instruction. Still, I had never heard of abortion and didn't know that the Church was against it.

At the time I was taking a course from John Crossett, a professor who was Socrates reincarnate. Through ruthless and unbelievably patient dialectic, he was single-handedly and courageously attempting to argue students out of the prevailing relativism and subjectivism. Crossett was helping some of us have the conviction in our minds and become desirous of asking hard questions and of getting at the truth. Many of the other professors on campus seemed committed to stripping us of confidence that we could know anything at all. In fact, some professors, a few of them card-carrying Marxists, would smoke dope with the students and rally the students to boycott classes in protest of various government actions. Those were confusing times, and I doubt that college campuses have improved any since.

I went to the meeting about abortion and asked when the advocates of abortion thought life begins. I said that I was prepared to write letters to have abortion laws liberalized but that I needed to know when life begins. The presenters started shouting at me, "sit down, shut up, we don't need your kind here. We don't need you right-to-lifers here." I was very confused because it was a very genuine statement and I didn't know why I had made them so mad. As mentioned, I had never heard of abortion before that afternoon and I certainly hadn't heard of right-to-lifers. I was perplexed by the statement "we don't need your kind here." The fashion of the time was that both males and females were doing our best to look like John Lennon. I had actually succeeded to a remarkable extent and was distressed that my conformity to the norm was not being acknowledged.

I remember walking across campus and having an epiphany. I thought, "if they can't defend their position about when human life begins, they may well be wrong and if the Catholic Church is right about abortion, maybe it is right about other things." It wasn't too long afterwards that I returned to the Church. Sunday mornings were a ghost town at Grinnell College. A handful of us lonely Christians made our way off to church.

From that time on I was a marked woman on campus. I had a few friends who were willing to reason with me about abortion. Before long I realized I was very much against abortion. My fellow students regularly accosted me with all the arguments in favor of abortion, and eventually some of us reasoned out why those reasons for abortion simply didn't balance against the life of a child in the womb. What if the baby is going to be born deformed? The world is overpopulated. Why shouldn't an unmarried pregnant woman be allowed to get on with her life? What if a woman has been raped? None of those concerns seemed to me to permit the killing of an innocent unborn child.

When *Roe vs. Wade* was decided, it barely dented my consciousness. I was in graduate school studying classical languages. I thought I would spend my life teaching students to read Latin and

Greek and the ancient classics. When I was studying at the University of Toronto, I looked up Lloyd Gerson, a fellow graduate from Grinnell who was teaching philosophy there. For some reason the topic of abortion came up. He told me he was very involved in the right-to-life movement and that I should get involved. I remember shortly thereafter biking across Toronto to the right-to-life office and asking how I could help. They needed people to speak in the high schools, and since I was going to be a teacher I decided that I should contribute in that way. It eventually got to the point where I was speaking several times a month, sometimes debating members of Planned Parenthood. I also began and ran the student pro-life group at the University of Toronto for the years I was studying there.

I was now very much committed to my Catholicism and had a circle of friends who also were fervent Catholics–much to the consternation of our fellow graduate students. They thought that we seemed intelligent and couldn't understand how intelligent people could be Catholic. They were particularly frustrated with our pro-life views and completely appalled at the possibility that we could support the Church's teaching on contraception (or the ordination of women). We formed a study group and read *Humanae Vitae* (in fact, we had several study groups–one on the thought of Aquinas, another on the documents of Vatican II, and yet another on the Bible). We discussed *Humanae Vitae* and became convinced of its truth. In spite of my acceptance of the Church's teaching on contraception, when asked about contraception in my right-to-life talks, I would quickly dismiss the question and insist that contraception and abortion were two different issues, for one was preventing a life from coming to be and the other was taking a life that had already begun.

When I started teaching at Notre Dame in the great books program there, I was assigned to teach the course on ethics. We were encouraged to include discussion of modern issues in our classes. I decided to have the students read *Humanae Vitae* and was surprised at how receptive they were to the teaching. It was at this time that Pope John Paul II was delivering his theology of the body talks. There was no internet service at the time, of course, but Gerry Wegemer, then a graduate student in English, was receiving them via fax from Rome. Every week he would slip a copy of the latest one under my office door. My thinking about *Humanae Vitae* was thus being formed by the theology of the body talks as they were being delivered. Ger wangled me into giving a series of evening sessions to students on theology of the body, and again I was impressed with how appealing the students found John Paul II's thought and his defense of *Humanae Vitae*. I also debated one of my colleagues at Notre Dame about contraception–a dear friend of mine who admitted during the debate that he had not read *Humanae Vitae* until the very afternoon of the debate, even though he had been living in contradiction to it for years. I was beginning to realize that a lot of the disobedience from *Humanae Vitae* was blind disobedience. I had the epiphany that when young people read and studied *Humanae Vitae*, they often accepted its teachings.

For some years I did sidewalk counseling outside of the local abortion clinic. I know that most of you have engaged in similar activity and that you probably share my experience that time spent in front of an abortion clinic is powerful time for pondering. After all, one is standing on the divide between life and death. I pondered why women were coming to get abortions. I had a vision of people throwing babies in a river and of those of us at the abortion clinic as lifeguards trying to reach into the river and save as many as we could. I wondered what was causing the babies to be thrown into the river. At some point it dawned on me–I had the epiphany–that these women were engaged in relationships that could not readily accommodate a pregnancy. When I pondered why that would be so, it occurred to me that contraception had enabled them to embark upon relationships for which a pregnancy would be a crisis.

At the same time, many of my friends were getting married and it seemed to me that those who were committed to chastity before marriage and the use of natural family planning within marriage had manifestly better relationships than those who were unchaste and who contracepted. I was seeing the lived out consequences of the violation of Church teaching and of compliance with Church teaching, and this was providing the support of lived experience to what I thought was the philosophical and theological soundness of Church teaching.

When I was seeking a topic for the book I was required to write for tenure at Notre Dame, Ger Wegemer kept pestering me to write a book on *Humanae Vitae*. He said, "You know it and love it and should write about it." I told him that was ridiculous. I had never taken any courses in theology, let alone moral theology, and that supporting *Humanae Vitae* was not a stance that was likely to win one tenure at Notre Dame. But one day I found myself looking at the Latin version of *Humanae Vitae* since I was puzzled by a few passages in the English translation. I decided *Humanae Vitae* needed to be re-translated. All the English translations had been based on the Italian version and did not properly convey the nuances of Latin, which was more philosophically more precise. I decided that to do a good translation I needed to consult all the documents cited in the footnotes. At that point I decided I might as well do a commentary as well as a translation, and soon the commentary grew into a book.

Some of you are familiar with work that I did on the word *munus* that appears in the first line of *Humanae Vitae*: spouses have the *munus* of transmitting human life, a *munus* entrusted to them by God. *Munus* is an important concept.[1] It refers to an important task that God asks people to do in this world. It is both an assignment and a gift. I realized more and more that the Church tries to lead people to understand that the connection between sexuality and parenthood is not one to be bemoaned but one to be embraced and celebrated. *Humanae Vitae* is as much about parenthood as it is about any other concept. I have long loved Karol Wojtyła's book *Love and Responsibility*, and more detailed work that I have been doing recently has led me to see what tremendous influence he had on the themes of *Humanae Vitae*. I hope

---

[1] "The *Munus* of Transmitting Human Life: A New Approach to *Humanae Vitae*," *The Thomist* 54/3 (July 1990): 385-427.

soon to write a book on John Paul II and *Humanae Vitae*. There may actually be something new in that book. Not a new idea of mine, but a new appreciation on some of the work of John Paul II and *Humanae Vitae* that is not of yet full appreciated. I will give you a preview in a moment.

That book I wrote on *Humanae Vitae* did not, of course, get me tenure. In fact, it worked against my getting tenure, combined (I suspect) with the fact that I had led demonstrations against Hans Kung and Mario Como. I rather miss those days! It would not be wrong to say that for a portion of my life, I was a recycled radical. But the work I did on *Humanae Vitae* launched me on a speaking and publishing career that has brought me here today.

Since there weren't many folks speaking on the Church's teaching on contraception, I began to get a lot of requests. I remember that during the twenty-fifth anniversary year I traveled and spoke nine weekends in a row. I took virtually every invitation I got since I thought interest would soon peter out. It hasn't, thanks be to God. I had begun to realize that the best contribution that I personally could make to the pro-life movement was to try to convince people of the wrongness of contraception. If abortion is very much a result of contraceptive lifestyles, then trying to reduce the number of those involved in such lifestyles should serve to reduce the number of abortions as well.

There were three items that I read that had a huge impact on my thinking. One was an article written by Fr. Ernest Fortin. He was arguing that the designation "right-to-life movement" for the movement that was fighting abortion was problematic in several respects.[2] Chiefly he argued that the focus on rights seemed to pit the mother and the child against each other; it put them in a rather litigious relationship as if it were a contest of the right of the mother to choose

---

[2] Ernest L. Fortin, "The New Rights Theory and the Natural Law," *The Review of Politics* 44 (October 1982): 590-612.

against the right of the unborn child to life. He pointed out that to speak of the mother/child relationship in terms of rights falsified the relationship. Rather, it was one naturally built on love and generosity and self-sacrifice. He noted that the Church had always viewed the chief harm that was done through abortion to be the harms done to the doctor who performed the abortion, to the woman who had the abortion, and to the society that permitted the abortion rather than to the child who died. The child, we believed, would be received lovingly by God, but the agents of abortion had endangered their immoral souls.

Two books solidified and advanced some of the thoughts provoked by Fortin. One was Alasdair McIntyre's book *After Virtue*[3] and another was Karol Wojtyła's *Love and Responsibility*.[4] These works put an emphasis on how an action affects the agent, how the performance of actions impacts a person's character. *Humanae Vitae* itself places a great emphasis on this personalistic approach to ethics. As mentioned, the emphasis on *Humanae Vitae* is very much on parenthood and what parenthood means for the parents themselves– how it is an opportunity for them to grow in love.

And now at last I have grown tired of talking about myself and will turn my focus to this theme of "conscious parenthood" and how it may be a good focus for cultivation of a pro-life culture as a means of constructing the civilization of love that John Paul II called for.

John Paul II may well have been responsible for the emphasis in *Humanae Vitae* on parenthood. His writings prior to the issuance of *Humanae Vitae*, especially his book *Love and Responsibility*, put a great emphasis on what he called "conscious parenthood," and I believe many of his concepts worked their way in *Humanae Vitae* through several avenues.[5] His writings after the publication of

---

[3] Alasdair MacIntyre, *After Virtue: A Study in Moral Theory*, 3rd ed. (Notre Dame IN: Univ. of Notre Dame Press, [1981] 2007).

[4] Karol Wojtyła, *Love and Responsibility* (San Francisco CA: Ignatius, 1993), p. 331.

[5] Janet E. Smith, "Conscious Parenthood," *Nova et Vetera* 6/4 (2008): 927-50.

Humanae Vitae also stressed this concept of "conscious parenthood." His theology of the body provides the theological underpinnings for the proper understanding of *Humanae Vitae*. The theology of the body has delivered not only fantastic conceptual advances but has proven to have a powerful ability to affect conversions. Certainly the promotion of his theology of the body by Christopher West and others has converted thousands to lives of chastity, and along with lives of chastity comes a more indelible pro-life commitment.

All of us in the pro-life movement have been trying to find some means of persuading the public that abortion is wrong. We use scientific, philosophical, and religious arguments to defend the humanity and rights of the unborn, we show grisly pictures, we try to educate the public about the bad consequences of abortion for the mothers and fathers of the babies aborted and of the culture that permits abortion. We attempt to pass protective legislation and to elect and appoint pro-life judges. I am in full support of these efforts, and I believe they are making an impact and will continue to do so. Yet one problem with such approaches is that they require an audience that is able to reason and to recognize a good argument when it hears one. We rarely have such an audience.

I am going to suggest yet another factor that we could emphasize, that we could add to our toolbox of approaches. I am not saying that it has been absent from the pro-life movement, but it is one that doesn't depend so much on an audience that can reason. Rather, it depends upon people consulting experience–a John Paul II focus. I am hoping that a certain appeal to the heart of people might help them grasp what their heads seem incapable of getting.

One experience that all of us have in some shape or form is the experience of family, even though the variety of families in which people grow up is ever more diverse. I have found in speaking with young people that they do recognize that among the deep desires of their hearts is the desire for a stable family, for a long lasting relationship. Many of them have despaired of those as a possibility, either because their parents have divorced or the parents of many of their friends have divorced. They begin to think that indissoluble marriages are not possible. Another deep desire of their hearts is to be good parents. God has very much planted the love of children in people's hearts. For several decades, such forces in society as some forms of feminism, environmentalism, and materialism/careerism have created a hostility towards children and babies as terrible impediments to the advancement of women, as pollutants, and expensive inconveniences. But the outbreak of child-bearing by celebrities is rather astonishing, and it seems to be an indication that even the glitterati are susceptible to the appeal of babies with all the love and joy and meaning and hope for the future that they bring. I want to suggest here that the emphasis on the wonderment and the natural responsibilities that come with parenthood is something that we should be emphasizing. Perhaps we need an organization into which we should enroll young people called "Future Parents of America." This emphasis on the joys of babies and parenthood might be a path we should travel as well as stressing the humanity and rights of the unborn.

In *Humanae Vitae* there is a section entitled "responsible parenthood." The Latin that is generally translated as "responsible parenthood" is *conscia paternitas*. The word "responsible" does not truly convey what the Latin word *conscia* connotes. When English-speakers hear of "responsible parenthood," they generally think of parents who perform their duties as parents well. In the context of *Humanae Vitae*, it is reasonable for readers to understand that "responsible parents" are those who realize that they are to raise children to be good citizens in God's kingdom. Those senses are present, but they do not capture adequately what Karol Wojtyła meant by "conscious parenthood."

The word "conscious" has several connotations for Wojtyła. Certainly the word "conscious" means that someone is aware of the reality that he holds in his consciousness. There is kind of a focus or lively attentiveness to the awareness. To speak of an agent acting "consciously" indicates that the agent knows what he or she is doing.

It also suggests that he or she is aware of the consequences of the action and accepts responsibility for those consequences. Wojtyła uses the word frequently, much more frequently than he uses the word "rational," a word that also can be used to indicate that one knows the reality and is accepting of reality. I suspect that Wojtyła speaks of conscious behavior more frequently than rational behavior because to speak of consciousness seems more to emphasize the act of a particular person more than rationality does. To think and act rationally for the most part links the action with some objective universal order, to speak of being conscious reflects the individual's personal appropriating of some truth. The subjective and objective come together more.

In *Love and Responsibility* Wojtyła does a great deal with the concept of conscious parenthood. It is key to his understanding of sexual ethics. He argues that maturity requires that people be conscious that sexual intercourse leads to parenthood. And he argues that consciousness is crucial to sexual responsibility. That consciousness will include several elements. It will include the consciousness that having a child is a very great wonderful act and that those who have children do us all the service of perpetuating the species. Wojtyła speaks of parents entering into the "cosmic stream of existence." But the good of a child is much much more than a good for the species. The life given to a child is a gift of infinite value to the child, for a new immortal soul has come into existence. Wojtyła speaks of parents as "co-creators" with God. As the first line of *Humanae Vitae* states, God has "entrusted to spouses" the tremendously important *munus* or gift of transmitting human life. Those who would embrace this great task should be conscious of what a great task it is. They would realize that children need parents who possess virtues and who have made a lifetime commitment to live a shared loving life together. One should chose as one's spouse one with whom one can be a good parent.

I have clearly resisted making this a scholarly address, but I do want to quote one key passage from *Love and Responsibility*. There Wojtyła states:

When a man and woman capable of procreation have intercourse their union must be accompanied by awareness and willing acceptance of the possibility that 'I may become a father' or 'I may become a mother." ... [Sexual union] is raised to the level of the person only when it is accompanied in the mind and the will by acceptance of the possibility of parenthood. This acceptance is so important, so decisive that without it marital intercourse cannot be said to be a realization of a personal relationship.... Neither in the man nor in the woman can affirmation of the value of the person be divorced from awareness and willing acceptance that he may become a father and she may become a mother.... If the possibility of parenthood is deliberately excluded from marital relations, the character of the relationship automatically changes. The change is away from unification in love and in the direction of mutual or, rather, bilateral, 'enjoyment'. (228)[6]

And further:

The proper way for a person to deal with the sexual urge is, on the one hand, consciously to make use of it for its natural purposes, and on the other to resist it, when it threatens to degrade the relationship between two persons to a level lower than that of love, lower than the level on which the value of the person is affirmed in a union with a truly personal character. Sexual (marital) relations have the character of a true union of persons as long as a general disposition towards parenthood is not excluded from them. This implies a conscious attitude to the sexual instinct: to master the sexual urge means just this, to accept its purpose in marital relations.[7]

The appeal to the native desire to be good parents has a power in some surprising places. When I first was counseling outside of abortion clinics, I would tend to argue with the women about the humanity and rights of the unborn child. I was quite ineffective. I started having more success when I would ask the young women if they ever wanted to be a mother. They would all say yes. I would try to paint of picture of that motherhood for them. I would talk to them about them holding their babies and rocking the to sleep and going to parks with them to play with their babies as they became toddlers. They seemed to like getting those images in their minds. I would then inform them that they if they were pregnant, they were already mothers and that what their babies

---

[6] *Love and Responsibility*, p. 331.

[7] *Love and Responsibility*, p. 229.

need from them now was the warmth of their wombs. I had some success with that strategy.

Now some of you might be skeptical and thinking that a culture that is so obsessed with recreational sex is not likely to be able to be lead to become pro-life through the avenue of the responsibility that is attached to parenthood. I would like to point to a few pieces of evidence, a few films that suggest there may be some promise to this approach.

Nature always asserts itself eventually. But let me express something that you already know: it is natural to love babies. Many of us were delightfully astonished years ago by the movie *Raising Arizona*, a movie in which a most unlikely cast of characters vie over possession of a baby. There have been other wonderful indirectly prolife/pro family movies. I suppose we should make a list of them. I have loved, for instance, *Mrs. Doubtfire* and *Life is Beautiful* and *Spanglish*.

This past year has featured some films that are pro-life and pro-parenthood in some interesting ways. The film *Juno* and the very crude *Knocked Up* may be sign that pro-life sentiments are infiltrating the culture and may have done so to a rather surprising extent. When something percolates to the surface in a mainstream Hollywood film, it may indicate that some deep and wide changes are taking place. A most amazing scene in the movie *Juno* is when Juno goes to an abortion clinic. Outside is a sweet if somewhat goofy Christian Chinese girl who is chanting something like: "All babies want to be borned." She and Juno are friends and have a little chat. As Juno continues into the abortion clinic, the pro-lifer calls out to her, "Your baby already has finger nails." The young woman manning the desk at the abortion clinic is another story entirely. While discussing some deviant sexual act on the phone with a friend, she asks Juno some crude questions–she even offers her a condom–and is rather surly and insensitive. When Juno begins to fill out the requisite forms, she notices that everyone in the room seems to be doing something with their fingernails and leaves the abortion clinic. I was astounded by the favorable presentation of the pro-lifer and the negative portrayal of the abortion clinic personnel. Some of my younger friends said they thought the explanation was that such was a realistic depiction of what has in fact been the experience of many women at abortion clinics.

Juno goes on to put her baby up for adoption. She realizes the great value the life of her baby is to the mother who is adopting the child and receives some wonderful loving care from her parents as well. My guess is that the percentage of young women putting up their babies for adoption this year will rise.

The movie *Knocked Up* is also very pro-life, though very crude. The young man–a pot-smoking shiftless loser of a young man who fathered the child in a one night stand–matures into a responsible person as he faces the responsibilities of fatherhood. The young woman never seriously considers abortion in spite of her mother's rather cavalier proposal to her that she do so. We are led to believe that her willingness to have the child has been nurtured by her love for her nieces and nephews. But the plot line follows the maturing of the young man. The closing scene of the movie has him cuddling his newborn and remarking that he failure to us a condom that evening of the baby's conception was the best thing that had ever happened. The audience that would be likely to watch a movie as crude as *Knocked Up* would likely be getting a message it would encounter no where else. What kind of infiltration of the film industry is going on?

There was also a powerful movie featuring an abortion that didn't have the commercial success of *Juno* and *Knocked Up*. This movie was a Romanian film entitled, *Four months, three weeks, two days*. It showed very coldly and graphically a young woman getting an illegal abortion. In order to get an abortion, she and a friend of hers had to have sex with the abortionist. It was a very hard film to watch. While the film seemed intent on getting viewers to see that illegal abortions are horrible, to my mind it simply made the point that abortions are horrible. It is very hard to give a realistic portrayal of abortion and not to have a good portion of the audience conclude that abortion is revolting. Reviewers generally found it to be artistically excellent–and

I agree that the performances were superb and it was very effectively filmed. The reviewers lamented that it did not receive any film awards. Some commentators were frustrated that movies that featured abortion as a rejected choice are those that have happy endings, and those that feature abortion as the choice that is made are dark and dismal and sad. Again, reality kicks in.

The starkness of the difference in these movies perhaps reflects the starkness of the difference that I mentioned of those who stand outside of abortion clinics. On one side is life and love and responsibility and the joys of family life; on the other side is death, and depression, and loneliness. While our culture is still in some respect spiraling downward, the fact that good and evil are being set in stark relief against each other, is, I think a positive development. Back when I was a college student, I feared that some of the trends in our society and in the world meant that eventually the Marxists would win and Christians would be greatly persecuted. Living in these times when the attack on the embryo is more fierce than ever, when such absurdities as homosexual unions are getting legal recognition, when people are salivating over the organs of our dying loved ones, we may tend to think that the forces of relativism and sexual license and the culture of death will surely prevail, but we may be wrong. I won't be around in forty years time, but I do know that the work of the noble souls in this room will surely have an impact for the good. I know that in addition to the great work done by this group in trying to persuade the world through its excellent scholarly work of the evil of abortion and other attacks on life, of equal importance is the witness that we give of our love for our children and our love for our elderly.

Much of my work has led me to maintain that rejection of the good of parenthood that is embedded in the acceptance of contraception has played a major role in the acceptance of abortion and in the advancement of the culture of death. Thus I wish to maintain that we need to heed the wisdom of *Humanae Vitae* that contraception is wrong and that parenthood is good. We may find a delightful responsiveness to this approach even in our very confused culture.

Again, we may find surprising allies in the lifestyles of such folks as Angelina and Brad, of Madonna, and Brittany, for they all seem to have a sense that in a nihilistic world, children can still offer a liferaft of meaning, sanity and happiness. Perhaps as they embrace the responsibilities of parenthood, they will come to recognize the preciousness of all life. And then perhaps they will better be able to grasp the cogency of the arguments of the prolife movement that is trying to protect all life.

Garrett Hardin and James Rachels: Gurus of a Post-Human Age

Anne Barbeau Gardiner

ABSTRACT: In this essay I shall look at the writings of two men who broke new ground in promoting the culture of death. Both died in 2003 and both are still highly regarded in academe: (1) Garrett Hardin, a biologist who taught Human Ecology at the University of California, Santa Barbara, worked actively in the 1960s for the legalization of abortion and for population control for ecology's sake. (2) James Rachels, a philosopher and medical ethicist at the University of Alabama, merited praise in *The New York Times* for having launched the campaign for euthanasia by denying the difference between killing and letting die. Both men may be called *post-human* because they grounded their support for the culture of death on contempt for the human race–Hardin reduced us to numbers, while Rachels leveled us with beasts. That both men rose to the top of their fields shows how secular academe today encourages post-human perspectives.

IN THIS ESSAY I shall look at the writings of two influential professors who died in 2003 but whose post-human teachings are still highly regarded in the academic world. The first is Garrett Hardin, a biologist who taught human ecology at the University of California, Santa Barbara, and the second James Rachels, a philosopher and medical ethicist at the University of Alabama who was credited in *The New York Times* with igniting the euthanasia debate. Both of these academics may be called "post-human" because each expresses a thoroughgoing contempt for human nature and sees nothing wrong with consigning the weak among us to a cruel death. Each rose to the top of his profession in America, a fact that reveals how completely our secular academic world has embraced the culture of death.

Garrett Hardin turns flesh-and-blood human beings into numbers on a page so that he can calmly consign vast numbers of people to a needless death. He complains that "traditional thinking" is "deplorably nonnumerate." Christianity is especially deficient in this area, having developed before there was "much appreciation of the importance of numeracy," but many ethicists and philosophers have also failed to realize how much "numbers matter." For Hardin, the great task before us today is to "marry" ethics to scientific "numeracy." While words may still have value, they now "require a numerate cast."[1] Hardin sees religious language as utterly disconnected from reality: "People need to be made allergic to such thought-stoppers as *infinity*, *sacred*, and *absolute*. The real world is a world of quantified entities: 'infinity' and the like are not words for quantities but utterances used to divert attention from quantities and limits."[2] Thus he dismisses as non-existent the transcendence of man over the material world.

For Hardin, reality consists only of *quantified entities*. Thus he was an all-out activist for legalized abortion as far back as 1963, and then spent then next forty years of his life promoting population control. This is why he heartily approved of a comparison between the spread of humanity and "the metastasis of cancer" made in 1955 by Alan Gregg, then Vice President of the Rockefeller Foundation. This comparison was meant to justify letting people in densely populated areas starve to death because "[c]ancerous growths demand food; but, as far as I know, they have never been cured by getting it."[3] For Hardin, human beings are not the crown of creation made in the image of God but rather earth's invasive disease.

Hardin is most famous for *The Tragedy of the Commons*, an essay recently described as "one of the most widely read of all environmental works."[4] This was his Presidential Address to the American Association

---

[1] Craig Straub, "Living in a World of Limits: An Interview with Noted Biologist Garrett Hardin," *The Social Contract* (Fall 1997), p. 9, accessible online at: http://www.garretthardinsociety.org; Garrett Hardin, "Extension of the Tragedy of the Commons" (1998), *The American Association for the Advancement of Science*, p. 2, accessible online at: www.garretthardinsociety.org.

[2] Garrett Hardin, *Filters against Folly: How to Survive Despite Economists, Ecologists, and the Merely Eloquent* (New York NY: Viking, 1985), p. 221.

[3] Garrett Hardin, "Living on a Lifeboat," *Bioscience* 24 (1974):10, and *Social Contract* (Fall 2001), p. 9, online at: http://www.garretthardinsociety.org.

[4] J. Edward de Steiguer, *The Origins of Modern Environmental Thought* (Tucson AZ: Univ. of Arizona Press, 2006), p. 213.

for the Advancement of Science (Pacific Branch) on 25 June 1968, a date that reveals how long post-human thinking has been acceptable in academe. Hardin thinks that we need to get rid of traditional morality because it makes "no allowance" for overpopulation.[5] There is no warrant in nature for the traditional belief in the "sanctity of life," he argues, because an individual life is "cheap, very cheap" where there is "a surplus of demanding human flesh." His phrase *surplus of flesh* turns human beings into a vast quantity of superfluous meat. Of course, an individual life would be significant if there were too few people on earth, but instead of a shortage we have (and here he coins a quantifying word) "a longage of people."[6]

Hardin's post-human zeal to reduce our numbers is just the kind of impetus that has propelled Western nations to a self-inflicted demographic winter. First he reduces us to numbers, next promotes the view (embraced by deep ecologists and Green parties) that our lives must be kept in "subservient position" to the environment, and then protests that he is simply showing "concern" for man's long-term survival when he makes the following chilling statement: that the "greatest gift" that we can offer to the "starving millions in poor countries" who appeal to us for emergency aid in time of famine is to give them "the knowledge that they are on their own." Such indifference would amount to genocide, and yet Hardin wants us to stand idly by with a clear conscience while millions starve to death in developing countries. Why? Because a famine would pave the way to a better future. In order to reduce "the number of people who are living a miserable life," he explains, it is necessary to reduce "the number of people who are alive in the next generation." Here he turns a starving multitude into a *number* that needs to be subtracted from the whole so as to reach the ideal population.

Along these lines he praises China for having let millions of its own people starve to death rather than accepting outside help in time of famine. By standing on its own, he says, China came "closer" to solving

---

[5] Garrett Hardin, *The Tragedy of Commons*, p. 6, accessible online at: http://www.garretthardinsociety.org/articles.

[6] Garrett Hardin, *The Limits of Altruism: An Ecologist's View of Survival* (Bloomington IN: Indiana Univ. Press, 1977), p. 116; *Filters*, pp. 13, 214.

its "population problem." On the other hand, India worsened its population problem by accepting outside help to save fifty million of its people from starving in 1965-1966. If India had only one-tenth of its population, he adds, life there would be "very comfortable." But how to get rid of what he calls "excess life"[7]? He shows that it can be done today chiefly by omission, by failing to help the destitute. For the post-human moralist, Dives may in good conscience refuse to give the scraps from his table to starving Lazarus.

Hardin complains that the global food program of the United Nations prevents millions of people from starving to death each year. Feeding the hungry masses frustrates the "corrective feedback of the population cycle" because wherever there is a "deterioration of food supply," it means a "low ratio of resources to population," and then if food is not provided from outside, "the population drops back to the 'normal' level–the 'carrying capacity' of the environment or even below." Yes, this "cycle" involves "great suffering," Hardin admits, but this is a "normal" cycle for countries that yield to "the temptation to convert extra food into extra babies." The phrase *extra food for extra babies* suggests that having another child is the sort of activity for which one may fairly be punished by famine. Again, Hardin insists that the multitude that starves today paves the way to a better life for the remnant: "Every life saved this year in a poor country diminishes the quality of life for subsequent generations." Not only should we allow millions to perish for lack of the food that we could easily give them, but we should also slam the door in the face of hungry immigrants: "World food banks move food to the people, thus facilitating the exhaustion of the Environment of the poor. By contrast, unrestricted immigration moves people to the food, thus speeding up the destruction of the Environment in rich countries."[8] He capitalizes the word *Environment* to show its relative importance in comparison to starving people.

In a subsection of *The Tragedy of the Commons* entitled "Freedom to Breed Is Intolerable," Hardin observes that when birds produce too large a clutch, their babies starve to death. But, he finds, this "negative

---

[7] Hardin, *Limits*, pp. 63-66; Straub "Interview," pp. 7-8.

[8] Hardin, "Living on a Lifeboat," pp. 6-7, 10, 11.

feedback" is unavailable to human beings. Why? Because the modern "welfare state" refuses to let the "children of improvident parents" starve to death. Thus, "overbreeding" no longer brings "its own 'punishment' to the germ line." In line with this criticism of the welfare state, Hardin deplores the enactment of the Universal Declaration of Human Rights by the United Nations in 1948, a document stating that "any choice and decision with regard to the size of the family must irrevocably rest with the family itself." Hardin calls this "right" to choose family size an "absolutist concept" and also "ethic imperialism" when it is imposed on nations that might otherwise engage in coercive population control. If people are given a choice about family size, he laments, those with no "conscience" will outbreed the rest. Note that here the word *conscience* implies having few or no children. To reduce population size, there should be "mutual coercion, mutually agreed upon by the majority of the people affected," and "substantial sanctions" for over-fertile parents. The phrase *substantial sanctions* hints that those with large families could be punished as criminals.[9]

Indeed, Hardin compares "mutual coercion" in regard to family size to "compulsory" taxes and laws against bank robbery to insinuate that having a large family might be as criminal as defaulting on one's taxes or holding up banks. He even warns that unless we accept "coercion" regarding family size, we will no longer be free: "The only way we can preserve and nurture other and more precious freedoms is by relinquishing the freedom to breed, and that very soon." Under "more precious freedoms," he includes the current licentiousness, for he states that the West is "just emerging from a dreadful two-centuries-long Dark Ages of Eros."[10] This post-human guru would give us, then, the false freedom of sexual license while depriving us of the real freedom to procreate.

Since he wants us to stand idly by while millions starve to death, it is no surprise that Hardin spent most of his "external time" from 1963 to 1973 fighting for legalized abortion. He is well known for having compared abortion to smashing "acorns to death with a hammer" and for calculating the "value of a tiny zygote" to be "just about zero." Writing

[9] Hardin, *Tragedy*, pp. 7-9.

[10] Hardin, *Tragedy*, p. 9; *Limits*, p. 69.

on the initial stage of human life, he took occasion to restate his "general principle," that "we cannot make an ethical advance until we realize that numeracy is a part of ethics."[11] Such heartlessness was what he called an *ethical advance*! Just as he had no regret for the millions of Chinese who starved to death when their country refused outside help, so he had no regret for the nearly fifty million of babies in the womb who died as a result of *Roe v. Wade*. After all, they were only numbers, and what duty can we have to numbers?

Sadly, Hardin maintained this post-human vision to the end. His legs had been weakened by polio, so he spent his long life walking by the strength of his arms–suffering that evidently did not awaken in him compassion for the weak. In a 1996 interview he declared that when the time came that he was confined to a wheelchair, he would send for Dr. Kevorkian.[12] Seven years later, in his late eighties, he committed suicide, along with his wife.

Hardin's post-human ideology, now spread by deep ecologists and members of Green parties, is based on the denial of Divine Providence, which the *General Catechism* defines as God's immediate and concrete care for all creatures, including human beings. Whereas Hardin would have us commit a heinous sin by letting millions starve to death for the sake of a future chimerical good, Our Lord demands that we do the right thing now and trust in the fatherly Providence of God for the future: "seek first his kingdom and his righteousness, and all these things shall be yours as well."

Another exponent of post-human morality is the philosopher James Rachels, best known for his 1975 article "Active and Passive Euthanasia," published in *The New England Journal of Medicine*. In a 2003 obituary, *The New York Times* noted that Rachels had broken new ground in his essay "by arguing that actively killing a patient with a terminal illness was morally no worse than letting the person die by

---

[11] "Living within Limits & Limits on Living: Garrett Hardin on Ecology, Economy, and Ethics: Interview by Frank Meile," *Sceptic* 4 (1996): p. 1, online at: www.lrainc.com; Hardin, *Filters*, pp. 124-25; Straub, "Interview," p. 7.

[12] "Interview by Frank Meile," p. 2.

doing nothing."[13] As I will show, what lay behind Rachels's advocacy of medical murder was a strange concept of humility.

Rachels cites approvingly what Darwin wrote in his notebooks in 1838 (around twenty years before *The Origin of the Species* appeared): "Man in his arrogance thinks himself a great work worthy the interposition of a deity. More humble and I think truer to consider him created from animals." Here Darwin calls it *arrogance* to believe, as Christians do, that man is a "great work" that came about by God's direct intervention. He calls it *more humble* to regard man as derived from animals without any divine action. Rachels embraces this viewpoint and declares dogmatically that, after Darwin, "we can no longer think of ourselves as occupying a special place in creation.... We are not a great work."[14] Here he presents himself as *humble* in Darwin's sense of the word, following him in declaring that man is nothing "special" in reality, certainly "not a great work" shaped by the hand of God.

Ah, but is this really being *humble*? Four centuries ago, the poet John Donne observed that certain philosophers pretend to an "impious humility" by holding a low view of man, as if his soul were "no more than the soul of a beast."[15] In his 1755 *Dictionary*, Samuel Johnson defined the word *impious* as "wicked" and "without reverence of religion," and he also defined *atheistical* as "impious." Thus, Donne's phrase *impious humility* means a wicked, atheistic version of humility by which man is reduced to the level of a four-footed beast. This is a parody of Christian humility, the first of the theological virtues. For, according to St. Thomas Aquinas, humility is the virtue that sees God (certainly not a beast!) in another human being.[16]

---

[13] Anahad O'Connor, "James Rachels, Ethicist, p. 62; "Ignited Euthanasia Debate," *The New York Times* obituary (September 9, 2003), accesible online at www.bradpriddy.com.

[14] James Rachels, "Darwin, Species, and Morality" (1987) in *The Legacy of Socrates: Essays in Moral Philosophy*, ed. Stuart Rachels (New York NY: Columbia Univ. Press, 2006), p. 15.

[15] John Donne, "18. Meditation," from *Devotions upon Emergent Occasions*, in *Seventeenth-Century Verse and Prose*, 2 vols., ed. Helen C. White et al. (New York NY: Macmillan, 1967), I: 109.

[16] *Summa Theologica*, II-II, q. 161.

Actually, Rachels reduces man not to a level with, but rather below, the beast. He remarks that the "greatest misconception of all" is to imagine that man stands at the apex of evolution; since evolution is random, the "cockroach" is a "better candidate" for the title of "highest achievement of evolution." The *cockroach*! Rachels is aware, of course, that Aristotle and "virtually every important thinker in our history" has regarded human beings as "dominating a world made for their benefit,"[17] and that his own post-human contempt for our nature goes against the philosophical consensus of three millennia. This doesn't bother him. He quips that all those philosophers were in the throes of vanity–"Humans are a remarkably vain species"–as well as "in the grip of the notion that humanity is somehow 'special' in some occult or hard-to-define sense."[18] His phrase *in the grip* implies they were not thinking freely, while the adjectives *occult* and *vain* imply that their views were weirdly religious and downright foolish.

At one point Rachels warns that a lofty view of human nature aids the pro-life cause: "an exaggerated sense of the cosmic importance of human beings" leads to "the sanctity-of-human-life ethic."[19] By the phrase *cosmic importance*, he seems to glance at the mystery of the Incarnation, the supreme act of humility by which God conferred an "exalted dignity" on the human race by becoming a man, a dignity not even "given to Angels."[20] By contrast, Rachels's view of our *cosmic unimportance* leads to our human life being treated as worthless.

Rachels follows Nietzsche in regarding Christians as the epitome of *arrogance* because they believe in Holy Scripture: "Christians have the astonishing arrogance to imagine that the entire universe was made for their benefit. They have persuaded themselves that they were created in the image of God, who loves them above all others and who made the

---

[17] "Nietzsche and the Objectivity of Morals" (1998) in *Legacy*, p. 144.

[18] "Value," *Legacy*, p. 66.

[19] "The Value of Human Life" (2002), in *Legacy*, pp. 59, 65-66.

[20] *Catechism of the Council of Trent for Parish Priests, issued by order of Pope Pius V*, trans. John A. McHugh and Charles J. Callan (Rockford IL: TAN Books, 1982), p. 48.

world for them. They believe in addition that they will never perish."[21] The implication here is that the Bible, from which these doctrines derive, is a source of *arrogance* rather than humility, and that we Christians will never be *humble* in his impious, atheistic sense until we abandon Holy Scripture. This should be easy to do, Rachels says, since Christianity has already been "virtually demolished" by *The Descent of Man*, in which Darwin asserts that every one of our mental characteristics can also be found in animals. In that work Darwin claims that there is "no fundamental difference between man and the higher mammals in their mental faculties" and that even our boasted use of language differs from other animals only in "degree." Yes, only in *degree*. Strange that there is no animal version of the *Divine Comedy*. Rachels contends that Darwin's exalted view of animals has been confirmed in our own time because the "best theory" of animal behavior today attributes not just rational powers to animals, but even "desires and beliefs."[22] Yes, *beliefs*. Strange that animals have not yet produced a Creed.

To puncture our Christian arrogance and instruct us in the new evolutionary *humility*, Rachels cites a passage from *The Origin of the Species*, where Darwin states that the word *species* refers to nothing in the real world: "I look at the term species as one arbitrarily given for the sake of convenience to a set of individuals closely resembling each other." Rachels agrees heartily that determinate species with fixed essences do not exist in the real world, but rather only multitudes of individual organisms exist, which are somewhat alike and somewhat unlike. This vision of the world as a chaos of disconnected particular beings requires a new morality, because "traditional morality" is based on the view that a man, as opposed to a dog or a cow, is "morally special" because of his species-membership. Now that this "old" view has "lost its foundations," thanks to Darwin, only individual "characteristics" can have moral value.[23]

What this means in practice, Rachels explains, is that to the extent

---

[21] "Nietzsche," *Legacy*, p. 149.

[22] "Darwin," *Legacy*, pp.18-19.

[23] Ibid., pp. 27-28.

a human being and a dog are alike, their treatment will be the same, but to the extent they are unlike, their treatment will differ. Treatment will depend henceforth not on someone's species-membership, but on his characteristics. And that's not all, for in this new dispensation, human beings will have "to assert a right to better treatment" when they differ from "other animals" in their characteristics. They will bear the burden of proof when asking to be treated better than a chimpanzee. But what about those who do not have the "psychological capacities" to "assert" themselves and ask for better treatment? They will be passed by, Rachels admits, because under the new evolutionary ethic, one's "mere physical existence would be as insignificant, from a moral point of view, as that of a slug." Yes, a *slug*–Darwinian humility reduces man to the level of a snail!

What fate does Rachels have in store for handicapped babies and brain-damaged adults? Having dismissed the "old" axiom that "moral status is determined by what is normal for the species," he has no qualms about killing them outright. He also defends abortion on the ground that "fetuses" may have "human bodies," but lack a "distinctively human consciousness."[24] Reduced to a cluster of "characteristics," the child in the womb can hardly expect to be treated better than that triumph of evolution, the cockroach.

Rachels sums up his position neatly when he says that according to the "new view" propounded by Darwin, it is no longer possible to deduce "right and wrong" from "the nature of things in themselves" because there are no *natures* in existence. It follows that "the natural world does not in and of itself manifest value and purpose" and that the natural law ethics derived from Aristotle must now be replaced with a "scientific" ethics based only on particular characteristics. Here is an example: while proponents of natural law theory have "often taken homosexual conduct to be a paradigm case of conduct that is contrary to nature," the new morality considers that if scientists should turn out to be right in saying that homosexuals have a different "hypothalamus," then our "moral view" will have to "accommodate" this "fact" and

---

[24] "The Legacy of Socrates" (1992) in *Legacy*, p. 132; "Darwin," p. 26, and "Legacy," p. 65, in *Legacy*.

public policies favoring heterosexuals must no longer be allowed to stand as a barrier to the "flourishing" of homosexuals. And here is another example: it should be considered as unreasonable to let someone die slowly when "the distinction between killing and letting die" is not "*itself* important."[25] Thus, the *impious humility* that sees man as no better than a beast leads straight to the public sponsorship of homosexuality and the killing of sick people like dogs.

In conclusion, there are several doors that open onto the Culture of Death, but virtually all of them have the same contempt for human nature written on them, whether in the form of Hardin's numeracy or Rachels's *impious humility*. Whichever of these doors we open, the same chamber of horrors is found inside. For ideas have consequences, and if we embrace the teachings of highly acclaimed academics who deny that human life is special and sacred, we will likely end up letting millions starve to death when we might save them, working to exterminate vast numbers by abortion and euthanasia, and applauding the current homosexual juggernaut. Pope John Paul II was right when he said in the *Gospel of Life* that attacks against human life are receiving "widespread and powerful support from a broad consensus on the part of society" today and that "we are in fact faced by an objective '*conspiracy against life*'." Our post-human age gives new meaning to the Apocalypse, where the times of the Anti-Christ are depicted as the rule of the Beast.

---

[25] On homosexuality, see "Legacy," pp. 126-29; "Killing and Starving to Death" (1979), p. 73; "The Principle of Agency" (1998), p. 198, all in *Legacy*.

PHILOSOPHICAL PERSPECTIVES

Personal Identity and the Genome Project

John J. Conley, S.J.

ABSTRACT: The findings of the Human Genome Project can strengthen the traditional philosophical argument from identity, which claims that a human being's status as a person–and the right to life rooted in personhood–is coterminous with his or her corporeal existence from conception until natural death.

ONE OF THE MOST INFLUENTIAL philosophical arguments against the practices of abortion and euthanasia has been the argument from personal identity.[1] According to this argument, a unique human being begins his or her existence at the moment of conception and ends his or her existence at the moment of natural death. Although the individual human being undergoes substantial changes at different moments of development in terms of capacity and achievement–a new-born infant cannot write a book and a nonagenarian is not a candidate for the decathlon–the unique personal identity of each human being perdures through these various changes. Just as a unique human being exists in a continuum from conception until natural death, the rights of each human being, of which the right to life is paramount, inhere in the individual throughout his or her progress through this continuum. According to the argument from identity, to place the boundary markers for human personhood later than conception or earlier than natural death is to deny the ontological fact that it is the same human being who emerges in conception as a unique individual, who emits brain waves in the first trimester of pregnancy, who cries at birth, who starts to reason at approximately the age of seven, and who survives a severe accident that might have inflicted severe brain damage. Concomitantly, to deny the right to life to any human being at

---

[1] For contemporary versions of the philosophical argument from identity, see Francis J. Beckwith, *Defending Life: A Moral and Legal Case Against Abortion Choice* (Cambridge UK: Cambridge Univ. Press, 2007) and Robert P. George and Christopher Tollefsen, *Embryo: A Defense of Human Life* (New York NY: Doubleday, 2008).

any stage of the developmental process is to commit a grave injustice, since it treats a unique, individual human being as an object to be disposed of by more powerful human beings.

It is the purpose of my paper to indicate how the recently completed Human Genome Project can strengthen the philosophical argument from personal identity. Obviously, empirical scientific data in and of itself can neither prove nor disprove a case for human personhood from the moment of conception. Nonetheless, recent genetic research has indicated how many distinctive physical and intellectual traits of the human person are established at the moment of conception when each human being receives his or her distinctive genetic endowment. The Human Genome Project's detailed map of the human genotype indicates how many of the personality traits considered as part of the human being's moral profile have a radical beginning in the moment of conception. Although metaphysically neutral in and of themselves, the findings of the Genome Project can bolster the argument from personal identity and the case against abortion supported by that argument by revealing the various ways in which the history of individual personhood begins simultaneously with the history of individual corporeality at the onset of conception.

HUMAN GENOME PROJECT

Sponsored by the National Institutes of Health and the U. S. Department of Energy, the Human Genome Project (1990-2003) pursued two major research goals: (1) the mapping and identification of the approximately 20,000 to 25,000 genes present in human DNA; (2) the determination of the sequences of the 3 billion chemical base pairs that make up human DNA. The term "genome" refers to all the DNA present in an organism, including but not limited to, its genes. The proteins present in DNA shape how an organism looks, functions, and behaves. In addition to the conduct of research into the human genetic constitution, the Human Genome Project was charged to provide storage, transfer, and analysis of the empirical genetic data generated by the research. From the inception of the project, one of its sub-projects (appropriately entitled ELSI) has subsidized papers and conferences dealing with the ethical, legal, and social issues posed by the new genetic profile of humanity sketched by the Genome Project's findings.[2]

Like other recent advances in genetic research, the findings of the Genome

---

[2] For the project's official findings, see *Human Genome Project Information* at http://www.ornl.gov/sci/techresources/Human_Genome/home.html.

Project indicate that certain traits of our intellectual capacity and moral temperament, as well as of our physical constitution, are shaped by our particular genetic endowment. It has long been known that the genetic code shapes our personal intelligence and our capacity to develop certain skills of the speculative and practical intellect. In addition to underscoring the contribution of our genetic endowment to our intellectual profile, the findings of the Human Genome Project underline how much our emotional temperament and moral character owe to our genetic constitution established at conception.

When I choose to tell the truth rather than a lie in a situation of social embarrassment, my action may well be a free act, inasmuch as it involves apprehension of certain goods, a weighing of alternative courses of action, and an election of the honest over the dishonest course. But my moral personality, which profoundly colors how I perceive and how I resolve this moral dilemma, seems to be deeply shaped by forces that predate and elude my limited zone of freedom. Collateral studies on the findings of the Genome Project are pinpointing the genetic causes of depression, elation, and other major mood-mental states–and it is not news to those involved in counseling how profoundly such states can color the perception, judgment, and activity of a moral agent affected by them. Recently publicized research exploring the data generated by the Human Genome Project suggests that such virtues as courage (and possibly such vices as foolhardiness) under the clinical guise of "risk-taking" have substantial genetic causes.[3] A genetics of vice and virtue is a humbling prospect, but contemporary genetic research indicates that the basic moral temperament with which moral agency must work in the effort to foster virtue and repress vice is rooted in each individual's genetic endowment.

Genetic Identity and Moral Personality

The Genome Project's portrait of the genetic determinants of emotional and moral temperament in the genetic constitution established at conception indicates how radically the history of each human person, and not only the history of each person's body, begins at conception. My history of cowardice and courage, industriousness and sloth, justice and bias owes far more to the genetic endowment that I have received from my parents than earlier

---

[3] The most influential of the studies arguing for a genetic influence on risk-taking is J.B. Savitz and R.S. Ramesar, "Genetic Variants Implicated in Personality: A Review of the More Promising Candidates," *American Journal of Medical Genetics*, 131B (2004): 2032.

generations could fathom. Environment, childhood history, and personal choice can counterbalance or modify such an endowment but not abolish it. This initial genetic constitution shapes the field in which we exercise our moral responsibility but it is neither the product of nor malleable by our moral responsibility.

My personal history has a decisive onset in the moment of conception inasmuch as my way of perceiving and reacting to the world, especially to other persons, is shaped by my particular genotype. My ways of exercising freedom and my characteristic honesty or dishonesty have roots in my genetic constitution as surely as do my blood type and my eye color, even if the latter (unlike the former) are not open to alteration through environmental influences and personal choice. The data generated by the Genome Project on the genetic roots of moral personality can strengthen the argument from identity's claim concerning the radical unity between the embryo and the mature adult in the trajectory of the genetically identical human individual. This unity is moral, spiritual, and emotional as well as physical.

Genetic Identity, Freedom, and Environment

To affirm the genetic roots of human moral personality is not to deny the influence of social environment on the development of moral character or to deny the reality of the personal exercise of free will. Indeed, the literature developed in tandem with the Human Genome Project indicates how the complementary contributions of genetics, environment, and self-determination to human personality can be affirmed. Throughout the papers written by researchers associated with the Human Genome Project, one finds a repeated distinction between "determinative" and "influential" genes that shape human behavior.

The discussion of the etiology of Alzheimer's disease reflects this differential rhetoric.[4] A particular genetic marker is determinative for a rare version of Alzheimer's disease called "familial Alzheimer's disease." This disease affects nearly everyone in a small, identifiable group of families that transmit the gene. Between the ages of thirty and sixty, family members begin to exhibit the alterations in brain chemistry (the emergence of the plaques and tangles typical of the disease) that are characteristic of disease. The typical behavioral decline, expressed through memory loss, loss of motor skills,

---

[4] For a presentation of the genetic evidence concerning Alzheimer's disease and inheritance, see the research findings of the Alzheimer's Association at http://www.ygyh.org/alz/inherited.htm.

aphasia, hallucinations, and delusion, also manifests itself during this early time span (thirty to sixty years old); hence, its common designation as "early-onset Alzheimer's." With familial Alzheimer's disease, no environmental factors or personal choices can alter the designated course of the disease. The genetic causation here appears to be determinative. To echo traditional language of the free-will debate, it could not be otherwise.

The other type of Alzheimer's disease, called "sporadic Alzheimer's disease," does not appear to have a determinative genetic cause. Also called "late-onset Alzheimer's," sporadic Alzheimer's disease typically affects people after they have reached the age of sixty-five. Researchers have identified a particular version of the APOE gene on Chromosome 19 as increasing one's risk of developing Alzheimer's disease later in life, although the influence of the gene on the onset of Alzheimer's in a particular individual seems relatively slight. In the etiology of sporadic Alzheimer's disease, environmental and personal-choice factors appear more influential than do the genetic. One's diet (especially the consumption of Vitamins E and C), one's history of injury (especially of serious head injury), and one's regular exercise of the brain tissue (especially through the use of puzzles, varied types of reading, and various types of problem-solving) appear to be more decisive in affecting one's chances of developing Alzheimer's disease late in life.

The findings of the Genome Project do not alter the basic components of a free human act. To use neo-Aristotelian language, the exercises of apprehension, deliberation, election, and execution remain what they always have been.[5] The intellect and will continue to author an act that by its intentionality and voluntariness remains distinct from the actions dependent purely on instinct. As Francis Collins, the head of the National Institutes of Health's team for the Genome Project, has remarked, our genetic constitution may hand us the deck of cards we have to play with, but we are the ones in our deliberate and calculated choices who play the cards in response to the various challenges that we confront as rational agents.[6] The findings of the project may provide a far more detailed and precise map of the biological constraints on our exercise of free will, but these simply complement the limitations on free human activity that we have long recognized in our accounts of human nature. Like our

---

[5] For a typical neo-Aristotelian presentation of the psychology of the moral act, see Martin D. O'Keefe, *Known From the Things That Are* (Houston TX: Center for Thomistic Studies, 1987), pp. 13-17.

[6] See Francis S. Collins, *The Language of God* (New York NY: Free Press, 2007).

environment, our family history, our political community, and our emotional temperament, our genetic endowment creates a framework in which we choose to act in ways that could have been otherwise–but these are still rational and voluntary choices that could have been otherwise. The new map of the genetic constitution of human nature modifies but does not abolish the paradox of an authentic freedom that is exercised in and limited by a creaturely, physical, and spiritual nature that possesses only a limited malleability.

CONCLUSION

The philosophical argument from identity has long argued that despite developmental changes, the same unique human being exists from the moment of conception until the moment of natural death. The data generated by the Human Genome Project and similar projects of genetic research indicate how deeply personal this individual human continuity is. The genetic constitution established at conception shapes the individual's moral and spiritual personality. Subsequent alterations to this personality through interaction with the environment and through the personal exercise of freedom always bear the trace of the initial genetic direction of the human person toward a particular moral temperament and away from another. Although much of this personal determination may be a softer type of influence than strict causal determination, it indicates that the history of the individual person has a radical beginning and orientation in conception. The development and transformation of the person through subsequent stages of development occur to an individual whose personal history is coterminous with his or her history as an embodied being.

Would Aquinas Change His Mind on Hominization Today?

Craig Payne

ABSTRACT: Those who claim that Aquinas would use modern embryo-logical analysis in his discussions of the human soul typically argue that this type of analysis would push the divine infusion of the intellectual soul back to the time of the fertilization of the zygotic cell, while Aquinas (given his lack of such embryological analysis) argues that this infusion comes a few weeks later in the embryo's development. This claim also entails that in order to be a faithful and accurate interpreter of Aquinas today, one must reject the biological notions put forward by Aquinas himself. One would then also reject the interpretations of Aquinas put forward by such authors as Pasnau, Donceel, Dombrowski, Deltete, and so on.

INTRODUCTION

A remarkable paradox within Thomistic anthropology is that, were Thomas alive today, he would revise some of his own arguments and conclusions *based on his own principles* of inquiry. It may seem suspiciously convenient to speak of what Aquinas "would" and "would not" say if he were "alive today," instead of merely reporting what he did in fact say when he was in fact alive. However, especially in the area of scientific advances in understanding, Aquinas himself makes the following point: "Our intellect's proper and proportionate object is the nature of a sensible thing. Now a perfect judgment concerning anything cannot be formed, unless all that pertains to that thing's nature be known."[1] In his description of the human constitution, therefore, Aquinas would certainly take advantage of advances in genetic and embryological information. "Thomism is bound to no particular scientific theory. St. Thomas...uses the theories current in his day by way of illustration, but with the proviso that these theories may well be discarded by a later generation and that such a discarding would have no

[1] ST I 84.8.

effect upon his thesis."[2] Aquinas would not, however, regard a change in *attitudes* toward something's nature as an actual advance in knowledge; for example, whether or not a society's attitudes change toward the acceptance or non-acceptance of infanticide would not represent any sort of advance in knowledge regarding the actual nature of the action itself. A societal change in attitudes may, in fact, arise from a willful rejection of knowledge, not an advance. At any rate, it remains true that, as Jean-Pierre Torrell has written, the greatness of the *Summa Theologica* lies in its ability "to inspire solutions to problems for future generations because of the breadth of the great intuitions that govern it. Therein lies, no doubt, the major reason for the *Summa*'s lastingness and its enduring fruitfulness."[3] These "great intuitions that govern" Aquinas's writing are a faithful and accurate guide to what he would and would not say were he alive today.

For example, since he based his biological discussions on the biology known to his day, Aquinas would adapt these discussions to the wealth of new scientific knowledge now available:

> Were he alive today, St. Thomas would without doubt hold the doctrine of immediate animation [i.e., that the human soul is immediately infused into the body at conception]. The fundamental principles of his philosophy of man are independent of his obsolete biology; indeed, when applied to modern knowledge, they provide formidable support for immediate animation. Stripping off the shell of the out-of-date science, we find the permanently valid kernel of his thought on the soul. This is not wishful thinking. It is simply the application of the Thomist axiom stated earlier: philosophy must have an empirical base.[4]

Since "philosophy must have an empirical base," the principles of inquiry involved do not themselves necessarily have to be changed.

---

[2] Gerald Vann, O.P. *The Aquinas Prescription: St. Thomas's Path to a Discerning Heart, a Sane Society, and a Holy Church* (London UK: Hague and Gill, 1940; reprinted, Manchester NH: Sophia Institute Press, 1999), pp. 94-95.

[3] Jean-Pierre Torrell. *Aquinas's* Summa*: Background, Structure, and Reception*. Benedict M. Guevin, O.S.B., trans. (Washington, D.C.: The Catholic Univ. of America Press, 2005), p. x.

[4] "An Approach to a Key Theological Question." American Bioethics Advisory Commission Report, Part 10. all.org/abac/clontx10.htm, n.p. Accessed 13 December 2005. It is worth adding that not only would Aquinas hold to immediate animation/hominization were he alive today, but he also would no longer consider the infusion of the rational soul to come at widely varying times for males and females.

However, the results obtained from those principles might change as the empirically-based information available for inquiry is expanded or corrected.[5] "Due to its dependence upon medieval biological data, which has been far surpassed by current scientific research," as one writer notes, "Aquinas's explicit account of human embryogenesis has been generally rejected by contemporary scholars."[6]

Those who claim that Aquinas would use modern embryological analysis in his discussions of the animating soul typically argue that this type of analysis would push the divine infusion of the intellectual soul back to the time of the fertilization of the zygotic cell, while Aquinas (given his lack of such embryological analysis) argues that this infusion comes a few weeks later in the embryo's development. Since this claim goes to the heart of one's definition of human-ness and the host of human-life issues related to that definition, it has provoked a number of studies and occasioned much controversy, especially since this claim also entails that *in order to be a faithful and accurate interpreter of Aquinas today, one must reject the biological notions put forward by Aquinas himself.*

Recent Problematic Accounts

Along with the extensive literature on the question of Thomistic anthropological hominization and its relation to natural law moral principles, as well as on hominization in general, in recent years some works have appeared offering what I consider to be profound misinterpretations both in the area of Aquinas's metaphysics and anthropology, and also in specific bioethical applications of these interpretations. In the bioethical area, two examples are *Sacred Rights: The Case for Contraception and Abortion in World Religions*, edited by Daniel C. Maguire, in particular Christine H. Gudorf's essay "Contraception and Abortion

---

[5] "Empirical means derived from experience; and, in this sense, both science and philosophy are derived from inductive facts. True, philosophy is predominantly speculative, while science is predominantly investigative; yet both are empirical to the extent that both are emergences from experience." Robert Edward Brennan, *Thomistic Psychology: A Philosophic Analysis of the Nature of Man* (New York NY: Macmillan, 1941), p. 52.

[6] Jason T. Eberl. "Aquinas's Account of Human Embryogenesis and Recent Interpretations." *Journal of Medicine and Philosophy* 30/4 (2005): 379-94, p. 380.

in Roman Catholicism"[7]; and *A Brief, Liberal, Catholic Defense of Abortion*, written by Daniel A. Dombrowski and Robert Deltete.[8] The latter work contains an exegesis of both Aquinas and Augustine that appears quite mistaken, as well as the argument that the Catholic Church's "immediate hominization" teaching regarding the human embryo arises out of two discredited scientific views from the 1600s.[9] In the Introduction to the first-mentioned work, Maguire refers to abortion as a "sacred right": "We believe that women should make the decision for abortion themselves and that it is a misuse of governmental power to take this sacred right from them."[10]

However, the example that provides the primary impetus to the present essay revolves around Aquinas's metaphysics and anthropology; this is Robert Pasnau's work *Thomas Aquinas on Human Nature.*[11] Pasnau's analysis of the "Treatise on Human Nature" in the *Summa Theologica*, although containing much of benefit, also puts forward many views of the soul, its nature, its immortality, and so on that are quite problematic; furthermore, Pasnau uses his account of Aquinas's anthropology to provide a chapter-long attack upon the Catholic Church's social teachings in the area of abortion. Pasnau writes:

> There is an unfortunate tendency to conflate interest in medieval philosophy, especially in the work of Thomas Aquinas, with sympathy for the Roman Catholic Church. Inasmuch as the Church's intellectual foundations lie in medieval philosophy, above all in Aquinas, sympathy for his work naturally should translate into sympathy for Catholicism. But the conflation is still unfortunate, because in recent years the Church has identified itself with a noxious social agenda–especially on homosexuality, contraception, and abortion–that has sadly come to seem part of the defining character of Catholicism. So it should be gratifying, for students of medieval philosophy, to see how in at least one of these cases Aquinas provides the resources to show something

[7] Daniel C. Maguire, ed. *Sacred Rights: The Case for Contraception and Abortion in World Religions* (New York NY: Oxford Univ. Press, 2003). Gudorf's essay is found on pages 55-78.

[8] Daniel A. Dombrowski and Robert Deltete, *A Brief, Liberal, Catholic Defense of Abortion* (Champaign IL: Univ. of Illinois Press, 2000).

[9] These discredited views are "preformationism" and the idea of the human "homunculus."

[10] Maguire, "Introduction," *Sacred Rights*, p. 6.

[11] Robert Pasnau. *Thomas Aquinas on Human Nature: A Philosophical Study of* Summa Theologiae *1a 75-89* (Cambridge UK: Cambridge Univ. Press, 2002).

of what is wrong with the Church's position.[12]

Pasnau's account of Aquinas's views of delayed hominization is also similar to that of Dombrowski and Deltete, and thus this essay is in large part a reaction contrary to this account. Pasnau's views, of course, could be passed over more easily had he put them forward as his own views, not as Aquinas's. As he himself writes, "This is not meant to be an exercise in neo-Thomistic metaphysics; it is a proposal about how we should understand Aquinas himself." He also somewhat candidly admits his readiness for "drawing conclusions about [Aquinas's] metaphysics that go beyond what the texts explicitly say."[13]

Pasnau's work is pitched at a level that is scholarly, yet accessible to the intelligent undergraduate. Therefore, if this respectably published and well-publicized work were *the* account of Aquinas's anthropology that a reader were depending upon for his or her understanding of Aquinas's views, that reader would come away seriously misled regarding some features of Aquinas's metaphysics and anthropology. Further, this hypothetical reader would especially misunderstand how Aquinas's teaching on the soul's animation of the human substance could possibly lead directly to the current bioethical views held by many Thomists and many of those sympathetic to Thomistic arguments. As Haldane and Lee put it, corrective responses are necessary "since there will be readers whose only knowledge of the issues in question will come from Pasnau's account, and since that account is contentious in substance, and advanced in advocacy of a particular moral interest.... Matters are other than as Pasnau has chosen to present them."[14]

This present essay, therefore, seeks to rectify the mistaken views presented in the writings mentioned by presenting a more or less traditional account of Thomistic anthropology along with the now-traditional view of the immediate hominization of the human being at the time of conception; along with this hominization goes the concomitant endowment of human rights and protections. The term "now-

[12] Ibid., p. 105.

[13] Ibid., pp. 138 and 85.

[14] John Haldane and Patrick Lee, "Aquinas on Human Ensoulment, Abortion, and the Value of Life," *Philosophy* 78 (2003): 255-78, p. 256.

traditional view" is used as opposed to Pasnau's description of the state of affairs: "Despite the official Church stance, there is a growing consensus among all parties to the dispute that, whatever be said after the first two weeks, it cannot reasonably be supposed that a one-week-old 'pre-embryo' counts as a human being."[15] Since Pasnau refers to the "growing consensus among all parties to the dispute," one must assume that he no longer considers those agreeing with the "official Church stance" (what is here called the "now-traditional view") to be legitimate parties to the dispute. Of course, if one polls only those on one side of an argument, one tends to discover "growing consensus" rather easily.

Modern Embryology and the Human Form

In fact, the issue of hominization has provoked such extensive discussion that one must wonder at Pasnau's claim that "Aquinas's view on these matters [i.e., on the delayed ensoulment of the embryo forming the human substance] is not widely known. Those who do know are generally not eager to advertise it, and indeed have often attacked it in scholarly circles."[16] Pasnau seems at the very least to imply that some sort of deliberate concealment of Aquinas's views has been going on amongst scholars, one presumes for ideological reasons related to their embarrassment or to the damage to their own arguments were Aquinas's actual teaching of "delayed hominization" (as it is called[17]) more "widely known." To the contrary, as argued by Haldane and Lee:

[15] *Thomas Aquinas on Human Nature*, p. 420 n17.

[16] Pasnau, *Thomas Aquinas on Human Nature*, p. 115.

[17] The terms "hominization," "ensoulment," and "animation," when referring to humans, will be used synonymously when used specifically by me in this work, even though many early Latin and Roman Catholic philosophers and theologians (including Aquinas himself) would separate them. In the Orthodox tradition, "As a general rule, the Greek Fathers (e.g., Gregory of Nyssa) held a theory not only of immediate animation but also of immediate hominization" (Dombrowski and Deltete, *A Brief, Liberal, Catholic Defense of Abortion*, p. 27). Aquinas, on the other hand, based on his insufficient embryological information, made a distinction between animation and hominization, arguing for the immediate animation of the embryo (i.e., the embryo is living and developing from the moment of conception) but not its immediate hominization (i.e., the embryo is not from conception infused with the intellectual soul making it human). See ST I, 76, 3 ad 3 and I.118.2 ad 2.

Quite contrary to this impression of concealment, however, it is a commonplace of informed, scholarly discussions in this area that Aquinas (along with other ancient and medieval writers) believed in late human ensoulment, often referred to as "delayed hominization," and there is an extensive scholarly and semi-popular literature on it contributed to by parties from different sides of the interpretive, philosophical, theological, and moral debates.... As it is, [Pasnau's] treatment of the matter suggests an overly hasty rush to judgment.[18]

Contra Pasnau, Haldane and Lee go on to point out, "Not only are scholars in the field generally well aware of Aquinas's views about human ensoulment, but the Catholic Church itself has made reference to such views in its public declarations promulgating a contrary position."[19] Consequently, this position has not only been known "in scholarly circles," as Pasnau puts it, but more popularly as well. For instance, in its 1974 *Declaration on Procured Abortion*, the Congregation for the Doctrine of the Faith states:

In the course of history...the various opinions on the infusion of the spiritual soul did not introduce any doubt about the illicitness of abortion. It is true that in the Middle Ages, when the opinion was generally held that the spiritual soul was not present until after the first few weeks, a distinction was made in the evaluation of the sin and the gravity of penal sanctions. Excellent authors allowed for this first period more lenient case solutions which they rejected for following periods. But it was never denied at that time that procured abortion, even during the first days, was an objectively grave fault. This condemnation was in fact unanimous.[20]

One of these "excellent authors" mentioned in this Declaration was of course Aquinas. Pasnau quotes Aquinas[21] as arguing regarding abortion before the infusion of the rational soul that "although this sin is serious, and should be counted as wrongdoing...still it is less than homicide."[22] In this same footnote, Pasnau also refers the reader to ST II-II.64.8 without quoting it. In this passage, Aquinas comments on Exodus 21:22 as follows: "He that strikes a woman with child does something unlawful: wherefore if there results the death either of the woman or of

---

[18] Haldane and Lee, "Aquinas on Human Ensoulment, Abortion, and the Value of Life," pp. 258-60.

[19] Ibid., p. 261.

[20] Sacred Congregation for the Doctrine of the Faith, *Declaration on Procured Abortion* (Vatican: Holy See, 1974), p. 7.

[21] *In quatuor libros Sententiarum*, Distinctio 31, Expositio (Pasnau's translation).

[22] Pasnau, *Thomas Aquinas on Human Nature*, p. 418 n7.

the animated fetus, he will not be excused from homicide." By means of this reference Pasnau is implicitly arguing for Aquinas's distinction between the killing of the non-animated early conceptus, which according to Aquinas is not to be seen as homicide, and the killing of the animated fetus, which is to be so seen. However, as has already been shown, this aspect of Aquinas's thought has already been known and discussed; it is not some sort of hidden-away or embarrassing revelation, as Pasnau seems to indicate. Furthermore, it is worth highlighting at this point that Aquinas, despite his delayed hominization view, did in fact see abortion after the first few weeks of pregnancy as homicide, and abortion before that time as a "serious" sin.

Continuing advances in embryology eventually led in 1987 to the following statement from the Roman Catholic Church:

> [R]ecent findings of human biological science...recognize that in the zygote resulting from fertilization the biological identity of a new human individual is already constituted. Certainly no experimental datum can be in itself sufficient to bring us to the recognition of a spiritual soul; nevertheless, the conclusions of science regarding the human embryo provide a valuable indication for discerning by the use of reason a personal presence at the moment of this first appearance of a human life: how could a human individual not be a human person? The Magisterium has not expressly committed itself to an affirmation of a philosophical nature, but it constantly reaffirms the moral condemnation of any kind of procured abortion.... Thus the fruit of human generation, from the first moment of its existence, that is to say from the moment the zygote is formed, demands the unconditional respect that is morally due to the human being in his bodily and spiritual totality. The human being is to be respected and treated as a person from the moment of conception; and therefore from that same moment his rights as a person must be recognized, among which in the first place is the inviolable right of every innocent human being to life.[23]

In other words, no matter the results of the philosophical dispute over hominization, determining "the first appearance of a human life" does not now depend on when the embryo begins to look human or begins to develop recognizably human organs and features, such as the cerebral cortex, but now depends on genetic testing. The human "form" (or soul) causes the material embodiment to develop into a mature example of that which it is, namely, a human. Therefore, the human being is

[23] Sacred Congregation for the Doctrine of the Faith. *Donum Vitae* (Vatican: Holy See, 1987), p. 1.

"ensouled" or "animated" at the time when it possesses all its potential to become a mature example of that which it is–that is, when the genetic "information" is available that is capable of directing all subsequent development. The new human being possesses all such potential from the time when it is conceived.

Internal genetic self-development, as it begins to occur, is thus the physical sign of the logically prior instantiation of the metaphysical form. The zygote has no innate "potential" to develop into anything other than what it already is. It is not a "potential person," as many today have put it. At whatever level of development, the animated conceptus is a potential doctor, or teacher, or farmer, or university student. However, it can only be these things in *potential* because of what it already *is*. It is a potential professor, but not a potential starling or gazelle; it will never be a starling or gazelle, although it may very well be a professor some day, because it already is a human and can never change its metaphysical substance, its form, as is seen physically in its genetic structure. As professor Robert P. George points out:

> Until fairly recently in modern history we lacked the knowledge of embryogenesis and early human developmental biology to say securely what we now know with certainty, namely, that even the early embryo is a complete, self-integrating human organism that by directing its own integral organic functioning develops himself or herself to the next more mature stage of his or her life. We now know securely that the difference between an embryo and a fetus, infant, child, adolescent, and adult is not a difference in *kind*, but is rather a difference *in biological maturity or stage of development*. Embryos and human beings are not different kinds of beings; an embryo is simply a human being in the earliest developmental stage.... The human embryo is not...merely a "potential person," whatever that might mean; rather the human embryo *is* a human being—a whole living member of the species *Homo sapiens*–in the embryonic stage.[24]

However, in Aquinas's time, these facts could not have been known, since they could only have been determined with knowledge of genetics and DNA coding. If Aquinas had known of DNA's potential for speciation and development, he would have recognized that the

[24] Robert P. George, "Sweet Reason." Review of *Human Life, Action, and Ethics: Essays by G.E.M. Anscombe*, edited by Mary Geach and Luke Gormally, eds. *First Things* 159 (January 2006): 56-59, pp. 58-59. Emphasis in original. For a more extensive discussion, see also George's *The Clash of Orthodoxies: Law, Religion, and Morality in Crisis* (Wilmington, Delaware: ISI Books, 2001).

animating form of the material embodiment of a human actually is infused into the human's matter at a much earlier stage than he had thought.[25] His ideas of delayed hominization were based on the superficial physical resemblance of a human embryo at an early stage of development to the embryos of other animals at similar stages of development. Genetically, of course, it is now known that the resemblance is in fact superficial:

> Modern biology has proved that the fundamental "disposition" or "organization" of living matter is genetic. We can now do what the ancients could not: we can distinguish the human embryo from embryos of other species. The perceptible form of the zygote, its genetic structure, may therefore be regarded as, so to speak, the outward and visible sign of its metaphysical form, that which makes it what it is, a member of the human species. The human zygote as we understand it today with DNA and RNA would in Thomas's understanding eminently satisfy as having the organized matter required for the infusion of a human spiritual soul.[26]

So, a Thomistic definition of human-ness today must take these developments within genetics and DNA testing into account. If Aquinas's Aristotelian embryological sequence of "vegetative," "animal," and finally "rational" forms were correct, surely the embodiment of these various forms would be manifested genetically, in a corresponding sequence of vegetative, animal, and finally human DNA codes. However, this of course is not the case–in fact, the very idea seems absurd–because the human form (and only the human form) is present from the very beginning of its embodiment, as revealed by testing the human zygote's DNA structure. Of course, this is not to say that the human form or soul is to be located in a human's DNA code, but rather that the DNA code is a necessary condition both to the embodiment of the human soul and to the soul's capacity, under normal conditions, to develop the hylomorphic union of form/matter into a mature embodied example of a human.

Aquinas makes a clear demarcation between the "sensitive [sensation-receiving] soul," which humans share with all creatures with sensory apparatus, and the intellectual soul. The sensitive soul is

---

[25] Aquinas's own writings on this matter in the ST are primarily found in I.118.2 and I.76.3.

[26] "An Approach to a Key Theological Question," n.p.

generated by the act of procreation, as is the case with all animals,[27] while the intellectual soul "comes from without," being begotten "through creation by God."[28] As the intellect is non-corporeal, it cannot be generated in a corporeal fashion. Aquinas thinks of the intellectual soul as supervening upon the sensitive soul, without thereby losing the powers of the sensitive soul, and so in Aquinas's view the developing human embryo does not possess the human form until it is infused by God with the intellectual soul.

However, Aquinas in these instances errs in his view of the development of the corporeal embryo; he is passing along the faulty embryological information available to him, virtually unchanged from the time of Aristotle. As Brennan writes:

> In matters of empirical observation, both Aristotle and Aquinas were men of their age, which was definitely a prescientific age. This means that extreme caution must be used to dissociate the permanent philosophic analyses from the useless and outmoded scientific formulas with which these analyses are often overlaid. The record of Aristotle's and Aquinas's theories in the field of science is, for the most part, without value, except as a moment in the history of their mental development.[29]

Aquinas does not think of the developing embryo as possessing the human form until that form animates a recognizably human embodiment. These mistaken scientific views need not threaten one's adoption of a Thomistic anthropology, since "the fundamental principles of his philosophy of man are independent of his obsolete biology."[30]

Aquinas and Donceel on Conception and Hominization

Whatever one's view of the topics under discussion, it at least is clear that Aquinas's position cannot legitimately be used as Pasnau uses it; as one review of *Thomas Aquinas on Human Nature* puts it, Pasnau's account of Aquinas, both in metaphysics and in anthropology, is both "contentious in substance, and advanced in advocacy of a particular

---

[27] ST I.118.1.

[28] ST I.118.2.

[29] Brennan, *Thomistic Psychology*, p. 4.

[30] "An Approach to a Key Theological Question," n.p.

moral interest."[31] The "particular moral interest" that Pasnau is interested in advocating is the pro-choice position on abortion, which he argues Aquinas would also uphold, at least in the case of abortions in the first six weeks of pregnancy and possibly up to twenty weeks or so. As has been argued, however, Aquinas's "view on these matters" relating to abortion does not seem to be presented by him in any well-established or dogmatic fashion, and would certainly vary depending on the empirical information available to him.

On the other hand, Joseph F. Donceel, whose writings on this question have influenced Pasnau and others,[32] argues that in Aquinas's hylomorphic view, the matter that receives the soul must be more highly organized as the soul itself is ranked higher in the scale of being; consequently "hylomorphism cannot admit that the fertilized ovum [or even] the early embryo is animated by an intellectual human soul."[33] As Stephen Heaney paraphrases this view, "Since soul and body must be proportioned to each other, it is argued, a rational soul cannot be present until the human body is formed enough to support it, i.e., until there are organs in place through which the rational soul can begin to exercise its proper powers."[34] This principle is stated succinctly by Aquinas himself: "The form does not surpass the proportion of the matter."[35] In another

---

[31] Haldane and Lee, "Aquinas on Human Ensoulment, Abortion, and the Value of Life," p. 256.

[32] Pasnau refers approvingly to Donceel as follows: "The Jesuit theologian Joseph Donceel makes this point forcefully [i.e., that those who think of the intellectual soul as being infused by God at the conception of the human are guilty of a sort of Cartesian dualism] in a 1970 article ["Immediate Animation and Delayed Hominization"], where he shows how many recent accounts of the soul's infusion, even those offered in Aquinas's name, have been blatantly Cartesian. Donceel remarks, in describing Aquinas's hylomorphism, that 'even God cannot put a human soul into a rock, a plant, or a lower animal, any more than He can make the contour of a circle square' (p. 82)" (*Thomas Aquinas on Human Nature*, p. 420 n19).

[33] Donceel, "Immediate Animation and Delayed Hominization," *Theological Studies* 31 (1970): 76-105, p. 80.

[34] Heaney, "The Human Rational Soul in the Early Embryo." Vanderbilt.edu/SFL/Thomist/Fertilization, n.p. Accessed 2 June 2007. See also Heaney's "Aquinas and the Presence of the Human Rational Soul in the Early Embryo." *The Thomist* 56 (1992): 19-48.

[35] ST II-II.24.3.

article,[36] Donceel quotes a similar argument from Henri de Dorlodot:

> A fertilized ovum, a morula, a fetus which has reached the stage resembling a gastrula, and even an embryo in the first period of its existence, do not possess the organization of a specifically human body. And the seat of the imagination and the vis cogitativa does not exist so long as the brain itself does not exist, and indeed as long as there are not present the first rudiments of the structure of a human brain.[37]

Donceel quotes Aquinas quoting Aristotle that the soul is "the act of a physical organic body which has life potentially" and points out that in this quotation the word "organic" means "having organs."[38] From Dorlodot and Aquinas, therefore, Donceel argues that the organic structure of the brain must be present in order for the soul to be its "act," an organic structure which arises somewhere between the third and fourth months of pregnancy. Donceel thinks that the idea that the zygote is animated by its own human soul at conception comes from the confusion of the soul as the formal cause of the human, which it is, with the soul as the efficient cause of the body, which, Donceel claims, it is not.

Perhaps arguing against this last point would serve to argue against the others as well, since the ensuing discussion would address not only the idea of the efficient cause of the body, but also the idea of delayed hominization. First of all, it must be conceded that Donceel is entirely correct in stating that Thomas himself separated between the soul as formal cause and as efficient cause. Donceel quotes from the *Summa Contra Gentiles*, "Form and matter combine together in one being, which is not the case with the effective principle together with that to which it gives being."[39] Although he does not quote a later passage, Donceel could well have done so: "The body is not formed by virtue of the soul of the begotten, as regards the body's foremost and principal parts, but by the virtue of the soul of the begetter.... All matter is similarly configured to its form; and yet this configuration results not

[36] Donceel, "Abortion: Mediate *v*. Immediate Animation," *Continuum* 5 (1967): 167-71.

[37] Henri de Dorlodot. "A Vindication of the Mediate Animation Theory." *Theology and Evolution*. E.C. Messenger, ed. (London: Sands and Co., 1949), p. 260.

[38] ST I.76.4.

[39] SCG II.68.

from the action of the subject generated but from the action of the generator."[40]

However, in context Aquinas is referring to the father's semen as the means used by the "action of the generator" and the "soul of the begetter" from which the body of the zygote begins to be organized; when he writes two sentences earlier that "the soul fashions a body like to itself," he is again referring to the *father's* soul (and not to the mother's),[41] not recognizing that the conceptus inherits genetic characteristics from both parents. According to Aquinas, the male's soul acting through his semen infuses the vegetative soul of the embryo; this "sensitive" soul begins in its turn the organization of the body by means of the "vital principle" of the father. The active power [*virtus*] of self-organization resides in the semen of the male, according to Aquinas, while the female provides the matter or material embodiment of the fetus. In this pre-modern view, the mother is thus the material cause of generation, while the father is the efficient cause.[42] The embryo eventually is infused with the intellectual soul directly by God, since the intellectual soul cannot be infused by a corporeal operation such as intercourse, or by a corporeal matter such as semen; this intellectual soul is thus the formal cause of the existence of the human being. One must then bring up, as Heaney asks, "How is such development [of a human being] possible at all without the presence of a human rational soul?"[43] Aquinas recognizes the principle that the effect cannot be greater than the cause; therefore, for Aquinas the development of the zygote is initiated by the organizing principle of the soul. However, in Aquinas's view, it is not the soul of the zygote which initiates this organization, but

[40] SCG II.89.

[41] SCG II.89.

[42] ST I.118.1.

[43] Heaney, "The Human Rational Soul in the Early Embryo," n.p. In context, the complete quote is as follows: "What is necessary for development toward a physically discernible individual at the primitive streak stage? I suggest Aquinas's answer (and mine) would be that it is the presence of a human rational soul.... Under favorable circumstances, the fertilized ovum will move through developmental individuality, then progressively through functional, behavioral, psychic, and social individuality. In viewing the first stage, one cannot afford to blot out subsequent stages. How is such development possible at all without the presence of a human rational soul?"

the parental soul: The formal cause of the zygote lies in the parent as maker, not in the conceptus as a sort of "artifact."

Clearly, even though Aquinas himself presents this view, this Aristotelian biology and account of conception is surely no longer required to hold in order to hold a Thomistic anthropology. The internal organization of the conceptus and the development of its internal organs come from an equally internal power already contained by the zygote at conception; moreover, the semen is no longer thought scientifically as containing any kind of "active power or spirit in the sense that Aquinas understood the term."[44] Again, if Aquinas were alive today and were to be presented with the information available regarding the self-directing activities of the embryo even at its earliest stages, the question asked earlier would still be completely pertinent: "Would Aquinas alter his views today?" If the answer is "Yes," as has already been argued, this transformation of views would also transform Aquinas's view of "delayed hominization": "The matter must indeed be commensurate with the form for an organism to develop to maturity. However, modern science makes abundantly clear that the sufficient matter for the development of the human person is the genome in the one-celled zygote.... Thus, the theories set forth for delayed hominization, often utilizing the thought of Aquinas as proof, become implausible," as Kevin O'Rourke has written.[45]

As Germain Grisez points out in his response to Donceel:

> St. Thomas's biological errors invalidate his anthropological conclusions [i.e., his conclusions as to when the intellectual soul is infused]. If St. Thomas had known about the specific and individual genetic uniqueness of the zygote which makes it biologically a living organism of the human species, he would have supported immediate animation [i.e., hominization at conception]. Moreover, Donceel's view disregards the fact that fetal development is a continuous process. Thus he does not explain why the fetus, which in his opinion cannot be a human body at the zygote stage, can be one after a few weeks.[46]

---

[44] Ibid., n.p.

[45] Kevin D. O'Rourke, O.P. "The Embryo as Person." *Life and Learning XVI: Proceedings of the Sixteenth University Faculty for Life Conference*, ed. Joseph W. Koterski, S.J. (Washington, D.C.: Univ. Faculty for Life, 2007): 281-96, p. 292.

[46] Grisez, *Abortion: The Myths, the Realities, and the Arguments* (New York: World Publishing Company, 1970), p. 283.

Consequently one could hold completely with Aquinas's essential principle–i.e., that a human rational soul is necessary to initiate the organization of the zygote, transforming matter into a living human body–and disagree with his view of what exactly occurs at conception–i.e., that the organizational soul is that of the parent rather than that of the conceptus itself. "For Aquinas, if effect is not to be greater than cause, a human soul must be responsible. Since for us the soul of one of the parents cannot be the cause, the cause must be the human rational soul of the zygote, right from the moment genetic uniqueness is established."[47] This "genetic uniqueness" is enough of an organic structure, as is evident from its subsequent development, to receive the God-given infusion of its own unique rational soul, the animating form of that development, which can then exercise its proper powers through that organic structure.

The infusion of the human soul at the time of conception is thus not "pointless," as Pasnau puts it,[48] but necessary; the cause of the human embryo's development as a human seems to be the embryo itself, its inner animating principle being the human form as given by God. The cause of the continued development of a *human* body is the presence of a *human* form.[49] "Evidence that a zygote or early embryo has an active internal principle guiding its ordered natural development into a being that actually thinks rationally is sufficient, I contend, to conclude that it is already a rational being," as Jason T. Eberl writes: "It has an active potentiality for rational thought and is thus informed by a rational soul."[50]

Some have misunderstood this crucial point; for instance, Pasnau argues as follows:

Modern proponents of what I call the moment-of-conception thesis like to appeal to science in defense of their approach, especially to the presence from conception of the

---

[47] Heaney, "The Human Rational Soul in the Early Embryo," n.p.

[48] "Without these physical capacities [dependent upon a certain level of brain development], the mind would be unable to function. At a minimum, it would be pointless for God to infuse the human soul at any earlier point" (*Thomas Aquinas on Human Nature*, p. 113).

[49] Haldane and Lee. "Aquinas on Human Ensoulment," p. 269.

[50] Eberl, "Aquinas's Account of Human Embryogenesis," p. 392.

> human genetic code.... Strangely, this sort of argument relies implicitly on the sort of reductive materialism that one would expect to be anathema to the pro-life movement. If to be human is to have a God-given soul, then the presence of the human genetic code at conception shows nothing about whether the embryo is a human being.[51]

However, one should note that the DNA code is a necessary but not (as a materialist might assert) a *sufficient* condition for human development. The infusion of the intellectual soul into the human embodiment is required, as the formal cause and organizing principle of the human substance, but the human minus the embodiment is not a human as humans know themselves today; in other words, the supposition "to be human is to have a God-given soul," as Pasnau claims, is not strictly accurate, or it is at best only half-accurate. Corporeal nature is also a necessary but not sufficient condition for a human being to *be* a human being.[52] As Gilbert Meilaender says, "The duality of our nature is such that we have no access to the free spirit apart from its incarnation in the body. The living body is therefore the locus of personal presence."[53]

In other words, *the soul does not animate the development of a human being unless it is embodied, and human embodiment may be recognized by the presence of human DNA.* In all other respects the human soul is more important and logically prior to the human body; as Aquinas asserts, "Man's being consists in soul and body, and though the being of the body depends on the soul, yet the being of the human soul does not depend on the body: indeed the body is for the soul, as matter for its form."[54] The body, including its DNA code, is a necessary but not sufficient condition for human existence; on the other hand, for humans to exist in their current condition, the reverse is also true: The soul is a necessary but not sufficient condition for human existence *as known today* (while not presently considering the post-mortem, pre-resurrection state). The mere presence of human DNA or "genetic identity"–as in a wart, for instance–is not enough to constitute a human being: "It is not

---

[51] Pasnau, *Thomas Aquinas on Human Nature*, p. 109.

[52] Ric Machuga. *In Defense of the Soul: What It Means to Be Human* (Grand Rapids MI: Brazos Press, 2002), pp. 19ff.

[53] Gilbert Meilaender. *Bioethics: A Primer for Christians* (Grand Rapids MI: Eerdmans, 1996), p. 6.

[54] ST I-II.2.5.

the case that merely possessing human DNA is sufficient for something to be a person [for if so] then hydatidiform moles–masses of placental tissue with the same genetic identity as an embryo–would also count as persons.... What separates a hydatidiform mole and a developing embryo is that the former can never, despite its intrinsic genetic structure and even if it is placed in a supportive uterine environment, develop into an organism with a functioning cerebral cortex; the latter can."[55] However, the presence of this human DNA or genetic identity in an embryo, along with the presence of the animating principle (the form, the soul) leading to its mature expression as a living, functioning human–these taken together *are* enough for us to recognize the presence of a human being.

Dombrowski and Deltete, in arguing for a "Catholic defense of abortion," seek to sidestep the use of these genetic criteria by pointing out that earlier foundational Catholic philosophers (primarily Aquinas and Augustine) admitted themselves ignorant regarding the beginning of human life:

> Augustine is explicit that he does not know (*ignoro*) when the human infant begins to live in the womb (*quando incipiat homo in utero vivere*), nor if human life exists in a latent state (*utrum sit quaedam vita et occulta*) before that point.[56]

But even if taken as stated, what is this supposed to demonstrate? As has been argued up to this point, one need only reply to this that Augustine's self-confessed ignorance on this matter, 1600 years ago, does not excuse one's ignorance today. The genetic requirements for the beginning of a human life are now known in a way that of course would not have been possible for either Augustine or Aquinas.

Speaking in Aquinas's Name

Nor is the position of this essay contrary to the principles of Aquinas's metaphysics, although it is contrary to Thomas's own thirteenth-century scientific mistakes. As Denis Bradley writes, "For Aquinas, the intellectual power is a necessary property of the human essence; what seems eminently reasonable to think is that this essential property,

[55] Jason T. Eberl. *Thomistic Principles and Bioethics* (London and New York: Routledge, 2006), pp. 130 n16 and 131 n29.

[56] Dombrowski and Deltete, *A Brief, Liberal, Catholic Defense of Abortion*, p. 23.

especially if it is regarded as a nonseparable property of the living human body, is a power contained in the body's determinate and determining form–the initial chromosomal program–that internally controls the development of the zygote." This idea, of course, does not equate the human form or intellectual soul with the human's "initial chromosomal program" or DNA code. An analogy might be the relationship between electrical current and a light bulb; the bulb contains within itself a "light-giving" system, but cannot actually give that light until it is infused with the animating principle of the electrical current. In this analogy, the light bulb is the human chromosomal program, and the electrical current is the rational soul infused by God (of course, such an analogy is not meant to imply that the soul is any sort of physical force such as is electricity). Bradley goes on to argue that Aquinas today–"Aquinas *redivivus*," as he puts it–would no longer find "compelling" the scientific views upon which authors such as Pasnau, Dombrowski, Deltete, and so on, base their position.[57] These authors "take up the outdated biology of these Catholic doctors, but cast aside their ethics–thus making a very selective use of Catholic tradition."[58]

The ethical prescription that one should protect innocent human life is more or less invariant in the Thomistic natural law tradition; however, the biological notion of what exactly constitutes that human life has advanced considerably since the time of Aquinas, given advances in empirical embryological knowledge. One might summarize this line of thought simply by saying that Thomistic biology is for the most part outdated; Thomistic ethics is not. Aquinas today would feel no compunction in casting aside his outdated embryology, while holding fast to the ethical obligations we have toward all humans, including those in the womb.

Contrary to Pasnau, Dombrowski, Deltete, and others, therefore, a Thomist today can be entirely true to Aquinas's principles (and not merely speaking "in Aquinas's name," as Pasnau puts it) in arguing that

---

[57] Denis Bradley, J.M. " 'To Be or Not To Be?' Pasnau on Aquinas's Immortal Human Soul," *The Thomist* 68 (2004): 1-39, p. 32.

58 Anne Barbeau Gardiner, "For Catholic Dissenters, Abortion Is Like Mowing Grass," Book Review of *A Brief, Liberal, Catholic Defense of Abortion* in *New Oxford Review* (October 2004), accessed at newoxfordreview.org, n.p. (12 Nov. 2007).

the hylomorphic union of soul and matter making up a human being is thus present from the conception of that human being. Aquinas consistently worked out a coherent account of human development based on his Aristotelian knowledge of conception and generation. However, his empirical knowledge of conception and generation was simply *wrong*. Given further empirical facts today, he with equal consistency would simply work out a different account of human development, one that indubitably would run counter to Pasnau's pro-choice advocacy. If one holds this view of the adaptability of Aquinas's principles, it can be seen that Pasnau is wrong to advance his own views by making of Aquinas a sort of frozen medieval museum piece stuck in an antiquated science.

Jacques Maritain and the Embryo: A Master's Muddles

James G. Hanink

ABSTRACT: Jacques Maritain champions both faith and reason. But Homer nods, and Maritain is sometimes muddled. Indeed, Maritain stoutly denies (1) that the embryo has a rational soul and (2) that the early fetus is a human being. Maritain, of course, would oppose both abortion and embryonic stem cell research. Still, he badly undermines the best reasons for doing so. In this essay I identify and criticize Maritain's "argument from complexity" and his "argument from virtual presence." Together, these arguments lead him to claim that the embryo is not *formally* a human. In addition, I assess Maritain's explicit efforts to link his inadequate embryology with what he presents as the core of a Thomist theory of evolution. Embryology, he insists, models evolution. To support his case, however, Maritain introduces a category of *transformational* change, the use of which proves incompatible with numerical identity over time. In the end, to our dismay, a series of unsound arguments finds Maritain putting at risk the unity of the human being.

IN *FIDES ET RATIO*, Pope John Paul II names Jacques Maritain as a champion of both faith and reason.[1] Despite this much deserved praise, for Maritain has surely taught us well, his account of the human embryo is badly flawed. In this particular regard, we had best recall Aristotle's remark that while Plato is a great friend, a greater friend is truth.

Jacques Maritain, it turns out, stoutly denies that the embryo has a rational soul. He claims that "[t]o admit that the human fetus, from the instant of its conception, receives the intellective soul, while the matter is still in no way disposed with respect to it, is in my view a philosophical absurdity."[2] Thus he denies that the embryo or

[1] *Fides et Ratio* §74.

[2] Jacques Maritain, *Untrammeled Approaches*, translated by Bernard Doering, preface by Ernst R. Korn (Notre Dame IN: Univ. of Notre Dame Press, 1997), p. 93. Maritain's discussion of the embryo first appeared as "Toward a Thomist Idea of Evolution" in *Nova et Vetera* 2 (1967): 87-136. He reviewed his 1967 text in 1972; see *Untrammeled Approaches*, p. 129 n36.

early fetus is a human being.[3] Already there is an irony to note, for Maritain would defend neither abortion nor embryonic stem cell research. In recent years, however, defenders of abortion often admit the humanity, but not the personhood, of the unborn. For Maritain, any human being is a person. Present-day defenders of embryonic stem cell research often deny the very humanity of the early embryo.

In any case, the core of what we might term Maritain's "argument from complexity," which is itself short and straightforward, is as follows:

1. A human being, *formally* understood, is a unity of a body and a rational soul.
2. A rational soul can only inform a suitably complex body.
3. But the human embryo is not a suitably complex body.
4. So the human embryo is not a unity of a body and a rational soul.
5. Therefore the human embryo in not *formally* a human being.

Maritain is entirely ready to specify the requisite complexity: "[T]he ultimate disposition which the intellective soul requires supposes a brain, a nervous system, and an already highly developed motor-sensitive psychism," one more advanced than in any animal.[4] This complex disposition is present only from the later stages of fetal development.[5]

A Critical Issue

Jacques Maritain's thesis on rational ensoulment, to use the technical expression, is initially critical for three reasons. *First*, how we come to be is critical to who we are. *Second*, to argue that the embryo or early fetus is not formally human but that abortion is always wrong invites confusion. *Third*, such a thesis, however metaphysically shorn, undermines the dignity of the pre-born.

---

[3] Ibid.

[4] Ibid.

[5] Ibid., pp. 96, 103.

John J. Conley, S.J., and Kevin D. O'Rourke, O.P., have already brought the ensoulment debate to the attention of this association.[6] But those of another mind have put a different view before a wider audience. Hans Kung has recently claimed that "[b]ecause the human person, says St. Thomas Aquinas, presupposes an *anima intellectualis,* an intellect, what distinguishes humans from animals, it is clear that at the beginning there is not a human person."[7] Thus, he concludes, "the problem of abortion is considerably reduced."[8] Even more recently, Lisa Jardine, chair of the United Kingdom's Human Fertilisation and Embryology Authority, opined that "[w]e have this one fatal impediment, which is the late 20th-century Catholic Church's commitment to fertilisation of the egg as being the moment of humanity."[9]

In making his case, Maritain–like Kung, on this occasion–also follows Aquinas. But Thomas worked from a sharply limited biological understanding, and it is because of this that he mistakenly thinks that the embryo lacks suitable complexity. We cannot, of course, fault him for not anticipating today's genetics. He did not know, nor could he know, that both a sperm cell and an ovum display organized life, albeit as *parts* of independent human beings, male and female. Nor could he know that the embryo is structurally, functionally, and systemically self-directing. So understood, the embryo is already an individual and distinct, though immature, human being. Given today's embryology, we dismiss Thomas's view that a power "acting by virtue of the generative soul of the father" (*Summa Contra Gentiles* II.89.8) directs the merely passive potency of embryonic development.[10] Such a view, plausible in light of

---

[6] John J. Conley, S.J., "Delayed Animation: An Ambiguity and Its Abuses," *Life and Learning XI*, pp. 159-68, and Kevin D. O'Rourke, O.P., "The Embryo as a Human Person," *Life and Learning XVI*, pp. 281-96.

[7] "Hans Kung Joins Abortion Debate in Mexico," *California Catholic Daily* (April 6, 2007).

[8] Ibid.

[9] See Sarah Boseley's interview of Jardine in *The Guardian* (May 28, 2008), p. 5, News & Features.

[10] For an analysis of what today's genetics bring to our knowledge of embryology, see P. Ide, "Is the Human Embryo a Person?" as presented to the Twelfth General Assembly of the Pontifical Academy for Life. For a thorough and accessible account

medieval embryology, is now of only historical interest. The bearing of today's embryology for Maritain's argument from complexity is apparent. Because its third premise is false, the argument fails.[11]

But Maritain, despite mistakenly accepting the argument from complexity, is not an apologist for early abortion. Nor, of course, was St. Thomas. Rather, Maritain appeals to the moral weight of the *virtual* humanity of the preborn. From conception, human nature is "virtually present" and "will pass through the embryo all during its evolutive development, until it attains its goal: a formally human being, a body informed by a rational soul."[12] The core of what we might term his "argument from virtual presence," simply stated, is as follows:

1. The human embryo is materially ordered to a complexity suitable for a rational soul and thus to formal humanity.
2. What is materially ordered to an ontological reality, such as formal humanity, is *virtually* such a reality.
3. So the human embryo is *virtually* a human being.

This "argument from virtual presence," I will contend, is not sound. But showing this will involve a close look at what "the virtual" means for Maritain.

A Special Question

But there is a further reason, both surprising and far-reaching, to examine Maritain's theory of rational ensoulment. He insists that it is critical to a Thomist view of evolution. To abandon delayed hominization would undercut Thomas's "rough outline of an anticipated

---

of the relevant findings of embryology, see Robert P. George and Christopher Tollefsen, *Embryo: A Defense of Human Life* (New York NY: Doubleday, 2008), pp. 27-56. Throughout their study, they deliberately refrain from any appeal to ensoulment.

[11] To be sure, the complexity of body is critical to ensoulment. Poetry, not philosophy, allows W. B. Yeats to fantasize, in his *Sailing to Byzantium*, that "once out of nature I shall never take / My bodily form from any natural thing / But such a form as Grecian goldsmiths make / of hammered god and gold enamelling / To keep a drowsy Emperor awake...."

[12] *Untrammeled Approaches,* p. 99.

philosophy of Evolution."[13] Embryology is a key to Thomas's evolutionary prospectus, which Maritain presents us by appealing to a few pivotal texts. Thus he draws our attention to Thomas's remarks on the tendency of "what is moved," that is, creation, toward the divine likeness. He outlines this tendency in his *Summa Contra Gentiles* III.22.7-8:

> [I]n regard to the last and most perfect act that matter can attain, the inclination of matter whereby it desires form must be inclined as toward the ultimate end of generation. Now, among the acts pertaining to forms, certain gradations are found. Thus, prime matter is in potency, first of all, to the forms of an element. When it is existing under the form of an element, it is in potency to the form of a mixed body; that is why the elements are matter for the mixed body. Considered under the form of a mixed body, it is in potency to a vegetative soul, for this sort of soul is the act of a body. In turn, the vegetative soul is in potency to a sensitive soul, and a sensitive one to an intellectual one.

Given this "transcategorical hierarchy," as Maritain calls it,[14] Thomas turns next to the coming to be of the human being:

> [A]t the start of generation there is the embryo living with plant life, later with animal life, and finally with human life. After this last type of form, no later and more noble form is found in the order of generable and corruptible things.

But Thomas's outline ranges beyond the embryo, an illuminating example, to the full trajectory of creation. Thus he continues:

> So, elements exist for the sake of mixed bodies; these latter exist for the sake of living bodies, among which plants exist for animals, and animals for men. Therefore, man is the end of the whole order of generation.

Indeed, what is true in the generation of things is true in their preservation: "[S]ince a thing is generated and preserved in being by the same reality, there is also an order in the preservation of things, which parallels the foregoing order of generation." Made in the image of God,

---

[13] Ibid., p. 92.

[14] Ibid., p. 89.

we share in this dynamic of generation and preservation. It is Providence that guides the overarching transition from the potential to the actual and sustains it in service to the order of being.

Just how, then, are we to link this trajectory with the embryo? Maritain finds an analogous "*evolutive movement*,"[15] common to both evolution and embryology. But he notes that only in the embryo does a soul, that is, a formal intrinsic principle, guide the development; we find nothing like this in the grand sweep of evolution. Yet Maritain still goes wrong, and he does so in three ways.[16] The first is in how he links a mistaken embryology to a metaphysics of evolution. The second is his account of the virtual. The third is his mishandling of the unity of the person.

On the Embryo and Evolution

Let's first explore the linking of the embryo with evolution. Maritain supposes that there is a structural similarity, an evolutive dynamic that embryological and evolutionary development share, and that this dynamic has explanatory merit for both. But his hypothesis is dubious. For he asks us to explain the increasingly clear–that is, genetically directed embryological development–by locating it within the speculative theory of a vast evolutionary development. Embryological structures and their development are empirically observable; they are exquisitely plotted. In contrast, the structures of the evolution of species, or any specific species, are empirically perplexing. No community of scientists can have ongoing empirical access to such structures. Nor is such an evolution repeatable. Partly because of this empirical elusiveness theorists of evolution are often at odds with one another.[17] (*A fortiori* it is the case among contemporary cosmologists.)

---

[15] Ibid., p. 93.

[16] Ibid., p. 115.

[17] Stephen J. Gould, for example, has raised the ire of John Maynard Smith, Richard Dawkins, and Daniel Dennett. See John Maynard Smith, *Did Darwin Get It Right*? (New York NY: Chapman and Hall, 1989), pp. 148-56; Richard Dawkins, *The Blind Watchmaker* (New York NY: W.W. Norton, 1996; 2nd ed.), ch. 9; Daniel C. Dennett, *Darwin's Dangerous Idea* (New York NY: Simon & Schuster, 1995), ch. 10.

Ernst Haeckel, an embryologist and early Darwinist, notoriously proposed an evolutionary reading of embryology. The embryo, he asserts, recapitulates the evolution of the human species. (Stephen Jay Gould has recently put in context Haeckel's falsified embryological drawings and their continuing use.[18]) But it is disconcerting that Maritain so uncritically links embryology with evolution. He even enlists, albeit gingerly, Karl Rahner: "[H]e looks with favor on the Thomist theory of the development of the human embryo; and [Rahner] notes very pointedly: 'Having accepted this, it can very well be said that the ontogenesis thus understood corresponds to human phylogenesis....'"[19] Here Haeckel's mantra of "ontogeny recapitulates phylogeny" comes to mind. (For the record, Stephen Jay Gould also points out that Darwinists have long abandoned this view.[20])

But if Maritain finds a theological ally in Rahner, he is also ready to dispute a pair of "hasty" theological conclusions. He claims that theologians have misled philosophers about the embryo by wrongly extrapolating from two points of doctrine. The first point is that abortion is a moral wrong at any point of gestation. Because of this, theologians suppose that the embryo is a human person. The second point, the Immaculate Conception, is that Mary was conceived without sin. Because of this, theologians suppose that she must have been human in nature from conception.

But Maritain argues that theologians mistakenly infer from the wrongness of abortion that rational ensoulment occurs at conception. We can avoid this mistake by noting that from conception, the embryo is virtually, but not formally, a human being. Maritain also argues that theologians misread the ontological import of the Immaculate Conception. From conception Mary was free from original sin as it exists virtually, but she was only formally free of it from the time of

---

[18] Stephen Jay Gould, "*Abscheulich*! – Atrocious! – the precursor to the theory of natural selection," *Natural History* 109/2 (2000): 42-50.

[19] *Untrammeled Approaches,* p. 95 n9.

[20] Stephen Jay Gould, *loc. cit.*

rational ensoulment.[21] For now, I will put *this* assertion aside.

THE QUESTION OF THE VIRTUAL

Given Jacques Maritain's strategic appeal to the virtual, it is time now to explore his account of the virtual. We might begin with his claim that since the virtual, though somehow real, is not entitative, it follows that only the formal has decisive ontological significance. Yet this supposed reality of the virtual is problematic. For a start, "virtual reality," in ordinary language, is not "the real thing." (It is realistic, but so too are nightmares.) Now, if by "virtual" we mean "potential," we still have problems. We might speak about the potential of, say, a scholar's pro-life contribution. But the "pro-lifer" must first be a real scholar. Ordinarily, if something is a virtual or a potential *Y*, it is already an actual, that is, real *X*. (Only a real nightmare portends a nightmarish reality.) To be sure, ordinary language can play fast and loose with the virtual and the potential. Maritain seeks a greater precision. Thus, in his discussion of the embryo he presents the virtual as a form of movement by which an efficient cause controls the instrumentality, throughout the causal process, which leads to the final effect.[22] Elsewhere he claims that "*[v]irtually* means much more than 'potentially'" and that it also "means 'implicitly,' but with the added idea of tendency."[23] As an example, he writes that "[a] grain of wheat is virtually a whole stalk of wheat."[24] But if a grain of wheat is germinated, it is as much a wheat plant as is a whole stalk of wheat, though obviously not so mature. Similarly, a "fertilized ovum," more properly, an embryo is as much a human being *in kind* as is an adult human being. The embryo is an individual and complete human being, though obviously not so mature. (To be sure, unlike a grain of wheat, an embryo does not have a period of dormancy, unless frozen.) So again Maritain's account of the virtual is problematic.

In any case, there is a good argument that helps correct ordinary

---

[21] *Untrammeled Approaches,* pp. 93-94.

[22] Ibid., p. 99.

[23] Ibid., p. 217 n26.

[24] Ibid.

language sloppiness and philosophical overreaching alike. This argument revisits the place of material development with regard to the virtual and the potential. Its core is simply put.

Virtual (and Potential) Presence, Revisited

1. That which is materially ordered to an ontological reality has some elements required for that ontological reality.
2. But a thing's having some elements required for an ontological reality does not itself make that thing either virtually or potentially such a reality.
3. So, a thing that is materially ordered to a formal ontological reality is not thereby virtually or potentially such a reality.

A sperm cell, for the topical example, brings a genetic contribution to a particular human being. Its specific contribution is a material and requisite element for a particular human being. But a sperm cell is neither virtually nor potentially a human being. Calling it such is wrongheaded. Consider, for example, the collegian with the potential for both scholarship and solidarity with "the least little ones." That student is not a virtual pro-life scholar, despite perhaps a tendency to become one in favorable circumstances. And if here we speak of a potential to become a pro-life scholar, it is not because of any material ordination to the modifications of mind and will that, say, a Thomist would see as marks of the ontological character of pro-life scholarship.

Maritain only weakens his case when, appealing to Thomas, he nonetheless claims that human nature is *virtually* present in a sperm cell.[25] To do so invites the following embarrassment.[26]

Against Maritain: Spermicide not Homicide

---

[25] Ibid., p. 93.

[26] Peter Singer claims that potentiality arguments against abortion have to extend to the potentiality of an ordered pair of sperm and ovum to become a person. But he conflates possibility with active potentiality. See his "Animal Liberation" in *The Moral Life*, ed. Louis B. Pojman and Lewis Vaughn, 3rd ed. (New York NY: Oxford Univ. Press, 2007), p. 888.

1. It is always wrong intentionally to kill an embryo, a virtual human being.
2. A sperm cell is also a virtual human being. (assumption)
3. Thus it is always wrong intentionally to kill a sperm cell, a virtual human being.
4. But a technician might licitly and intentionally kill a sperm cell secured in a fertility test, even if the test is morally wrong.
5. So, either (a) it is not always wrong intentionally to kill a sperm cell, a virtual human being, or (b) a sperm cell is not a virtual human being.
6. If (a), then it is not always wrong intentionally to kill an embryo.
7. If (b), then neither is an embryo is a virtual human being.
8. But Maritain claims that it is always wrong intentionally to kill an embryo and that an embryo is a virtual human being.

Here we might also point out that if the embryo is, in fact, an actual human being, then he or she is not merely a virtual or potential human being.

Let's briefly return now, as a postscript to the vicissitudes of virtuality, to Maritain's second theological point of reference. It has been put aside but not forgotten. What about the Immaculate Conception and its import for the embryo? Is it not odd to say, with Maritain, that Mary was free from original sin in that while for us original sin exists *virtually* in the embryo but for Mary it was not so?[27] After all, is not Mary's then virtual freedom, that of a not yet existing human being, a pale substitute for the real freedom of an actual human being? But suppose we return to our own case. It hardly seems plausible to say that we were conceived without real original sin!

On the Unity of the Human Being

We can next consider just how Maritain's thesis of delayed hominization mishandles the unity of the human person. It is in this context, too, that we again see how his misdirected link between the embryo and evolution comes into play. On the one hand, he does not want to appeal

---

[27] *Untrammeled Approaches*, pp. 93-94.

to the dynamic and sustained ordering of potency to act in a way that jeopardizes the unity of things, that is, of a thing's being what it is and not another thing. Yet, on the other hand, he thinks (with St. Thomas) that our development from (1) merely living, to (2) living with sensation, to (3) living with reason gives evidence to three distinct and corresponding souls: vegetative, animal, and rational.[28] Whatever the pedigree of this claim, we cannot but rightly wonder how this succession of souls can avoid undercutting the unity of the human being.

Maritain attempts to answer this pressing question by carefully qualifying the distinctive changes in the embryo's development. To this end, he notes that the embryo's remarkable transformation does not jeopardize its numerical identity. For this transformation rests on

> a corporeal substance *numerically one* (one and the same suppositum) which is transformed from one stage to another (as a mere seed at first, developing and then *evolving* according to the vegetative life characteristic of the vegetable kingdom, then as a more perfect organism, developing and then *evolving* according to the sensitive life characteristic of the animal kingdom).[29]

It is just here, Maritain continues, that there is a striking parallel with evolutionary development:

> In order that at the end of this process it may become *formally something else*, substantially something else, that is, informed by a different soul–we would say today that it recapitulates in itself in the intra-uterine development of that being which is the head of material creation, *the evolution of life* which after centuries has attained its final end in man.[30]

So, we have an interpretative key to an extraordinary phenomenon: embryology models evolution.

This passage serves Maritain's project in that it introduces a new

---

[28] Lee Silver has recently suggested that since the embryo has a vegetative but not a sentient life, he or she is not yet a human being. For how this proposal conflicts with the unity of the human being, see George and Tollefsen, *Embryo*, pp. 166-73.

[29] *Untrammeled Approaches,* pp. 94-95.

[30] Ibid.

distinction to supplement the familiar *accidental change* and *substantial change*. For example, if one toasts a slice of bread, it undergoes an accidental change. If one eats the toast, it becomes a part of one's body. Becoming something else, the toast undergoes a substantial change.

There is a loss of numerical identity. Enter now Maritain's distinctive and evolutive change that somehow preserves the numerical identity of that which undergoes change. We can term this *transformational* change. In change of this sort, one thing becomes another without the loss of its numerical identity, despite the change's being far more basic than an accidental change. In the case of the embryo, moreover, the initial powers of the vegetative and the sensitive souls are taken up by the rational soul that, we recall, can only inform a body of adequate complexity.

Yet Maritain's distinctive transformational change, though at first reading it might seem resourceful, leads to needless complexity. Consider the following argument:

Argument against Embryonic Transformational Change

1. Ordinarily, a succession of forms causes a substantial change.
2. We ought not to introduce a distinct transformational change without an empirical or conceptual reason to do so.
3. The development of the embryo does not indicate an empirical reason to do so.
4. Nor does the development of the embryo indicate a conceptual reason to do so.
5. So we ought not to claim that the embryo undergoes transformational change.

Each of us is *numerically* the same living being from conception to death, as Maritain recognizes. But what he fails to recognize, in effect, is that each of us has but a single life and a single body. Our "to be" is to live this life. The soul, the form of the human being who lives but a single life, is one soul. This precludes transformational change as the vehicle for a succession of souls that could only obscure the unity of the human being.[31] No doubt, Maritain's inability to grasp the implications of contemporary genetics tempted him to introduce transformational change as a device by which to hold on to the numerical identity of the human being during *in utero* development.

A Last Objection, A Last Reply

But perhaps my case against Maritain's delayed hominization is too hasty. John Conley, S.J. and Kevin O'Rourke, O.P. argue that it is too soon for the Catholic Church to teach definitively on the time of rational ensoulment. Questions remain about the import of early cellular totipotency and twinning.[32] Micro-metaphysics is a work in progress.

Yet Maritain's position seems untenable, though it is seldom noted or challenged.[33] But something like it, a generic gradualism *sans* metaphysics is common. Let this gradualism be a last objection to my case. It is the most rhetorically persuasive objection to the thesis that the embryo is a human being.

The gradualism objection is as follows. Most change is incremental. Often, the more we know about a major change, the more we recognize how just gradual it is. Breaking news: An ice shelf in Antarctica comes detached! Yet the changes that led to it were gradual. Happy Birthday: One turns 64! But the changes that led to it were gradual–all 63 plus years of them. And doesn't this gradual pattern of change, with examples ready at hand, also point to the holistic character of nature? Consider the coming to be of the human being. How could it transpire

---

[31] Maritain, of course, does not want to undermine the unity of the human being despite introducing an argument that does so. He fares better in maintaining the unity of the human species in his account of evolutionary development. See *Untrammeled Approaches*, pp. 129-30.

[32] John Conley, S.J., "Delayed Animation: An Ambiguity and Its Abuses," *Life and Learning XI*, pp. 166-67, and Kenneth O'Rourke, O.P., "The Embryo as a Human Person," *Life and Learning XVI,* p. 294.

[33] In "Is the Human Embryo a Person?" P. Ide briefly notes Maritain's "mediatist" position; see n9. James Arraj summarizes it in his *Can Christians Still Believe?* (2004); see ch. 2, "Evolution and Human Origins." Nicholas F. Gier gives it favorable notice. See his *God, Reason, and the Evangelicals: The Case Against Evangelical Rationalism* (Lanham MD: Univ. Press of America, 1987), p. 220. Gier cites Maritain against evangelical "rationalism" in opposing abortion.

in the brief process of conception? Surely humanity is a gradual and holistic development.

But the gradualism objection fails to do justice to the richness of change. Specifically, it denies substantial change. Of course, most changes are not substantial. Neither the shifting nor the melting of an ice shelf is metaphysically substantial. Why, even turning 64 isn't a metaphysically substantial change. We remain numerically the same people we were at 21–and *in utero*. Yet other changes, even if common, are substantial. Hydrogen and oxygen, suitably conjoined, give us water. Bread and wine, if digested, give us nourishment. And what about the substance, as it were, and thus the significance of a human act? Only when intention, as its form, shapes mere physical behavior can we identify a human action and grasp its meaning–and intention can do all this with immediacy.

But suppose that we deny substantial change. Suppose that, while thinking that every thing is what it is, we assume that whatever changes does so in degree but not in kind. If so, we will pay a steep price. For in denying substantial change, we deny that there is anything brand new under the sun. But there is so much that is brand new, including the water that a chemistry experiment produces, the nourishment a meal provides, and the conference paper that we write. Indeed, our species is relatively new species, however creation and evolution gave rise to it by way of substantial changes.

To deny substantial change is, indirectly, to deny unity. Hydrogen is what it is, oxygen is what it is, and neither is water. Bread is what it is, wine is what it is, and neither are enriched cells in our bodies. A physical behavior is what it is, an intention is what it is, and there's many a slip twixt the cup and the lip. Unity is, indeed, the transcendental in virtue of which everything is what it is and not another thing. So, to abandon substantial change is to forfeit the individuality and intelligibility of *what is.* But once these are forfeit, we forfeit the referential intelligibility of language. In the question before us, the nature of the embryo, we thus frustrate our understanding of the nature of the human person in coming to be.

Rhetorical and Literary Perspectives

Invective, Irony, Sarcasm and Other Negative Tropes in Pro-life Rhetoric

Robert F. Gotcher

ABSTRACT: Invective and other negative rhetoric is common enough in both secular and religious efforts to eliminate abortion in our society. Standard Catholic moral analysis places limits on its use, especially in public, antagonistic debates. A more personalist analysis, emphasizing the effect that the rhetoric has on the speaker and the existing and potential bonds of communion between the speaker and the hostile hearer, even further limits the situations in which such rhetoric may be used.

PRO-ABORTION RESPONSE TO RHETORICAL TROPES

Some friends and I were recently discussing whether the phrase "pro-aborts" is inflammatory. On the one hand, the label itself reveals most directly the actual position of those it is designed to designate, and therefore should not be offensive. I don't think that I would be insulted by being called "pro-fetus keeper" or "pro-embryonic cell saver," or even "pro-product of conception," although the latter is a minimalist description since I believe that the "product of conception" is a human being.

We have a psychological fact here. Pro-lifers do not mind their real position being made explicit in labels. Pro-abortioners, or whatever we call them, have to hide behind euphemisms. For pro-life advocates, the more clearly the label reflects their actual position, the happier they are. On the other hand, there is no honest label that one could use for people who want other people to be able to kill their babies legally that would not be inflammatory.

The phrase "pro-choice" is a shell game. If people do not believe that unborn children ought to be protected by law, if they want abortion to be an option in our society, even if the procedure is not something that they are enthusiastic about, they are pro-abortion, because unless it is illegal it will be provided. Would we say that someone who is not enthusiastic about murder but did not think that it ought to be illegal in our society is neutral about murder? If there were poison in someone's water and one knew something about it and did not actively seek to eliminate it, and if people started drinking this water, would that person not be rightly called "pro-poison"? Why does calling advocates of legal abortion "pro-aborts" make them angry? Are they so irrational that being labeled truthfully makes them unable to think clearly about the issue?

On the other hand, there is something about the tone of the phrase "pro-abort" that is jarring. Does the label do something more than simply reflect the admittedly immoral position of the person so labeled? Does it attempt to injure the person and therefore constitute a sin? This got me to thinking about the tone of some of the other pro-life rhetoric that I have heard over the years.

As a result I have developed a set of questions that I would like to address in this essay. What is the value of polemics in general and of invective and irony in particular within human interaction, and especially within Church life and evangelization? Are there times and circumstances where negative rhetoric is useful, where invective is inappropriate, where irony, or even sarcasm, might help to promote the Gospel of Life? If invective is useful, to what degree? What are the rules? How does one know? Do we draw the line at the other person's taking offense? Why or why not?

In order to begin to answer these questions, I will first look at the current trend toward negative rhetoric in our culture, and then at the use of negative rhetoric in the pro-life movement. I will do a standard moral analysis of the object, the intention, and the circumstances that are involved when one is using negative rhetoric as a way to help distinguish between sinful and non-sinful uses of such rhetoric. Finally, by looking at the question from a personalist perspective and by focusing on the spiritual impact that negative rhetoric has on the acting person, I will draw some preliminary conclusions. I suggest that we should be extremely cautious in using even legitimate negative rhetoric in any public forum. For the sake of our own souls, we should be cautious about this in our more private interactions and in our own interior discourse.

AN AGE OF PERSONALLY NEGATIVE RHETORIC

Our Culture in General. While preparing this essay I read a book by Al Franken called *Lies (and the Lying Liars Who Tell Them): A Fair and Balanced Look at the Right.*[1] In one of the first chapters Franken takes on conservative commentator Ann Coulter. He not only accuses her of lies but also criticizes her and many other politically conservative commentators of poisoning the atmosphere of public discourse with personally demeaning and destructively negative rhetorical language. Three chapters of the book are devoted to an analysis of this tone. The ironic part of this criticism is that Franken himself employs such negative rhetoric throughout the book. For instance, the title of the second chapter is "Ann Coulter: Nutcase." His argument seems to be something like "They started it" rather than "I'll take the high road."

Rhetoric nowadays, especially in the new media, relies heavily on invective, irony, sarcasm, and the like to achieve an emotional reaction. The sneering tone is often referred to as "snarky." It demonstrates a presumption of intellectual superiority that is captured in the label that some liberal commentators have tried to pin to themselves, the "brights." Al Frankin and Ann Coulter define the atmosphere. Many others liberal and conservative talk radio personalities and bloggers exhibit it as well.

The trend to negative rhetoric appears to be a part of a general culture shift in the last few decades away from even pretended civility in personal or public conversation and dialogue. For instance, Leslie Savan devotes the largest of her ten chapters in her book on pop phrases[2] to the ubiquitous presence of negative rhetorical jibes in our everyday speech. The chapter called "Don't Ever Think about Telling Me 'I Don't *Think* So': The Media, Meanness and Me" takes up one third of the book.

The Pro-life Movement and Negative Rhetoric. There are some

---

[1] Al Franken, *Lies (and the Lying Liars Who Tell Them): A Fair and Balanced Look at the Right* (New York NY: Dutton, 2003). The title is ironic. Franken is not pretending to be fair and balanced in the book. He is making fun of the slogan form typical of the Fox News Network.

[2] *Slam Dunks and No-Brainers: Pop Language in Your Life, the Media, and Like...Whatever* (New York NY: Knopf, 2005).

signs that this negative rhetoric is affecting the broad pro-life movement. On the one hand, the most important public pro-life activists avoid the use of invective and irony in their rhetoric. A perusal of the webpages of National Right to Life[3] and of Healing the Culture,[4] for instance, turns up very little of it, although the language is direct. Their approach appears to focus primarily on argumentation, reason, and vivid presentation of the truth.

On the other hand, other public promoters of the pro-life cause, especially in the secular media, use the negative rhetoric that is the stock-in-trade of those media. Ann Coulter, for instance, uses irony to insinuate the stupidity of the members of the Supreme Court when she says, "With even liberals backing away from *Roe*, apparently the last group of people on Earth to realize the Supreme Court's abortion jurisprudence is a catastrophe is going to be the Supreme Court."[5] She is renowned for having said, "Abortion is the sacrament [of the Democratic party] and *Roe v. Wade* is Holy Writ."[6] Rush Limbaugh coined the phrase "feminazis" to refer to "any female who is intolerant of any point of view that challenges militant feminism. [He] often use[s] it to describe women who are obsessed with perpetuating a modern-day holocaust: abortion."[7] Other examples of such rhetoric can be found in common epithets such as "Dr. Death" for Jack Kevorkian and the phrase "Planned Barrenhood" as a substitution for Planned Parenthood.

Not all uses of such rhetoric are in the secular press. If you have ever read the blog of Catholic apologist Mark Shea, you know that he is an expert at pithy and pointed headlines. He is specifically known for his frequent links to articles that he headlines, e.g., "Gay brownshirts on the march!" Following the example of his literary mentor, G.K. Chesterton, he often uses rhetorical juxtaposition to point out a real connection

---

[3] http://www.nrlc.org/.

[4] http://www.healingtheculture.com/.

[5] "Abortion Stops a Bleeding Heart," January 25, 2006. http://www.anncoulter.com/cgi-local/article.cgi?article=97.

[6] Ann Coulter, *Godless: The Church of Liberalism* (New York NY: Crown Forum, 2006).

[7] See http://www.ontheissues.org/Celeb/Rush_Limbaugh_Abortion.htm.

between two realities that are apparently unconnected, such as in a recent post entitled "The Abortion Industry: Finishing What Hitler Started,"[8] in which he discusses abortion in Israel. For Shea, the abortion industry is "Murder, Inc."[9] Even my fellow blogger on the HMS Weblog resorts to invective, as when he called an actress from the television series *Grey's Anatomy* "Planned Parenthood's Hollywood spokesbimbo."[10] One often finds such rhetoric on bumper stickers: "'Vote Pro-Choice' Satan,"[11] "Abortion: A Doctor's Right to Make a Killing,"[12] and "I Think... therefore I'm Pro-Life."[13]

NEGATIVE RHETORIC IN THE HISTORY OF THE CHURCH

Ecclesiastical Writers. Negative tropes in rhetoric, of course, are not something newly discovered by American conservatives or liberals in the 1990s. Their value, affirmed in ancient textbooks on rhetoric, reveals a long and distinguished history, even in Christian literature. For example, the following is a passage from Patriarch Alexander of Alexandria's letter to Alexander of Thessalonika concerning the activity of the priest Arius and his accomplices in the fourth-century Trinitarian controversy:

> The ambitious and covetous calculation of rascally men has produced plots against the apparently greater dioceses. Through intricate pretenses such individuals are attacking the orthodox faith of the church. Driven wild by the devil at work in them for pleasures at hand, the skipped away from every piety and trampled on the feat of God's judgment.[14]

One of my students even calls Athanasius's *Oration Against the Arians*

---

[8] http://markshea.blogspot.com/2008_05_01_archive. html.

[9] http://markshea.blogspot.com/2008_05_01_archive.html.

[10] http://www.exceptionalmarriages.com/weblog/BlogDetail.asp?ID=39751.

[11] http://www.christianshirts.net/bumperStickers.php/.

[12] http://www.childrenoftherosary.org/bumpmain.htm.

[13] Ibid.

[14] "Alexander of Alexandria's Letter of Alexander of Thessalonica" in *The Trinitarian Controversy*, ed. William G. Rusch (Philadelphia PA: Fortress Press, 1980), p. 33.

a "rant." St. Thomas Aquinas also used pointed irony, as Jean-Pierre Torrell remarks:

> If we feared, for example, that he may have been too timorous in the troubled university situation, these writings do not lack in vigor or firmness or even, as M.-M. Dufeil has underscored, in a "sarcastic irony which bursts forth at intervals" in the *Contra Impugnantes*.[15]

The Bible. Invective and irony appears frequently enough in the Bible. Saint Paul spares no rhetorical venom when speaking of those who would require gentile converts to be circumcised: "Look out for the dogs, look out for the evil-workers, look out for those who mutilate the flesh" (Phil. 3:2)[16] and "O foolish Galatians! Who has bewitched you, before whose eyes Jesus Christ was publicly portrayed as crucified?" (Gal. 3:1). "Would that those who are upsetting you might also castrate themselves!" (Gal. 5:12, RNAB).

Jesus himself was not immune from such rhetoric. "And [Jesus] said to them, 'O foolish men, and slow of heart to believe all that the prophets have spoken! Was it not necessary that the Christ should suffer these things and enter into his glory?'" (Lk. 24:25). The New Testament prize for invective, however, has to go to Jesus's diatribe against the scribes and Pharisees:

> "But woe to you, scribes and Pharisees, ...hypocrites! ... hypocrites! ... blind guides, ... You blind fools! ... You blind men! ... hypocrites! ... You blind guides, straining out a gnat and swallowing a camel! ... hypocrites! for you cleanse the outside of the cup and of the plate, but inside they are full of extortion and rapacity... hypocrites! ... whitewashed tombs, which outwardly appear beautiful, but within they are full of dead men's bones and all uncleanness.... So you also outwardly appear righteous to men, but within you are full of hypocrisy and iniquity... hypocrites!... You serpents, you brood of vipers." (Mt. 23:13-33)

Although Jesus did not use biting sarcasm, some argue that he used

---

[15] Jean-Pierre Torrell, *St. Thomas Aquinas*, Vol 1: *The Person and His Work*, trans. by Robert Royal, revised ed. (Washington, D.C.: The Catholic Univ. of America Press, 2005), p. 91.

[16] All biblical quotations are from the Revised Standard Version unless otherwise indicated.

irony, such as when he named Simon bar Jonah "Peter," knowing full well what an unstable and unreliable character Peter was. He certainly was being ironic when he called Nathaniel a "true Israelite, a man without guile" since Jacob himself was a man with a great deal of guile, as shown by the ruse that he used to deprive Esau of his father Isaac's blessing.

The fact that various Church Fathers and Scholastics, not to mention Christ and St. Paul, used invective, irony, and even sarcasm, would seem to justify its use in pro-life activism. But a close moral analysis will reveal severe limits on its use, especially in light of the specific nature of the pro-life movement itself.

Moral Analysis, Definitions, Invective

First, let's define our terms. Invective is defined as insulting language.[17] It is usually called *contumelia* in Latin theology. It is a label applied to a person, institution, idea, or event that highlights some negative aspect of that person or things. It is usually personal. To say "Mark is an idiot" is more clearly and directly insulting than saying "Mark's idea about shoes is idiotic." The first is more easily interpreted as an offense against charity. But even the second is often interpreted as a personal attack because we tend to identify ourselves with our ideas.

Irony and Sarcasm. Rhetorical irony is saying the opposite of what one means. This can be distinguished from situational irony, where an event occurs that is contrary to what one would expect in a situation, and dramatic irony, where the audience knows the true significance of the events on stage when the character or characters in the play do not.[18] An example of rhetorical irony occurs when a golfer has been boasting about his skill at the game of golf and has a high score. A fellow golfer might say, "Boy, you sure *are* good at golf!" Our culture is very confused about what irony is, and often uses the word "sarcasm" for irony. Sarcasm comes from the Greek word for flesh-tearing. According

---

[17] Merriam-Webster's Online Dictionary. "Of, relating to, or characterized by insult or abuse." http://www.merriam-webster.com/dictionary/invective.

[18] John da Fiesole, http://disputations.blogspot.com/2008_03_01_archive.html; http://disputations.blogspot.com/2008_03_01_archive.html.

to *Merriam-Webster*, it is a "harsh or bitter derision or irony, ...a sharply ironical taunt; sneering or cutting remark."[19] The difference between irony and sarcasm is that sarcasm is always personal and relatively harsh, whereas an ironic remark can be about an impersonal situation and need not be harsh.

The Use of Language. The fundamental theological principle about human language, flowing from the Incarnation of the *Logos* and the basis of the eighth commandment, is that human language is meant to express the truth and to build up others and society. It is not intended to cause injury. As A. G. Sertillanges said:

> When we want to awaken a thought in anyone, what are the means at our disposal? One only, to produce in him by word and sign states of sensibility and of imagination, emotion and memory in which he will discover our idea and make it his own.[20]

The bible warns repeatedly about using language to harm another: "But I say to you that every one who is angry with his brother shall be liable to judgment; whoever insults his brother [says to him *raca*!] shall be liable to the council, and whoever says, 'You fool!' shall be liable to the hell of fire" (Mt. 5:22). "Let no evil talk come out of your mouths, but only such as is good for edifying, as fits the occasion, that it may impart grace to those who hear" (Eph. 4:29). Language is supposed to be edifying, to impart grace, not to cause harm:

> With [the tongue] we bless the Lord and Father, and with it we curse men, who are made in the likeness of God. From the same mouth come blessing and cursing. My brethren, this ought not to be so. Does a spring pour forth from the same opening fresh water and brackish? Can a fig tree, my brethren, yield olives, or a grapevine figs? No more can salt water yield fresh. (James 3:9-12).

The *Catechism of the Catholic Church* warns journalists specifically not only to be devoted to the truth, but to communicate the truth in charity:

> By the very nature of their profession, journalists have an obligation to serve the truth

---

[19] Dictionary.com, Unabridged (v. 1.1). Random House. http://dictionary.reference.com/browse/sarcasm (accessed: January 25, 2008.

[20] Sertillanges, p. 34.

and not offend against charity in disseminating information. They should strive to respect, with equal care, the nature of the facts and the limits of critical judgment concerning individuals. They should not stoop to defamation. (§2497)

OBJECT

Moral analysis considers the three sources of the morality of an act: the object, the intention, and the circumstance. I would like to consider each one of these and its impact on the morality of the use of invective, irony, and sarcasm. First of all, formal invective and sarcasm by nature intend an injury. According to St. Thomas, who considers verbal injuries inflicted extrajuridically in his *Summa theologiae* II-II, qq. 72-75, "reviling" (contumelia, q. 72) dishonors a person in the sight of a third party but "derision" (q. 75) intends to instill shame in the person derided.

Reviling (*contumelia*) is to dishonor a person, by word to deprive a man of the respect due him from another: "a man's faults are exposed to the detriment of his honor" (II-II, q. 72). In reply to objection 3, St. Thomas points out that it is a moral fault that is highlighted. One doesn't just say "you are blind," but "you are a thief." Derision, on the other hand, is intended to elicit shame in the hearer, not dishonor from a third person (q. 75). Formally to sin in using these tropes one must intend injury. In this case the intention to injure is part of the object.

Sarcasm by nature seems to include an *ad hominem* component, an intent to injure, especially in the context of hostile exchanges. Author Oswald Sobrino gives us a great lesson about sarcasm, the twin sister of that other personal and cultural poison, cynicism:

> [S]arcasm is a force for evil in our lives. Even if we do not know its exact origin in each case, it is surely certain that Satan delights in the harm it causes everyone concerned and the division it brings among Christians and thus uses and exploits sarcasm to advance his cause.

Yet, sarcasm, in spite of its obvious toxic effect on us and others, is quite common and often appears as a compulsion and habit that the sarcastic person himself can fail to recognize.[21] Some would even argue

---

[21] Sobrino, "The Spirit of Sacrasm," Wednesday, Jan. 23, 2008. http://catholicanalysis.blogspot.com/2008/01/spirit-of-sarcasm.html.

that any use of irony is contrary to the good. John da Fiesole states on his blog: "Irony has no place in the kingdom of God."[22]

INTENTION

On the other hand, some would argue justifiably for the use of such language on the basis that the intention is not to injure, but some social good. St. Thomas states that material reviling is not necessarily sinful:

If, on the other hand, a man says to another a railing or reviling word, yet with the intention, not of dishonoring him, but rather perhaps of correcting him or with some like purpose, he utters a railing or reviling not formally and essentially, but accidentally and materially, in so far to wit as he says that which might be a railing or reviling. Hence this may be sometimes a venial sin, and sometimes without any sin at all. (II-II, q. 72, a. 2)

Calling a Spade a Spade. For instance, some argue that they use such language in order to unveil the truth, to call a spade a spade. There are certain contexts where irony can be an effective device for clarifying the genuine position of the opponent. Such appears to be the case in the phrase "Planned Barrenhood." This purpose is an aspect of the admonition of St. Paul for the Christian to bring the darkness of the sinner to light: "Take no part in the unfruitful works of darkness, but instead expose them. For it is a shame even to speak of the things that they do in secret; but when anything is exposed by the light it becomes visible, for anything that becomes visible is light" (Eph. 5:11-13). Judie Brown of American Life League says that civility in dialogue must not silence the truth. If others are offended by a frank and direct statement of the truth about them or something they hold dear, that does not mean that one should not speak that truth:

"Civility" should not require deception. "Civility" should not be based on a false premise of protecting the consciences of those who publicly defy basic Church teachings. "Civility" does not avoid judgment of what is objectively evil, such as the act of abortion and its advocacy by persons in political life. There is no "reasoned" Catholic argument in defense of such atrocious behavior, regardless of what the signers

[22] John da Fiesole, http://disputations.blogspot.com/2008_03_01_archive.html. A rebuttal by Mike Potemra, on NRO's The Corner, http://corner.nationalreview.com/post/.

[of a statement defending the support of pro-abortion politicians] may think.[23]

Persuasion and Correction. Other uses of negative rhetorical tropes might include persuasion or correction. One, for instance, may use invective or irony to sway public opinion about a person or position. For instance, when St. Paul tries to persuade the believers in Ephesus not to live as the Gentiles, he highlights their depravity:

> Now this I affirm and testify in the Lord, that you must no longer live as the Gentiles do, in the futility of their minds; they are darkened in their understanding, alienated from the life of God because of the ignorance that is in them, due to their hardness of heart; they have become callous and have given themselves up to licentiousness, greedy to practice every kind of uncleanness. (Eph. 4:17-19)

Note, however, that he does not resort to sarcasm or even irony in this passage.

Humor. Finally, one might use irony or epithets to amuse, rather than revile, as when St. Thomas says:

> It belongs to wittiness to utter some slight mockery, not with intent to dishonor or pain the person who is the object of the mockery, but rather with intent to please and amuse: and this may be without sin, if the due circumstances be observed. On the other hand if a man does not shrink from inflicting pain on the object of his witty mockery, so long as he makes others laugh, this is sinful. (q. 72, a. 2 ad 1).

St. Thomas states that lightheartedness reduces sin (q. 72, a. 2 ad 3).

Double Effect. On the other hand, whatever our intention, negative tropes can have both our intended virtuous effect and an unintended negative effect. In such cases, the principle of double effect applies. Even when we do not intend the second effect, we cannot ignore it. We have to consider whether the positive good achieved by our intended goal is sufficient to justify the unintended negative effect, and whether the unintended injury to the person helps achieve the virtuous end we seek. Language is for upbuilding of all hearers, whether it is taken in jest

---

[23] Judie Brown, "Sacrilege, scandal and murder–or civility?", Released November 14, 2007, http://www.all.org/article.

or not. St. Thomas warns:

> Nevertheless there is need of discretion in such matters, and one should not use such words without moderation, because the railing might be so grave that being uttered inconsiderately it might dishonor the person against whom it is uttered. On such a case a man might commit a mortal sin, even though he did not intend to dishonor the other man: just as were a man incautiously to injure grievously another by striking him in fun, he would not be without blame (q. 72, a. 2).

Thomas continues:

> Just as it is lawful to strike a person, or damnify him in his belongings for the purpose of correction, so too, for the purpose of correction, one may say a mocking word to a person whom one has to correct. It is thus that our Lord called the disciples "foolish," and the Apostle called the Galatians "senseless." Yet, as Augustine says (*De Sermone Domini in Monte* ii, 19), "seldom and only when it is very necessary should we have recourse to invectives, and then so as to urge God's service, not our own" (q. 72, a. 2 ad 2).

Circumstances

Another factor to consider in determining the morality of a rhetorical act is circumstance. Do different circumstances justify different usages?

Privacy. When one is in private, one is often more free with using epithets as a kind of verbal shortcut. I will use invective among close friends when I am pretty sure the significance (sign-value) of the epithet will be understood and when I am not intending to malign the person, but only to communicate a certain idea about him. For instance, when I was writing my dissertation a colleague and I would refer to it, in jest, as "Rahner is the Antichrist," because part of my purpose was to counter the influence of a Rahner-inspired interpretation of *Gaudium et Spes*.[24] Now, neither my colleague nor I think that Rahner is the Antichrist: we just said it as a kind of a short hand for our mutually held position on a number of theological controversies.

When can a person let his hair down and use cant, jargon, and

---

[24] Robert F. Gotcher, "Henri de Lubac and Communio: The Significance of de Lubac's Theology of the Supernatural for an Interpretation of Gaudium et Spes," Doctoral Diss., (Marquette University, 2002).

verbal shortcuts? An important consideration these days is an unjustified presumption of privacy. Can we get away with it in this internet age? The Internet is a public forum. We need to be aware that anything we say will be known to the opponents of life. Further, what is said in private can scandalize even those who agree. One home-schooling mom, for instance, comments upon some of the things said in private among home-schoolers by saying:

> My husband had been an atheist many years ago and says that if he still was one, what he sees in home-school behavior and what is coming over the home-school email would have made him never want to convert or have anything to do with these people. So in my own life and dealing with fallen away people I am very sensitive over what battles I am going to pick. Because these people catch wind on what we are discussing.[25]

As for a public use on, say, a blog, I tend to avoid being negative for two reasons. First of all there is the possibility that the real meaning of the term used (its sign-value) will not be clear to some of the readers, leading to a situation where I have to explain that "I didn't mean that!" Second, for many people, their only knowledge of the person insulted may be what I have said about them. I prefer to let people represent their own idiocy, rather that people relying on me as some kind of authority who can do the interpreting for my loyal readers. For instance, I might say of a friend, "Kevin Miller is a chowderhead" because of some less than intelligent post he has made. Someone who has never met him might come to think of him as a chowderhead pure and simple. It would be arrogant of me to put myself up as such an authority to be trusted.

Equals vs. Unequals. One must be careful not to use aggressive rhetoric against those who are not as intellectually gifted because it comes off sounding like bullying. Making fun of someone who is intelligent but said something stupid is different from mocking someone who is, in fact, less intelligent. That is snobbery. Even St. Paul, who called the Galatians stupid, also said that we need to be considerate of the weak (1 Cor. 8:7-13).

Public Debate. Irony in the context of a friendly debate where there

---

[25] Flying Stars blog. http://mrsnancybrown.blogspot.com/2007/10/is-dumbledore-real.html. Saturday, October 20, 2007.

is fundamental good will on both sides, as irony in the context of an obviously loving relationship between two persons where there is no question of ill will, usually does not come off sounding mean-spirited. Some families have a culture of teasing that is very good-natured. G.K. Chesterton seems to have been genuinely friendly with George Bernard Shaw and others whom he debated, even though they opposed each other with some pretty negative rhetoric: "I am not so much disposed to quarrel as to argue; and I value more than I can easily say the generally genial relations I have kept with those who differ from me merely in argument."[26]

Sometimes negative rhetorical tropes are used in a public forum where the person referred to is not being directly addressed or even present, such as in a speech. Since, however, the forum is public, it is possible for the person eventually to hear the epithet. In our age one must be very careful about using such language, for it is easily distorted and amplified by the media.

Personalist Analysis: The Culture of Life

The previous analysis has been a standard, textbook moral analysis of invective, irony and sarcasm. Such a standard analysis already indicates significant limits on the use of negative rhetoric in pro-life activism. Looking at the question from a more personalist approach, the kind of approach advocated by the Second Vatican Council and by John Paul II in *Veritatis splendor*, we find such language is even more restricted.

The meaning of a personalist morality is articulated clearly in the 1976 *Document on the Theological Formation of Future Priests* of the Congregation for Catholic Education, in a passage that encourages a return to a Thomistic moral reasoning:

> On the contrary, [St. Thomas Aquinas] placed it within the unitary plan of systematic theology viewing it as the study of the process by which the human person, created in the likeness of God and redeemed by the grace of Christ, tends toward his full realization, according to the demands of his divine calling, in the context of the

[26] G.K. Chesterton, *The Thing* (New York NY: Sheed and Ward, n.d.), pp. 8-9.

economy of salvation historically realized in the Church.[27]

John Paul II emphasizes the subjective dimension of personalist morality in a key passage of *Veritatis splendor* §78: "In order to be able to grasp the object of an act which specifies that act morally, it is therefore necessary to place oneself in the perspective of the acting person." As John Grabowski describes the more personalist approach:

> [T]his focus on the human person redeemed by Christ and called to communion with the Trinity requires an account of how a person can grow in moral goodness or holiness. It is not enough to offer juridical criteria for analyzing isolated acts that are unconnected from one another and the person who authors them. Rather, one must consider the role human acts play in the *moral becoming* of the person. While human finitude means that there are real limits to the freedom men and women possess, they still possess the ability to define themselves as moral beings through their freely chosen behaviors and attitudes. That is, human beings create for themselves a specific moral character through their free choice and actions.[28]

In this approach one is concerned about the human dignity and the supernatural destiny of everyone involved in a situation, about how behavior affects the growth in holiness of the persons acting, and about the potential and existing bonds of communion between persons.

Icon of the Culture of Life. Two events have had a long-lasting impact on me. The first was a tour that I made of the exhibition hall at the Steele County Free Fair in Minnesota. There were two booths at different ends of the exhibition hall. The one I ran across first was the pro-life booth. It was manned by an elderly lady who was kind, gentle, and not aggressive. On the other hand, the "pro-choice" booth was manned by a young man in a black tee-shirt with a strident slogan. He stood in front of the booth with his arms crossed across his chest and a scowl across his face. One can experience this contrast in front of abortion clinics.

The second was a pro-life march on the capitol building in St. Paul. There were nearly 10,000 people who marched from the Cathedral to the

---

[27] Quoted in Servais Pinckaers, O.P., *Morality: The Catholic View* (South Bend IN: St. Augustine Press, 2003), p. 44.

[28] John Grabowski, *Sex and Virtue* (Washington, D.C.: The Catholic Univ. of America Press, 2004), p. xi.

Capitol, listened to speeches, and sang hymns. One also noticed how peaceful the crowd was. What one noticed about the crowd was that it consisted primarily of families–men, women, and children who witnessed to life. One also noticed how peaceful the crowd was. There was no anger, no stridency. It is as if the rhetoric about the dignity of the human person were represented iconically. And this was not a calculated attempt to manipulate, but it flowed from the inner integrity of the persons involved.

On the fringe, however, a group of ACT-UP type homosexual activists were protesting the march. Their behavior was coarse, their slogans and placards were obscene. Their ugliness contrasted with the beauty of the men, women, and children who were standing up for life. The contrast between the grace-filled and the demonic could not have been greater.[29]

The goal of the pro-life movement is not only to stop abortions but to create a culture of life, to be a contrast to the culture of death in word and deed.[30] In fact, individuals and groups in the movement become beautiful icons of the culture of life. This is accomplished not only by being right about life issues but by an interior transformation into the kind of person who respects the dignity of the human person, even and especially the enemy, in word and deed–the cultivation of virtues. The more pro-life activists imitate the harsh methods of their opponents, the less contrast there is. There are three particular characteristics of the culture of life that our rhetoric should manifest–personal holiness, mercy, and friendship.

Personal Holiness. The goal of the pro-life movement is not simply victory, whether in argumentation or legislation, but to create a culture of life. A culture of life begins with personal holiness. Alasdair McIntyre distinguishes between the cultivation of virtue in pursuit of the goods of personal excellence and that of the goods of cooperative effectiveness, in other words, the difference between something that

---

[29] I recently asked my twenty-two year old daughter, who was in grade school at the time, whether she remembered this particular march and what she remembered of it. She not only remembered it very clearly, but specifically remembered the obscene things being shouted by the contra-march protesters.

[30] See John Paul II's *Evangelium Vitae*, especially §78ff.

increases the goodness of the acting person and something that gets something done.[31] As John Paul II says in *Veritatis Splendor*:

> Human acts are moral acts because they express and determine the goodness or evil of the individual who performs them. They do not produce a change merely in the state of affairs outside of man but, to the extent that they are deliberate choices, they give moral definition to the very person who performs them, determining his profound spiritual traits. (VS §71)

The true aim of Christian moral action is not primarily the establishment of a specific extrinsic state of affairs, even if it is seen as "a better state of affairs for all concerned" (VS §74), but the interior transformation of the acting person and the establishment of the conditions for the movement of others towards participation in the interior transformation–the kingdom. When we say "the ends do not justify the means," we are saying more than a deontological "the rules are the rules." We are saying that personal holiness trumps the achievement of a social end. One has to risk failing to achieve a successful outcome if the means of accomplishing it diminishes one spiritually, whether it is technically sinful or not. Even at the risk of losing a debate and diminishing the chances of an immediate victory in public policy.

The question is: What kind of person does using such language make me? How does it affect my relationships with God and others? According to *Veritatis splendor*, a Christian judges the morality of an act by the Christian's relationship with the Lord:

> The Christian, thanks to God's Revelation and to faith, is aware of the "newness" which characterizes the morality of his actions: these actions are called to show either consistency or inconsistency with that dignity and vocation which have been bestowed on him by grace. In Jesus Christ and in his Spirit, the Christian is a "new creation," a child of God; by his actions he shows his likeness or unlikeness to the image of the Son who is the first-born among many brethren (cf. Rom 8:29), he lives out his fidelity or infidelity to the gift of the Spirit, and he opens or closes himself to eternal life, to the communion of vision, love and happiness with God the Father, Son and Holy Spirit. As Saint Cyril of Alexandria writes, Christ "forms us according to his image, in such a way that the traits of his divine nature shine forth in us through sanctification and

---

[31] Alasdair MacIntyre, *Whose Justice? Which Rationality?* (Notre Dame IN: Univ. of Notre Dame Press, 1988). He begins discussing the difference between excellence and effectiveness on p. 27 and uses the distinction throughout.

justice and the life which is good and in conformity with virtue... The beauty of this image shines forth in us who are in Christ, when we show ourselves to be good in our works. (VS §73)

Mercy. A pro-life activist first of all shows his interior and profound commitment to the culture of life by being a merciful person, demonstrating an obvious respect for the dignity of every human person, even those who are profoundly wrong and those who are sinners. This precludes ever scoring even a valid point at the expense of the personal dignity of an opponent, including the president of the National Organization for Women and Senator Ted Kennedy.

The use of language should not only be just, but charitable. Negative rhetoric is not the second line of defense after more charitable approaches fail, invective itself is used when it is the most charitable option available in context. This reasoning is similar to the reasoning that is at the heart of John Paul II's argument against capital punishment (*Evangelium Vitae* §56). For John Paul II, the effective exercise of justice requires mercy: "The experience of the past and of our own time demonstrates that justice alone is not enough, that it can even lead to the negation and destruction of itself, if that deeper power, which is love, is not allowed to shape human life in its various dimensions."[32]

There may be situations in which it is justified to use invective, irony, or even sarcasm, but for the sake of the pro-life activist's soul and for the sake of the culture of life, he may do well to restrain himself in order to show respect for the personal human dignity of his enemies. The "newness" that John Paul II says the pro-life movement is to demonstrate in the culture of life (VS §73) is justice tempered by mercy. In showing mercy to the enemies of the culture of life, by treating them gently when justice might demand a stronger response, is to initiate them into the kingdom.

Friendship. Ever since the time of Plato, philosophers and theologians have emphasized the importance of establishing a relationship of

---

[32] *Dives in Misericordia* §12. See Kevin E. Miller, "The Role of Mercy in a Culture of Life: John Paul II on Capital Punishment" in *Life and Learning VIII: Proceedings of the Eighth University Faculty for Life Conference*, ed. Joseph W. Koterski, S.J. (Washington, D.C.: Univ. Faculty for Life, 1999), pp. 405-42.

trust and friendship in persuading another of the truth. I have seen many situations in which the use of invective and sarcasm, while not necessarily being the sole cause, was an exacerbating factor in a quasi-permanent rupture between people whom otherwise agree on important fundamentals. I cannot think of a situation where I have seen invective used in an argument that led to overcoming the barrier of hostility. I have rarely seen a situation in which polemic actually achieved a change of mind on the part of an opponent in a public debate. We are not going to be as open to a person who exhibits hostility. "A soft answer turns away wrath, but a harsh word stirs up anger" (Prov. 15:1).

A recent book on rhetoric describes the closing effect invective can have during a debate:

> Within limits it is reasonable in persuasion to use connotations that advance the writer's purpose. But when emotional language is carried to the point of name calling, it provokes an unfavorable response from intelligent readers, especially when name calling is substituted for logical thinking.[33]

In rhetoric, one of the three means of persuasion is *ethos*, the character of the person.[34] According to a secular writer's handbook, "*Trustworthiness is the kind of persuasion that comes from the character or personality of the persuader.*"[35] In *The Message in the Bottle*, Walker Percy says that a bearer of news is more easily accepted if he exhibits good faith in his mien.[36] If we have demonstrated a concern for the person by good will, outside of the context of our disagreement, that person is more likely to listen to us. Percy offers a wonderful description of the type of newsbearer who is most easily received by another:

> For if a perfect stranger puts himself to some trouble to come to me and to announce

---

[33] James M. McCrimmon, *Writing With a Purpose*, Seventh Edition (Dallas TX: Houghton Mifflin, 1980), p. 212.

[34] Aristotle, *Rhetoric*, Bk 1, Ch. 2.

[35] McCrimmon, loc. cit.

[36] Walker Percy, *The Message in the Bottle: How Queer Man is, How Queer Language Is, and What One Has to Do with the Other* (New York NY: Farrar, Straus and Giroux, 1975), pp. 132-36.

a piece of news relevant to my predicament and announce it with perfect sobriety and with every outward sign of good faith, then I must say to myself, What manner of man is this that he should put himself out of his way for a perfect stranger–and I should heed him.[37]

The pro-life activist is a bearer of good new, the Gospel of Life. One hears many stories of clinic workers converting on a clinic sidewalk because of kindness of sidewalk counselors. The Second Vatican Council's *Gaudium et Spes* says that the Christian's own behavior is not a little responsible for the spread of atheism (GS §20).[38]

WHAT ABOUT JESUS?

As stated earlier, Jesus himself engaged in negative rhetoric, the most notable example in Matthew 23. What allows him to get away with it and can we imitate him?

Prophetic rhetorical context. The first point to consider is the rhetori-cal contexts of Jesus's world and our own society. Jesus lived in a time and culture in which prophets, like the court jesters of medieval courts, could address political situations. In ancient Israel, what the rulers deman-ded was *evidence of divine authority*. The question of the scribes and Pharisees was not whether Jesus should say the things he did, but whether he had the authority to do and things in the name of God (Mk 11:28).

While an American with a classical liberal education understands that rhetorical context affects significantly the *ad hominem* nature of language used, very few Americans have a genuinely liberal education, and there-fore have no exposure to the rhetorical sciences. In the American culture, language is either true or a lie, gentle or vicious.

---

[37] Ibid, pp. 135-36. Percy also reminds us of the importance of sobriety (p. 135) for sharing the good news with others. Another means of showing good faith is to show real knowledge of the person's predicament and to associate the news we bring with their predicament. Hence, a pro-life advocate can show that the pro-life message, the Gospel of Life, addresses the personal concerns (predicament) of a pro-abortion advocate, he may be able to persuade him to the side of life.

[38] In a literary example, one scholar has made the point that in J.R.R. Tolkien's *The Lord of the Rings*, Sam's intemperate use of the epithet "sneak" for Gullum may have undercut what little goodness Gollum still had that might have been the basis for his ultimate cooperation in Frodo's quest.

Language that seems negative is taken as personal. For example, it is presumed when politicians resort to negative campaigning, that the opposing side will take offense, be angry, or hold a grudge. The emphasis on campaign reporting, for instance, is often on how the candidates *feel*.[39] Hence, the American context may not be the best context for negative rhetoric because of the presumption that the rhetoric is intended to be personal.

Purity of Heart. The second reason why Jesus was able to use negative rhetoric when others are not able to do so, is that in his use of such language he was free from a desire to harm the other person. Those affec-ted by original sin are less likely to be able to separate their desire for truth and justice from their desire to harm or destroy the enemy. The book of Jonah is instructive. Jonah's attitude toward the Ninevites was one of ill will. His hope was that the Ninevites would be punished, not that they repent and be saved. When they did repent he was disappointed. Purity of motivation in dealing with one's enemies is quite rare and demands a purity of heart that is possible only when one has advanced in the path to holiness. As C.S. Lewis states, human beings find it difficult to distinguish between the sinner and the sin. In his science fiction novel *Perelandra*, Lewis describes the experience of a man who is for the first time able to experience absolutely justified hatred because it is directed not at a human person, but a damned angel:

> Then an experience that perhaps no good man can ever have in our world came over him–a torrent of perfectly unmixed and lawful hatred. The energy of hating, never before felt without some guilt, without some dim knowledge that he was failing fully to distinguish the sinner from the sin, rose into his arms and legs tell he felt that they were pillars of burning blood. What was before him appeared no longer a creature of corrupted will. It was corruption itself to which will was attached only as an instrument. Ages ago it had been a Person: but the ruins of personality now survived in it only as weapons at the disposal of a furious self-exiled negation. It is perhaps difficult to understand why this filled Ranson not with horror, but with a kind of joy. The joy came

---

39 "A visibly angry Sen. Hillary Clinton lashed out Saturday at Sen. Barack Obama over campaign literature that she said he knows is 'blatantly false,' while Obama called her outburst 'tactical.'" In "Clinton tells Obama: 'Shame on you'; Obama fires back," CNN, Feb. 23, 2008. http://www.cnn.com/2008/POLITICS/02/23/clinton.mailings/index.html (accessed June 30, 2008). Whether a seasoned politicians is *really* angry when he is *visibly* angry is not a question often asked by the average reader.

from finding at last what hatred was made for. As a boy with an axe rejoices on finding a tree, or a boy with a box of colored chalks rejoices on finding a pile of perfectly white paper, so he rejoiced in the perfect congruity between his emotions and its object.[40]

The opposition to the pro-life position is neither as absolutely evil as being the demon who possessed Weston, nor are pro-life activists sure to be of such purity of heart that they can separate their desire to convert the opposition and their desire to destroy it.

Conclusion

Invective and other negative rhetoric are common enough in both secular and religious efforts to eliminate abortion in our society. Standard Catholic moral analysis places limits on their use, especially in public, antagonistic debates. A more personalist analysis, emphasizing the effect the rhetoric has on the speaker and the existing and potential bonds of communion between the speaker and the hostile hearer even further limits the situations in which such rhetoric may be used.

In hostile situations careful argumentation, rather than dismissive or biting wit, is more fruitful and effective because it is more charitable and merciful. Negative rhetoric runs the risk of undermining any hope of communion. There is an *ad hominem* component to it when it is used as a rhetorical device, as well as a certain intellectual arrogance, especially in our culture that is ignorant of the distinction between negative rhetoric and personal ill will. The best way to demonstrate a person's error to himself or to a third party is to simply tell or show what the person did or said, with the addition of whatever moral or technical analysis is necessary, if the error of the words or actions is not obvious.

As Archbishop Joseph Naumann of Kansas City, Kansas, in discussing a column responding to his public request that Kansas governor Kathleen Sebelius to refrain from receiving communion, said:

In logic, this type of argument is termed *ad hominem*. It is an attempt to attack personally one's opponent in a debate, rather than make substantive arguments about the issue being debated. It is usually an indication of a weak position by the person

---

[40] C.S. Lewis, *Perelandra* (New York NY: Scribner, 1972), p. 132.

making the *ad hominem* argument. What is needed is a substantive discussion of this important social and moral issue, not personal attacks![41]

The real question is this: is the pro-life movement intending to influence minds or hearts, to lead others to conversion? Or, is our goal our victory and their defeat our holiness and the inclusion of the enemy in the civilization of love? The movement's use of negative rhetoric will reflect the decision its members make on these questions.

---

[41] "Archbishop Addresses Questions that Earlier Column Raised," Catholic Culture Webpage, online at: http://www.catholicculture.org/library/view.

Death Scenes in Literature from the Nineteenth Century to Current Fiction

Jeff Koloze

ABSTRACT: This paper considers five elements found in the nineteenth-century depiction of death scenes. (1) Dying characters have the benefit of being in a comforting place before they die, and (2) they have contact with a caring human being. (3) Removal of pain of the individual dying is a significant concern; (4) material goods, in contrast, are insignificant to the dying. Finally, (5) spiritual solace can be found in the death scenes. After showing how these elements are depicted in significant passages in the novels of Dickens, the paper then documents how the elements can be discovered in early twentieth-century novels; by century's end, however, the elements were almost completely absent. The paper examines contemporary twenty-first century novels whose death scenes include the five elements and suggests that future research is needed before a literary trend of novels rediscovering the nineteenth-century standard can be established.

FICTION READERS who wish to satisfy their desire not so much to be educated by the literature they read as to be entertained by it would do well to focus on nineteenth-century novels. Almost every novel written in the century that saw the rise of the novel as the dominant means of prose expression can rise to the stature of a "good read." This can be attributed to the tendency that nineteenth-century novels have of generally following the four-part plot structure (exposition, crisis, climax, and dénouement), which gives readers, not necessarily a happy ending, but a sense of completion or fulfillment, a practice that endured until realism and other literary movements at the end of the nineteenth century encouraged fiction writers to alter the model that had worked well since the late eighteenth century. While readers may not be concerned with the didactic value of such novels if their intent is to enjoy the writing, what do they enjoy when they encounter many death scenes of significant characters in these novels–death being an unpleasant topic in literature that disturbs the idea of a "good read"?

By "death scenes" I mean those scenes in fictional works that depict a human being at the last stage of living, one who is dying naturally and not because of judicial decree or military activity. Perhaps the presence of numerous death scenes in the masterworks of nineteenth-century fiction indicates that authors used them as vehicles for sentimentality. Perhaps the death scenes illustrate social protest in a manner befitting a non-didactic mode of nineteenth-century novels. It would have been preachy for a novelist to write: "It is not right that the poor should die as they do in an environment where industrial development is eradicating the agrarian society from which they have come. It is not right that the rich should not care for their poor brothers and sisters." But the death scenes in nineteenth-century novels convey the ideas of the preceding two quotes much more effectively by giving readers enduring images and powerful vocabulary.

Twentieth-century literature may have lost the bearings of its ancestor. While dying characters in nineteenth-century novels were treated with respect, the dying in twentieth-century works are often dehumanized, belittled, and reduced to entities that likely to benefit from euthanasia. What the twenty-first century has to offer is still in formation, but some commentary about recent works can be provided. Examining death scenes in all literature in all genres is beyond the scope of this paper, so I would like to restrict my field of study to American and British literature, beginning in the nineteenth century.

I. Nineteenth-century Death Scenes

Of all the nineteenth-century British authors one could select, the reader naturally gravitates to Charles Dickens–"naturally" because there are many enduring images of characters at the moment of death in Dickens's work, so many that a reader may not be able to conclude which character's death is the most poignant. Focusing on some of the more famous episodes in his fiction will suffice to document certain elements that compel readers to remember the scenes, to linger over the details of the characters' dying moments, and perhaps to learn how the deaths of fictional characters can apply to their own lives. I will consider the deaths of characters spanning Dickens's career: Smike in *Nicholas Nickleby* (1838-39), Nell in *The Old Curiosity Shop* (1840-41), Richard Carstone (and, in contrast, Lady Dedlock) in *Bleak House* (1852-53), Mr. Dorrit in *Little Dorrit* (1855-57), and Johnny in *Our Mutual Friend* (1865).[1] All of these episodes include five elements that appear to be essential for reader appreciation of the death scenes: a comforting place in which to die, contact with a caring human being, removal of pain of the individual dying, little concern with material goods, and spiritual solace.[2]

A comforting place to die. The first element common to the major death scenes is that the dying characters occupy a comforting place in which to breathe their last moments. The setting for Smike's death is idyllic:

---

[1] Charles Dickens, *Bleak House* (1852-1853; New York NY: Barnes & Noble Classics, 2005); *Little Dorrit* (1855-1857), ed. John Holloway (Harmondsworth UK: Penguin Books, 1967); *Nicholas Nickleby* (1838-1839), ed. Michael Slater (Harmondsworth UK: Penguin Books, 1978); *The Old Curiosity Shop* (1840-1841, New York NY: Dodd, Mead, 1943); *Our Mutual Friend* (1865, New York NY: New American Library, 1964).

[2] Some death scenes in nineteenth-century literature are mentioned briefly in major works, primarily for the sake of character development, and need not be discussed here. Such is the case with William Makepeace Thackeray's *Vanity Fair* (1847-48; Great Illustrated Classics, 1864; New York NY: Dodd, Mead, 1943), where the pitiful state of Sir Pitt is reduced to this: "For this was all that was left after more than seventy years of cunning and struggling, and drinking and scheming, and sin and selfishness–a whimpering old idiot put in and out of bed and cleaned and fed like a baby!" (444), this followed immediately by a notation of his death. Thomas Hardy's *The Mayor of Casterbridge* (1886; Ware, Hertfordshire UK: Wordsworth Classics, 1995) can be included here as well; the final words of Susan Henchard are relayed by another character at great length to illustrate that she was a fine woman (93).

> On a fine, mild autumn day, when all was tranquil and at peace, when the soft sweet air crept in at the open window of the quiet room, and not a sound was heard but the gentle rustling of the leaves, Nicholas sat in his old place by the bedside, and knew that the time was nearly come. So very still it was, that every now and then he bent down his ear to listen for the breathing of him who lay asleep, as if to assure himself that life was still there, and that he had not fallen into that deep slumber from which on earth there is no waking. (862-63)

Nell's death occurs in the abandoned abbey church where she and her grandfather eventually dwell after an extensive journey across England. For over a hundred pages before her death Dickens describes how much Nell loved to be in the former abbey buildings, to wander in the graveyard adjacent the church, and to reflect on the buildings' former ecclesiastical use. Her death is described as reverentially as the environs are:

> There, upon her little bed, she lay at rest. The solemn stillness was no marvel now.... Her couch was dressed with here and there some winter berries and green leaves, gathered in a spot she had been used to favour. "When I die, put near me something that has loved the light, and had the sky above it always." (542)

Two death scenes in *Bleak House* are worthy of discussion regarding dying characters' need to have a comfortable place to die because of the contrasts they provide at the moment of death. Lady Dedlock, trying to flee the ignominy of having given birth to Esther Summerson out of wedlock, is discovered not in a comfortable place, but "on the step at the gate [of the graveyard], drenched in the fearful wet of such a place, which oozed and splashed down everywhere" (756).[3] In contrast, Richard Carstone, the young man whose obsession over the Jarndyce and Jarndyce will led to his

---

[3] The 1985 BBC dramatization of the novel enhances the sentimental value of this scene, but is unfaithful to the narrative. *Bleak House* (1985), performed by Diana Rigg, Denholm Elliott, Philip Franks, T.P. McKenna, Brian Deacon, Robert Urquhart (Videodisc, Warner Home Video, 2005). Although mother and daughter do meet, there is no communication between them in the novel as there is in the video adaptation; the novel makes this clear when Esther affirms that the figure reclined on the step "was my mother cold and dead" (756). The film version, however, provides Lady Dedlock with an opportunity, haltingly rendered by Lady Diana Rigg, to indicate that she is there because her deceased lover, Esther's father, is buried beyond the locked gate of the cemetery.

demise, is "lying on a sofa.... There were restoratives on the table; the room was made as airy as possible and was darkened, and was very orderly and quiet" (806). Even though her father's death occurs in luxurious surroundings, Mr. Dorrit imagines himself back in the Marshalsea debtors' prison, the place where he was most happy. Johnny finds rest at the Children's Hospital in the last of Dickens's finished novels, *Our Mutual Friend*. Despite the fears of the woman to whose care he had been entrusted, Johnny wakes "to find himself lying in a little quiet bed," surrounded by toys designed to make the little child comfortable, such as a "Noah's ark, the noble steed, and the yellow bird, with the officer in the Guards doing duty over the whole" (367).

Contact with a caring human being. The second element common to the death scenes, contact with a caring human being, is crucial–not only for the person dying, but also for the reader to extract as much emotion and didactic value out of the scene as possible. Nicholas Nickleby witnesses the death of Smike, who was "the partner of his poverty, and the sharer of his better fortune" (862). Smike's estimation of Nicholas is clear. His death imminent, since Nicholas has told him that they "shall meet again," Smike affirms that he "can even bear to part from you" (863). Just before the moment of death, "They embraced, and kissed each other on the cheek" (864). Nell's death is tragic in that the person whom she loved the most in the world, her grandfather, is not present at the moment that her death is first conveyed to the reader. Perhaps this is dramatic justice for the sake of the reader, for it is her grandfather's gambling habit that led them to dire straits; having him present at the death of so reverent and self-sacrificing a young woman would be sacrilegious.[4] Richard in *Bleak House* is surrounded by all of his beloved: his wife Ada, Esther, Esther's future

---

[4] Two pages later, however, it is obvious that "they" (her friends and, presumably, her grandfather) were around Nell when her death occurred two days earlier: "They had read and talked to her in the earlier portion of the night, but as the hours crept on, she sank to sleep" (544).

husband who was Richard's stalwart friend, and the guardian of Ada, Esther, and Richard. Having the guardian present was most important because Richard had become hostile towards him, presuming that he was blocking his inheritance from the Jarndyce will. Mr. Dorrit dies with the satisfaction of having not only his Little Dorrit around him, but also his brother Frederick, with whom he has reconciled. Doctors and hospital staff care for Johnny in his last days at the Children's Hospital, but also present is Mrs. Boffin, who cares for the little boy as though he were her own son.

Removal of pain of the individual dying. Third, most scenes of characters' dying moments involve or mention the removal of pain; the pain is often physical, but many scenes depict the removal of mental pain or anxiety. While "there was no rallying, no effort, no struggle for life," Smike's death occurs in the context of "little pain, little uneasiness" (862). The absence of pain at Nell's death is one of three constituent superlatives used to describe her on her deathbed: "No sleep so beautiful and calm, so free from trace of pain, so fair to look upon" (542). Richard experiences extreme anguish in *Bleak House* for having offended his benefactor, who can only reply to the confession by uttering "well" five times–said for the express purpose of removing his mental anguish (of "comforting him" 807). The narrator makes it a point to state that Mr. Dorrit "had been sinking in this painless way for two or three days" (712). Johnny asks whether the other children in the hospital ward are there so that their pain can be removed, and such is the little boy's selflessness that he understands "that the reply included himself" but only after they "made him understand" (367).

Little concern about material goods. Fourth, there is little concern at the moment of death about material goods. The only material good that Smike possesses at the moment of his death (a lock of his beloved's hair, wrapped in "two slight ribands") will be restored to him once he dies. Smike asks Nicholas to remove this lock once he is dead "so that no eyes but his might see it" and then to replace it around his neck "that it might rest with him in the grave" (864).

Throughout *The Old Curiosity Shop* Nell treasures no material good, whether in the curiosity shop where they first lived or on the road as they fled from London and those who would torment them. She loves only her grandfather. Even when he steals money from her to satisfy his gambling obsession, Nell cannot accuse her grandfather, so much does she love him and so constant is her devotion. Richard reduces the hundreds of pages of his anxiety over the Jarndyce will at the moment of his death in *Bleak House* to an interrogative:

> "It was a troubled dream?" said Richard, clasping both my guardian's hands, eagerly.
>
> "Nothing more, Rick; nothing more." (808)

During his last days Mr. Dorrit slowly eliminates the extraneous items that his wealth had purchased. Little Dorrit helps him to sell "a pompous gold watch" and "his sleeve-buttons and finger-rings...and it is as likely as not that he was kept alive for so many days by the satisfaction of sending them, piece by piece, to an imaginary pawnbroker's" (712). Johnny's only possessions are the toys that greeted him when he first came to the hospital; he gives them to a child with a broken leg. After giving these toys away, as well as "a kiss for the boofer lady [Mrs. Boffin]," "Having now bequeathed all he had to dispose of, and arranged his affairs in this world, Johnny, thus speaking, left it" (369).

Spiritual solace. Finally, many scenes offer spiritual solace to the dying individual. If spirituality is not essentially linked with the character, then spiritual solace is expressly offered for the reader. The account of Smike's death contains two such spiritual references. In the first instance Smike recalls Nicholas's affirmation that they would see each other again. The second reference occurs while Smike is dying. He sees "beautiful gardens, which...were filled with figures of men, women, and many children, all with light upon their faces; then whispered that it was Eden–and so died" (864). The description of Nell at the moment of death reverses the chronological order of the created world: "She seemed a creature fresh from the hand of God, and waiting for the breath of life; not one who had lived and suffered death" (542). Nell is so transformed after death that the narrator first proclaims that, as she was known in life, "[s]o shall we know the angels in their majesty, after death." The schoolmaster who befriended Nell and her grandfather closes the chapter, reflecting on heavenly justice, and asks the rhetorical question: "If one deliberate wish expressed in solemn terms above this bed could call her back to life, which of us would utter it!" (543). Richard's protracted death scene ends with his plea for forgiveness for having "married [his wife] to poverty and trouble[;] I have scattered your means to the winds." Forgiveness must be obtained, he asserts, "before I begin the world" (808)–this last dependent clause has become a metaphor for his death. At his brother's death, Frederick Dorrit directly invokes God to vow that he would take care of Little Dorrit. Within that same night, "[t]he two brothers were before their Father; far beyond the twilight judgment of this world; high above its mists and obscurities" (715). Johnny's limited religious experience is illustrated by two incidents. Above his bed in the Children's Hospital "was a coloured picture beautiful to see, representing as it were another Johnny seated on the knee of some Angel surely who loved little children" (367). The possible allusion to Christ escapes him as does the cause (man's inhumanity to man) of his being in the hospital in the first place; Johnny later asks the doctors if the children were all brought to the hospital by God.

II. Twentieth-Century Death Scenes

Twentieth-century literature, in contrast, offers many examples of characters whose last moments either continue or lack the elements discussed in the memorable death scenes above. A passage from Evelyn Waugh's *Brideshead Revisited*[5] will illustrate that a continuity with the nineteenth-century standard of depicting death

[5] Evelyn Waugh, *Brideshead Revisited: The Sacred and Profane Memories of Captain Charles Ryder* (1945; Boston: Little, Brown, 1973).

scenes was still functional. However, passages in two of James T. Farrell's works *(New Year's Eve/1929*, published in 1967, and his *The Death of Nora Ryan*, published in 1978)[6] clearly suggest that, while some of the nineteenth-century elements can be identified in these works, most are significantly altered or absent.[7]

An important death scene in Evelyn Waugh's *Brideshead Revisited* (1945) involves Lord Marchmain, the patriarch of the family whose history the narrator relates. Lord Marchmain has the satisfaction of being in his home when his last moments occur, and he receives exemplary medical care during his final hours. His

---

[6] James T. Farrell, *The Death of Nora Ryan* (Garden City NY: Doubleday, 1978); *New Year's Eve/1929* (New York NY: The Smith, 1967).

[7] As mentioned above regarding nineteenth-century works, some characters' deaths in twentieth-century novels, while important in helping the reader to understand the personalities of other characters, are too brief for study here. Such is the case in major works such as Henry James's *The Bostonians* (1886; New York NY: Modern Library, 1956), where Miss Birdseye's death extends over two independent clauses: "Miss Chancellor and Miss Tarrant had sat by her there, without moving, each of her hands in theirs, and she had just melted away, toward eight o'clock. It was a lovely death" (413). *The Big Money* portion of John Dos Passos's *U.S.A.* trilogy, *I. The 42nd Parallel; II. Nineteen-Nineteen; III. The Big Money* (New York NY: Modern Library, 1937) contains a brief passage where Mary French's father died alone and in great pain: "His face, rough with the grey stubble, was twisted and strangled, eyes open" (124). Zhivago in Pasternak's masterpiece (1958) suffers great pain during his heart attack, and the narrative describing his death increases the alienation of his character in its final moments. The film adaptation makes it seem as though Zhivago suffered the heart attack on the trolley because he thought he saw his beloved Lara walking down the street; however, there is no cause for his sudden heart attack in the novel, thus increasing the sense of futility of life expressed in his death scene.

Non-canonical works that include or disregard many of the five elements include Olive Schreiner's Undine (New York NY: Harper & Brothers, 1928), whose main character dies at novel's end; Robert Herrick's *Sometime* (New York NY: Farrar & Rinehart, 1933), whose depiction of Felix's death ends the novel; Karl Ashton's *Illegal Nurse* (New York NY: Godwin, 1936), where the death scene is an infanticide which is only suggested by the barest of narratorial detail; Gillian Tindall's *The Youngest* (London UK: Secker & Warburg, 1967); and Michael D. O'Brien's *Strangers and Sojourners* (San Francisco CA: Ignatius Press, 1997). The death scene in O'Brien's work contains all five elements: Anne dies in her home, in the presence of her aged husband, and has spiritual solace from a beloved priest; there is no concern over material things at her death. Although she is dying of cancer, no pain is mentioned; in fact, whatever fear or anxiety she experienced is eliminated: "I want you to know that the shadows went away. They've gone forever. I'm not afraid anymore" (545).

family surround him, and he has the benefit of "the simple, genial" Father Mackay to provide the last sacrament for this ostensibly fallen-away Catholic (339). Although the family is in financial peril (174-75), there is no concern about this expressed at the moment of Lord Marchmain's death.

Two items in the nineteenth-century catalog of elements in death scenes are interconnected in this case. Although no physical pain is expressed in the scene, Lord Marchmain's spiritual solace and anxiety over his sins are intertwined:

> "Now," said the priest, "I know you are sorry for all the sins of your life, aren't you? Make a sign, if you can. You're sorry, aren't you?" But there was no sign. "Try and remember your sins; tell God you are sorry."...
>
> I suddenly felt the longing for a sign, if only of courtesy, if only for the sake of the woman I loved, who knelt in front of me, praying, I knew, for a sign....
>
> Suddenly Lord Marchmain moved his hand to his forehead; I thought he had felt the touch of the chrism and was wiping it away. "O God," I prayed, "don't let him do that." But there was no need for fear; the hand moved slowly down his breast, then to his shoulder, and Lord Marchmain made the sign of the cross. (338)

Farrell's *New Year's Eve/1929* depicts the life of Beatrice Burns, a sensuous young woman whose goal is to spend New Year's Eve at a party. This attempt to enjoy life masks the futility of overcoming tuberculosis. Although there is no specific death scene in the novel, one can argue that the entire novel is a prolongation of Beatrice's dying. She loses a connection with her father (he leaves her apartment in the initial pages, and the reader does not see him again). She is unable to reciprocate the affection of a man who sincerely loves her (she loses him by page 25). Her desire to have sex is unfulfilled by the end of the book.

At the novel's end, the reader finds Beatrice on New Year's Day with all of the five elements of the nineteenth-century standard for death scenes unmet. Instead of a comforting place to die, Beatrice surveys "her unmade bed. She had slept all day, and now it was dark outside. The first day of this New Year was gone. She ran her hand through her uncombed hair, and let the sight of her unmade bed depress her" (139). Instead of contact with caring people, she bemoans that a friend of hers “hadn’t shown up, and he should have come by now. He knew that she’d expect him to come so that they could talk over last night’s party” (139). The end of the novel is replete with instances of her emotional distress, thus negating the element of removal of pain. Beatrice “didn’t have the will power to make up her mind and decide what she would do. It was even too much of an effort to get dressed” (139). Beatrice’s anxiety and concern about material things is expressed in the penultimate paragraph of the novel. When “Beatrice opened her eyes, and looked at the bare, whitish-grayish ceiling” and realized “That, she told herself, was her life,” her emotional reaction is swift: “She collapsed into tears. She shook with sobs, rolled over on the bed, and, with her face sunken into the soiled pillow slip, she continued to sob” (144). Finally, being agnostic, there is no spiritual solace for Beatrice. The novel ends with the pitiful thought, “I don’t want to die, she told herself like a frightened little girl” (144).

Set in 1946, *The Death of Nora Ryan* is another Farrell novel in which few of the nineteenth-century standards can be identified. The novel considers the effects that a debilitating stroke has on Nora Ryan, the matriarch of a Chicago family. Nora Ryan will not recover from the stroke, and so her children arrive from across the country for her last days. However, the children do everything but spend time in Nora’s presence. While she rests comfortably in her bedroom in a daughter’s house, her children are almost always depicted in another room. (One daughter does enter Nora’s bedroom when she is already in a coma.) The only contact Nora has with caring people are her attending physician and two nurses called in especially to care for her. While several characters wonder whether Nora is in pain, they make no effort to try to read their mother’s face, or to ask her directly (although the effort may be futile, since Nora has lost the capacity to speak). Nora herself is unconcerned with material goods; she is a devout Roman Catholic and prays not for her children’s financial or professional success as much as she prays that those of her children who have lost their faith will return to it. The children, however, are concerned about material goods, specifically, the costs associated not only with maintaining everybody in the house during her final illness, but also the financial costs of Nora's care if her dying becomes prolonged.

One paragraph in the four-hundred page novel is solely devoted to Nora's perspective, and her thoughts show just how removed from the nineteenth-century elements, except for spiritual solace, her own death scene is:

> Nora Ryan could only see part of the room. Sometimes something looked familiar, a face, an object, something. But it didn't look the way it used to. The space of her world had changed. She could hear talking; she heard the doctor saying that her right side was paralyzed and that she could not feel anything on that side. But she had dreams of pain there. As she lay with one eye open, seeing and watching, the world stopped. On the right of her, there was nothing. It was as if there were a wall in the room blocking out everything on that side. She was helpless, as helpless as a baby. But she had no mother. She dreamed one night that she was a baby and she recognized her mother in the dreams. Was her mother dead? Her mind was too weak and tired to try to remember. An automatic acceptance was imposed upon her by her condition. She was living from one minute to another. The only thing she knew was that she was dying. God was calling her but she could do nothing but lie here helpless until He called her for the last time. (350)

III. Late Twentieth-Century and Contemporary Fiction

Late twentieth-century fiction bifurcates, consistent with the two approaches towards the dying evident in society: one that is life-denying and one that is life-affirming. Life-denying novels follow the trend of earlier twentieth-century novels, largely disregarding the nineteenth-century elements and stripping away sentimentality and human compassion in death scenes. Life-affirming ones contain the five elements, incorporating them with significant changes (most notably, a more realistic approach towards dying and an absence of sentimentalism).

The life-denying approach is illustrated in three contemporary novels, two by British authors Ann Widdecombe and Tony Sullivan, the third by the American author Laurie Blauner.[8] Ann

---

[8] Laurie Blauner, *Infinite Kindness* (Seattle WA: Black Heron Press, 2007).

Widdecombe's *The Clematis Tree*[9] describes the tribulations of the Wellings family as they care for their handicapped son who was struck down by a drunken driver at age four. Now eleven, Jeremy is wheelchair-bound and unable to communicate except by grunting (often loudly in public to the embarrassment of his parents) and is slowly losing his ability to swallow food so that the family and his caregivers must use feeding tubes.

Jeremy's death scene manifests several of the nineteenth-century elements. In a way, his death occurs in a comfortable place; he is at home, sitting in his wheelchair "in the shade of the lilacs at the top of the slope on the other side of their back yard." He has his family members around him–his mother and father and his attentive Aunt Isobel. Even the next door neighbor trimming his hedges has affection for Jeremy. When Jeremy's wheelchair rolls down the slope, advancing towards the stream at its base, his father realizes what is happening and struggles to catch up with the chair. Jeremy eventually rolls into the water, where his father "went on staring, unwilling to disturb his son's peace" (268). The seconds lost at this moment guarantee that Jeremy will die by drowning.

Involving a futuristic view of life in Britain under legalized euthanasia, Tony Sullivan's *The Virtues of Volanasia*[10] contains one death scene that poignantly describes the final moments of a ninety-nine-year-old woman whose granddaughter had applied on the woman's behalf for "volanasia" (voluntary euthanasia). The "gerry-house" in which the woman resides is far from a comforting place to die:

> The place was thick with bodies[;] it was a swamp of aged flesh. The air was clamorous with voices, drenched with the nauseating stink of ordure and disinfectant, topped off with the sickly sweetness of an air-freshener. The light was gluey as though we were underground. (158-59)

The absence of any compassionate person is described just as

[9] Ann Widdecombe, *The Clematis Tree* (London UK: Phoenix, 2000).

[10] Tony Sullivan, *The Virtues of Volanasia* (Lewes UK: Book Guild, 2005).

depressingly:

> At first we could not find an attendant; everyone we came across was an inmate, appallingly old. Some wandered about distractedly, others sat abandoned in wheelchairs, calling out weakly for assistance...and had I not been so appalled and sickened I might have noted that in the midst of this loathsome chaos they often created a little oasis of human warmth and kindness for themselves.... (159)

When asked whether any other family members cared for the woman, the granddaughter retorts: "They all cleared off long ago and left her on my hands. Bleeding nerve! How am I supposed to afford it?" (160). Her response perfectly summarizes the concern for material goods, a significant element for the granddaughter, not for the old woman, who remains silent throughout the episode. Shortly after the granddaughter's statement, the old woman signs the suicide note requesting that she be put to death. The actual killing of the elderly woman, which is not depicted, is reduced to the demonstrative pronoun "this" that is embedded in the solicitousness of the narrator, who finds the scene sickening, not in any moral sense, only a physical one. "Are you all right?" the narrator's companion in the volanasia activity asks. "Why don't you leave? I'll finish this off then meet you in the car park" (160).

Laurie Blauner's *Infinite Kindness* (2007) follows Ann Russell, a nurse in the Crimean War, as she readjusts to life in London. Ann lost her fiancé in the war, and, at age thirty-two, she seems to be interested only in continuing the inspiring work of Florence Nightingale. Ann is convinced that she has chosen the correct career after she receives a message from God to "continue" her own work in a London hospital (141). However, unlike Nightingale's efforts to alleviate pain, Ann interprets the divine command as an affirmation of the killing that she has already accomplished at the hospital. The killings for which Ann is responsible begin indirectly. For example, a patient commits suicide by overdosing on drugs that Ann left at her bedside. The moral objection of this suicide cannot be traced to Ann because, after all, the patient took the pills herself. Her move towards active killing occurs when she thinks that she could "help" (in quotations in the original) an abandoned newborn named Carrot (106). Just before her command from God, Ann has progressed to the killing of two patients.

Consistent with her interpretation of nursing as a desire "to end the needless suffering" (142)–a definition of nursing that she formulates immediately after the divine command–Ann begins her killing career in earnest. She kills a blind old man who asks to be killed; she asserts that Florence Nightingale, the nurse exemplar, had killed two soldiers, severing their arteries (this claim is asserted twice, on 204 and 211); her benefactress's death is called a "release" (213); she strangles and then shoots two Abyssinian soldiers (229-30). Paradoxically, she feels more alive after the killings (233).

In contrast, the life-affirming approach towards the dying is represented in two contemporary American novels. These authors' novels not only hearken to the characteristics found in nineteenth-century works, but also, without that century's sentimentality, provide the reader with much more linguistic play and dramatic power.

Janice Thompson's *Duty to Die*[11] begins with a death scene typical of thc fiction that illustrates a life-denying perspective. Ashley Cooper is being euthanized under the provisions of the newly-enacted "Duty to Die" federal law that allows the active killing of persons suffering from incurable illness, later defined as illnesses that pose a "financial burden to society" (17). What would be a comforting place to die, a sanitary hospital room, is a location that only increases her anxiety. The only person in the room attending her death is a nurse whose consoling words are, "It's only a matter of time"–said while she was "yawning impatiently" (19). Ashley reviews her life as a successful corporate executive, but the italicized words "*Help me!*" and "*Daddy?*" suggest that what is occupying her mind even more is a need to connect with the nurturing love of her family. An agnostic, her only religious thought is the recollection of an aunt chastising her for lying. The repetition

---

[11] Janice Thompson, *Duty to Die* (Uhrichsville OH: Promise Press, 2001).

of "It was almost over now, almost over..." at the end of this scene indicates that she will soon die.

Of course, she will not succumb to the euthanasia drip. She is saved by a representative of an outlaw band of medical personnel who use "intervention" as a way to rescue persons about to be euthanized. Dramatic torque continues until the end of the novel with what appears to be a repeat death scene just as gloomily reported as the opening scene: "Drip, drip, drip.... Ashley gazed at the IV bag to her right" (237). What first reads as an act of euthanasia, however, is transformed into a life-affirming event:

> The pain was overwhelming. But it was almost over now, almost over. The inevitable was upon her. She was lost in a fog, a haze, drifting....
>
> Then words of a young doctor rang out, shattering the darkness: "It's a girl." (238).

The larger plot of Jane St. Clair's *Walk Me to Midnight*[12] concerns Susan Rutledge's fight against a murderous suicide-assisting physician named Alexis Hedeon. A significant subplot in the narrative concerns an AIDS patient who considers using Dr. Hedeon's suicide method. St. Clair's novel is the latest in contemporary fiction that illustrates a death scene in a life-affirming manner. Receiving hospice care, Kyle is able to spend his last moments in his own home, surrounded by his wife Lorie, his daughter Erica, his pastor, and Charlotte, a hospice nurse who is not only compassionate but also realistic about what duties must be performed to aid the dying man in his last moments. Unlike Dickens's characters whose pain is specifically removed at the time of their deaths, St. Clair does not mask the unpleasantness of Kyle's last moments:

> About a half hour later he began to struggle, gasp, and gurgle as he breathed.
>
> "Cheynestokes breathing," Charlotte explained. "Loud and rapid intakes followed by no breaths, sometimes for longer than thirty seconds."
>
> "Can you do something about it?" Susan demanded.

---

[12] Jane St. Clair, *Walk Me to Midnight* (Waterford VA: Capstone Fiction, 2007).

> "Gurgling is caused by congestion," she replied. "If I suction it out, it'll make him even more uncomfortable. We'll raise his head up a little, and play some more music to drown out the noise. Most families freak out when they hear Cheynestokes."
>
> Kyle's mouth was now hanging open, and the irregularity and noise of his death rattle was disconcerting. It sounded like a very loud coffee percolator–a noise so loud it penetrated walls. (166)

While the purpose of the preceding dialogue about Cheynestokes may be to educate the reading public about the physiological events that naturally occur at the moment of death, unpleasant though they may be,[13] the last moments of Kyle's life balances these negatives with strong positive images that provide spiritual solace not only for Kyle and his family but also for the reader, who has probably been disturbed by the intensity of Cheynestokes's description. Kyle speaks with his grandfather, who has been dead for eight years and who is apparently in his grandson's presence. Erica asks her mother, "Why is that angel and Jesus standing by Daddy?" (166). Kyle's last words are, "Lorie, it's beautiful here" (167).

Earlier, the pastor and the hospice nurse recognize that the dying think they see their deceased relatives coming to greet them at the moment of death. The pastor acknowledges that dying persons experience "the tunnel and the light thing.... That's pretty universal and cross-cultural." The hospice nurse responds with: "'Also the dead relative on the other side,' Charlotte added. 'There's nearly always someone they know to greet them when they cross over'" (163).

The pastor's use of the simple word "thing" and the nurse's presumed emphasis of the word "always" could suggest that their comments may be interpreted as dismissive. This rhetorical ploy counters the charge that such a passage would remain maudlin if Kyle's words were not considered from a secular perspective. The

---

[13] The starkness of this scene contrasts against a contemporary novel that tries to mimic this condition. Describing her mother's death in Anna Quindlen's *One True Thing* (1994), the narrator conveys the difficulty of her mother's breathing with a repetition of the onomatopoeic "eh" for each breath taken (185).

explicitly religious elements of Kyle's last moments, especially when uttered by the characters themselves and not the narrator, should strike the reader as being more compelling than a narrator's mere mention of a spiritual value to the death. In this way, contemporary life-affirming fiction improves the Dickensian formula.

The examples cited above can support three claims: that nineteenth-century fiction set the standard for the depiction of death scenes; that twentieth-century authors altered that standard by altering or eliminating certain elements; and that late twentieth-century and early twenty-first century authors may be revisiting the nineteenth-century standard, either to restore their work to the older standard or to develop aspects of death scenes that have lain dormant for a century.

Two qualifications need to be made. First, the corpus of works consulted in this study is relatively small; more research is needed to determine not only whether other twentieth-century works abandoned the nineteenth-century elements, but also whether twenty-first-century authors are re-examining the five elements.[14] Second, perhaps some elements have been missed in the exploration of the samples. If literature can be compared to an archaeological dig, then some items within the literary works or artifacts surrounding those works may have been completely overlooked. More research needs to be conducted in this area as well.

Despite these objections, some conjectures can be made about what appears to be a changing, if not growing, literary trend. Perhaps twentieth-century authors abandoned the nineteenth-century standard in the interest of pursuing artistic freedom–abandoning not so much the five elements of the death scenes, but what they may have considered as a too facile plot structure in favor of what were new fictional styles at the turn of the twentieth

---

[14] Among the other works consulted for this paper are the following: William Jeremiah Coughlin, *Her Honor* (New York NY: New American Library, 1987); Jodi Picoult, *Mercy* (New York NY: Pocket Books, 2001); Steven Snodgrass, *Lethal Dose* (Orlando FL: ICAM, 1996); Terry Trueman, *Stuck in Neutral* (New York NY: HarperCollins, 2000); Stephen White, *Kill Me* (Thorndike ME: Center Point, 2005).

century. The sentimentality found in nineteenth-century novels where the problems are resolved in the dénouement would not fit well in a twentieth-century novel where alienation and an unsatisfactory (often unhappy) ending are the norm. Alternatively, if twentieth-century authors abandoned the nineteenth-century standard because they had a vested interest in dehumanizing the dying and opening the culture to the idea of eliminating not so much the suffering, but the persons experiencing suffering themselves, then future research must be conducted using biographical and Marxist criticism to determine the forces at work in the authors' lives.

Similarly, twenty-first-century authors may be reacting against the twentieth-century trend by restoring literature to its foundation of respect for the dying–a balance that was destroyed when the twentieth century disregarded those elements that should feature in every dying person's experience. This restoration may be attributed either to contemporary authors' own life-affirming values, to their sense of being advocates on a philosophical level of the rights of the dying to be treated as human beings, or to a desire to produce meaningful works of literary merit–none of which is mutually exclusive.

Finally, only the addition of more works over perhaps one more decade can determine whether a literary trend is occurring. Death is not a pleasant topic for literary discussion, and authors' and critics' discussion of it could easily veer towards the morbid. However, if the trend to produce more meaningful fictional works faithful to the literary heritage of the nineteenth century continues over the next decade, death and dying may become a fascinating and a life-affirming topic for literary studies.

Life is Beautiful: The Theological Aesthetic Argument for Life

Matthew Lewis Sutton

ABSTRACT: Most arguments for the pro-life position are arguments from the transcendental of Truth–it is true that we must uphold the inherent dignity of human life–and the transcendental of the Good–it is good always and everywhere to will the good of human life by all involved. The question is then, what about the third transcendental of Beauty. Is there an argument for Life from the transcendental of Beauty? My thesis is that by using the theological aesthetics of the Church Father Irenaeus of Lyons ("the glory [beauty] of God is the living man") and the theological aesthetics of the twentieth-century theologian Hans Urs von Balthasar ("Beauty is the word that shall be our first"), one can make the powerful argument for Life from the transcendental of Beauty. In short, we should be for Life because we should be for Beauty.

WHEN I LIVED on the East Side in Milwaukee, I would join the pro-life group at my local church in their Saturday morning protest of the nearby abortion clinic. On one Saturday I brought with me my one-year-old daughter. While I was holding my sleeping baby and we were all praying, a pregnant woman was being escorted into the clinic. She focused her eyes completely on getting herself as quickly as possible into the clinic without looking at us. But she stole a look. She briefly looked at me holding my young child who was sleeping in my arms so sweetly. At that moment, the woman began to cry–sob would be the right word–but she still went into the clinic. I do not know if she decided to abort her child, yet somehow seeing a father holding his sleeping child–the beauty of this image–she was overwhelmed. Ever since that episode, I have been asking myself, why did she cry? What was it about the beauty of this image made her question the goodness and truth of her actions? Why did she cry? It certainly was not through reasoned discourse, catchy protest chants, or even an academic paper that started to persuade her that she was doing something wrong and denying something true.

In this paper, I will offer my answer to why I think she cried. I have become convinced that it was the glory of God manifesting itself through created beauty. God as Beauty Itself was trying to convert her about the goodness and truth of human life. I have come to understand what the twentieth-century Catholic theologian Hans Urs von Balthasar wrote about beauty in his work *Love Alone is Credible* when he said:

> In the experiences of extraordinary beauty–whether in nature or in art–we are able to grasp a phenomenon in its distinctiveness that otherwise remains veiled. What we encounter in such an experience is as overwhelming as a miracle, something we will never get over.[1]

In this passage von Balthasar helps me understand that extraordinary beauty can overwhelm by its own power of being beautiful. The miracle of beauty can make people get over what has overcome them. Beauty can overwhelm a pregnant woman about to abort her baby with the weight of the goodness, the truth, and the beauty of the life that she is about to end. With its own evidential power, beauty itself is an argument for life.

Most arguments for the pro-life position are appropriately arguments from the transcendental of truth–it is true that we must uphold the inherent dignity of human life–and the transcendental of goodness–it is good always and everywhere to will the good of human life by all involved.[2] The question, then, is this: What about the third transcendental of beauty? Is there an argument for life from the transcendental of beauty?

My thesis is that by using the theological aesthetics of the Church

---

[1] Hans Urs von Balthasar, *Love Alone is Credible*, trans. David C. Schindler (San Francisco CA: Ignatius Press, 2004), pp. 52-53.

[2] Though it has a complicated history, the idea of the transcendentals comes from ancient Greek philosophy. With the Christian use of this philosophy in the early and medieval ages, the transcendentals were understood as a created thing's beauty, goodness, and truth participating in the beauty, goodness, and truth of God; thus, created things, inasmuch as they are beautiful, good, and true, transcend themselves as they participate in God.

Father Irenaeus of Lyons ("the glory [beauty] of God is the living man") and the theological aesthetics of the twentieth-century theologian Hans Urs von Balthasar ("Beauty is the word that shall be our first"), one can make the powerful argument for life from the transcendental beauty. In short, we should be for life because we should be for beauty.

The theological aesthetics of Irenaeus, who flourished during the last half of the second century, provide structure for this paper. In his most famous work, commonly called *Against the Heresies*, Irenaeus argues against several forms of the Gnostic heresy present in early Christianity and tries to offer as complete as possible a presentation of Christian revelation in its internal obviousness, irrefutability, and irresistibility. Irenaeus's theology has at its center the idea of recapitulation. Already present in Paul's letters to the Ephesians and Romans, the theology of recapitulation presents Jesus Christ as the fulfiller or recapitulator of what humanity, as well as the cosmos, was meant to be at its origin. Jesus Christ in his being and his work brings the human person (Adam) to its perfection in him (as the new Adam).

At the "stilled center" of Irenaeus's theology of recapitulation, according to von Balthasar, is the notion that the human person is capable of receiving the weight of the glory of God.[3] It is summed up in probably his most often invoked idea, that "the glory of God is the living man, and the life of man is the vision of God."[4] I would like to focus on the first part of this idea, namely, that man fully alive is the glory of God. For Irenaeus, human life ultimately leads to the glory of God.

How are we able to start with Irenaeus from the life of man and end at the glory of God? For von Balthasar and for Irenaeus, inasmuch as he has a theological aesthetics, the connection between the life of man and the glory of God is traversed by transcendental beauty. Life leads to

---

[3] Hans Urs von Balthasar, *The Glory of the Lord: A Theological Aesthetics*, vol. 2: *Studies in Theological Style: Clerical Styles* [cited subsequently as GL II], trans. Andrew Louth, Francis McDonagh, and Brian McNeil (San Francisco CA: Ignatius Press, 1984), pp. 74-75. See also Aidan Nichols, *The Word Has Been Abroad: A Guide Through Balthasar's Aesthetics* (Washington, D.C.: The Catholic University of America Press, 1998), p. 70.

[4] Irenaeus, *Against the Heresies*, in *The Scandal of the Incarnation: Irenaeus Against the Heresies*, ed. Hans Urs von Balthasar, trans. John Saward (San Francisco CA: Ignatius Press, 1990), IV: 20, 7.

beauty and beauty leads to the glory of God. These two moves–from life to beauty and beauty to God's glory–make up the two parts of this paper in order to present an argument for life from the transcendental of beauty.

LIFE LEADS TO BEAUTY

For Irenaeus, the living human person is the glory of God because he is God's artwork.[5] The artwork of a master sculptor gives glory not only to the subject of the sculpture but also to the artist. The living man is the Creator's central artwork, and thereby man glorifies the Creator as the master artist. Man full of life radiates the beauty and glory of the Creator. Living man is inherently beautiful, according to Irenaeus, because he is the created artwork of the Creator and he gives glory to the Creator by being fully alive.

Irenaeus makes this connection between the life of man and the glory of God through his understanding of living man as a beautiful artwork. One way to see that this is true theologically is to offer the converse. The death of man means ugliness.

In the April 18, 2008 edition of *Yale Daily News*, Aliza Shvarts reported that for her senior art project she had inseminated herself artificially as many times as possible over a nine-month period and then "performed self-induced miscarriages" by using abortifacients.[6] She explained that after taking these abortifacients, she would "then experience cramps and heavy bleeding."[7] She collected this blood and intended to display it as her senior art project with video recordings of the forced miscarriages as well as of the cups of blood from the miscarriages. While this might be thought a hoax, some truly terrible morbid prank, as Yale University officials did at first, Shvarts produced some partially convincing evidence that she did do this project and wanted it accepted as her senior art project. Far from being a practical joker or even a deranged lunatic, she turns out to have been an

---

[5] Von Balthasar, *GL* II, 74.
[6] "Shvarts Explains Her 'Repeated Self-Induced Miscarriages," *Yale Daily News*, April 18, 2008.
[7] Ibid.

intelligent and articulate young woman. Shvarts explained that this project is indeed art in all of its intentional ambiguity and claimed that

> the most poignant aspect of this representation...is the impossibility of accurately identifying the resulting blood. Because the miscarriages coincide with the expected date of menstruation (the 28th day of my cycle), it remains ambiguous whether there was ever a fertilized ovum or not. The reality of the pregnancy, both for myself and for the audience, is a matter of reading. This ambivalence makes obvious how the act of identification or naming...is at its heart an ideological act, an act that literally has the power to construct bodies.[8]

In a more enigmatic and therefore supposedly profound way, she explains: "it is the intention of this piece to destabilize the locus of that authorial act, and in doing so, reclaim it from the heteronormative structures that seek to naturalize it."[9] She said in an interview with the *Yale Daily News*: "I believe strongly that art should be a medium for politics and ideologies, not just a commodity.... I think I'm creating a project that lives up to the standard of what art should be."[10] There are many things disturbing about this young woman, her art project, and her explanation. While her project was derided by the university and many of her fellow students, she had the support from her senior project advisor. It is still possible that she did not do this project; conclusive evidence has not been produced, her project has not been displayed, and the faculty members involved have not publicly confirmed or denied the project although they were disciplined by the university officials. Nevertheless, Shvarts has continued to claim that she did this project and that it is was real art.

For the most part, there was disgust at what Shvarts claimed she had done, but the critique was not based on the morality of the issue. It was on taste. While it was in bad taste, said the Yale Women's Center, she should be defended because her art project was "an appropriate exercise

---

[8] Ibid.
[9] Ibid.
[10] "For Senior, Abortion as a Medium for Art, Political Discourse," *Yale Daily News*, April 17, 2008.

of her right to free expression."[11] What Shvarts did was to create what can be called anti-beauty art. Ignoring her manufactured diatribe, Shvarts in reality produced a forced meditation on death and ugliness. This Yale student's artwork points to the perversity, and sometimes the demonic character, of the anti-life position. If the embryo is not a human, it can certainly be discarded, but it can also be used to further a political ideology. If there is no "real presence" of a human person in the miscarriage bleeding, then it is organic material that can be used to fabricate a work of "art."

The main fault, of course, rests with the artist. She should have known better and have been expelled from the institution, but the fault is not hers alone.[12] Like many of the young, she takes to an extreme what she has learned from her teachers. Youths tend to seize an idea and then they run with it–hard, fast, fearlessly–until their youthful body hits their 30s-40s and then, apparently, tempered realism sets in. This young artist seized the idea art as "intentional ambiguity," a deconstruction of heteronormative identification of the body, taught to her by her art professors, who in turn defended her artwork. The blame must also fall on them. We should not stop there. The fault falls on the culture of death. Her artwork manifests the core principle of the culture of death.

Abortion and other anti-life positions are anti-beauty. At the pro-life protests of abortion clinics there is usually someone holding a picture of an aborted baby with severed limbs. The subtext of that image is that this is ugly, and therefore abortion is wrong. It connects for the viewer ugliness with immorality–no beauty, therefore no goodness. This usual kind of argument is made in holocaust films, images, and writings. The image is an emaciated, barely living human being in a grim concentration camp who has been made ugly by National Socialism's anti-life ideology. The subtext in holocaust art is that National Socialism is wrong because it is ugly.

The great portrayal of the anti-life as not beautiful and of the pro-

---

[11]"Reaction to Shvarts: Outrage, Shock, Disgust," *Yale Daily News*, April 18, 2008. For an insightful critique of Yale student reactions, see Ian Marcus Corbin, "On the Banality of Abortion as Art," published online at *First Things: On the Square* (www.firstthings.com/onthesquare/?p=1053), April 23, 2008.

[12] Shvarts was allowed to graduate with a degree in English but not in Art.

life as beautiful was made in the film *La vita e bella* (1997). Its English release *Life is Beautiful* (1998) is the source of this paper's title. In this film, the contrast is made between the beautiful relationship of the main character (Guido Orefice) and his son (Joshua) and his wife (Dora) against the backdrop of the ugliness of the Nazis who are ceaselessly inflicting death. What is stunning about this film, which received the grand prize at Cannes Film Festival and three Academy Awards, including Best Foreign Language Film, is that the more that the death, the evil, and the ugliness of the Nazi death machine entered the world, all the more did the goodness, the truth, and the beauty of human life and relationships triumph. The subtext of the argument is that Nazism is wrong because it is ugly, but life is good because it is beautiful.

The climactic scene in the film makes the point clearly. The main character, Guido, is being chased by the SS troops, but in the midst of this tragedy, he is playing a simple hide-n-seek game with his son Joshua. The goodness and beauty of this simple father-and-son game are perceived as even more beautiful and life-affirming because it is being played against the backdrop of death, evil, and ugliness represented by the SS troops who murder Guido while Joshua is hiding. We are made to realize how beautiful this father-son game is because it is set in the context of death and ugliness. Here comedy is mixed with tragedy in order to show ultimately that life and beauty triumph. White is always perceived more distinctly when it is put against a backdrop of black.

I think that the pro-life movement must continue to show the anti-life movement as truly embracing the ugliness of death–the severed limbs of the unborn child just like the mass graves of Jews and Christians killed in concentration camps. In addition to this argument, the pro-life movement must also set before people the images of beauty that are embraced by the pro-life position.[13] This idea means that along with the billboards of smiling chubby babies and the brochures of happy couples holding their recently delivered child, the pro-life movement

---

[13] A culture of life must generate artwork that communicates the beauty of life. Pope Benedict XVI has made this his prayer intention for May 2008: "That Christians may use literature, art, and mass media to create a culture which defends and promotes the values of the human person." We need to use the gift of human culture to manifest the dignity of being human and thereby the glory of God revealed in human culture.

must share the even more profoundly beautiful image of the heroic choice for life in the midst of our culture of death. We need to set before people the image of a boyfriend saying to his pregnant girlfriend that he wants to have this child or the image of parents saying to their pregnant daughter that they will help her raise this child or the image of a community helping a struggling new mother keep her child while still going to school. The point is to show the tragedy and difficulty of the unexpected and in many cases burdensome pregnancy–in a sense, a new human life should be burdensome–but also showing the heroic act, the beauty of making the right choice. Not just the saccharine images of chubby, happy babies, but also the profoundly beautiful image of a baby accepted against the backdrop of the tragedy of the unexpected, irresponsible pregnancy. Life is full of tragedy, pain, suffering, and unexpected pregnancies. The pro-life movement needs to say that in the midst of this culture of death, we must still choose what is beautiful, what is right, and what is true. We must still play hide-n-seek even when the SS troop death squad approaches.

Beauty Leads to the Glory of God

I would like to do more in this paper than advocate for a kind of chiaroscuro–light in the midst of darkness–advertisement campaign for the pro-life movement. What I am suggesting here is that life leads to beauty. We should be for life because it is beautiful. In this next part, I would like to show that theologically life is beautiful because it radiates the glory of God. All of this, of course is to help us answer why the woman on her way to abort her child cried when she saw the image of a father holding his dear sleeping child. Hans Urs von Balthasar can help to explain the connection between beauty and the glory of God in order to answer this question.

Hans Urs von Balthasar (born in Lucerne, Switzerland in 1905; died in Basel, Switzerland in 1988) was a major Catholic theologian of the twentieth century who wrote eighty-five books and over five articles; he translated almost a hundred works, edited over sixty volumes of the works of the physician and mystic Adrienne von Speyr, and co-founded with her the secular institute called the *Johannesgemeinschaft* (Community of St. John). Henri de Lubac, his teacher and a major theologian in his own right, called von Balthasar "the most cultured man of his time." Pope John Paul II called him "an outstanding man of theology and of the arts, who deserves a special place of honor in contemporary ecclesiastical and cultural life." And Pope Benedict XVI, who worked with von Balthasar on several projects including the journal *Communio*, said: "I am convinced that his theological reflections preserve their freshness and profound relevance undiminished to this day and that they incite many others to penetrate ever further into the depths of the mystery of the faith."

It is impossible to summarize his significance for twentieth-century theology (Catholic and Protestant), philosophy, literature (German and French), and drama. In the fifteen volumes that he wrote from 1961 to 1987 the three transcendentals, Beauty, Goodness, and Truth, serve as the framework. He uses them to recover the essential relationship between the transcendentals and the analogy of being. Von Balthasar's interpretation of the analogy of being, which he received from the Jesuit philosopher Erich Przywara, is that God as Being itself is related to all created being not only because he created it but also because he predestined created being to have its definitive end (*telos*) in Being itself. For von Balthasar, the analogy of being must relate closely with the Christian doctrine of participation. Created being is not just a static analogy of Being itself. It is interiorly directed toward an intimate sharing in divine life (cf. 2 Peter 1:4).

With his interpretation of the analogy of being as participation in the life of God, von Balthasar now joins the Christian theological idea of the transcendentals. Since God is Being itself, he is also Beauty, Goodness, and Truth.[14] Anything that has created being as well as beauty, goodness, and truth necessarily participates in the intimate divine life because God is the source of all being as well as beauty, goodness, and truth. Thus, created beauty, goodness, and truth transcend finitude in order to find their definitive end in God. Within all created being, inasmuch as it is beautiful, good, and true, God has given it an

---

[14] "Part of Balthasar's theological project is a reinterpretation of Being via the three transcendentals and the analogy of being." Ed Bloch, Jr., "Introduction" in *Glory, Grace, and Culture: The Work of Hans Urs von Balthasar*, ed. Ed Block, Jr. (New York NY: Paulist Press, 2005), p. 8.

interior missionary character toward himself as Beauty, Goodness, and Truth itself.

With its definitive end in God, all the transcendentals necessarily relate to each other. Any time there is beauty, there is also goodness and truth. Any time there is goodness, there is also truth and beauty. Any time there is truth, there is also goodness and beauty. The three transcendentals are intimately connected because they have their origin and goal in God who is the source and *telos* of all created beauty, truth, and goodness.

The first part of the trilogy, called *The Glory of the Lord*, presents von Balthasar's theological aesthetics, that is, his relating the transcendental of beauty to the analogy of being. It is an argument that attempts to recover beauty as an entryway for the human person's encounter with God. When he looks for the first word out of all the words possible for his fifteen-volume masterwork, he chooses the word beauty: "Beauty is the word that shall be our first."[15] In a retrospective statement on the first part of his trilogy on beauty, von Balthasar said that he called it *The Glory of the Lord*,

> Because it is concerned, first, with learning to see God's revelation and because God can be known only in his Lordliness and sublimity [or better translated "glorious-ness"] (*Herr-heit* and *Hehr-heit*), in what Israel called *Kabod* and the New Testament *Gloria*, something that can be recognized under all the incognitos of human nature and the Cross. This means that God does not come primarily as a teacher for us ("true"), as a useful "redeemer" for us ("good"), but to display and to radiate himself, the splendor of his eternal triune love in that "disinterestedness" that true love has in common with true beauty.[16]

In other words, the human encounter with the revelation of God is known through his radiating beauty, or what the biblical witness called glory. God came not just to teach or to redeem, but primarily to reveal his glorious beauty because this revealing is what teaches and redeems.

---

[15] Hans Urs von Balthasar, *The Glory of the Lord: A Theological Aesthetics*, vol. 1: *Seeing the Form* [cited subsequently as GL I], trans. Erasmo Leiva-Merikakis (San Francisco CA: Ignatius Press, 1982), p. 18.

[16] Hans Urs von Balthasar, *My Work: In Retrospect*, trans. Kenneth Batinovich and Brian McNeil (San Francisco: Ignatius Press, 1993), 80.

For example, it is the glory of the Lord manifested in the cloud of smoke by day and the pillar of fire by night that convinces Israel to leave Egypt and journey to the promised land (Ex 13:17-22). It is the glory of the Lord that dwells on Mount Sinai, manifesting the potent, fiery presence of the Lord who gives the Law to Israel (Ex 19:16-20). It is the glory of the Lord that descends upon the first temple built by Solomon, revealing God's kingly dwelling in the Holy of Holies in Jerusalem (1 Kgs 8:1-11). It is the glory of the Lord that overshadows Mary in whom the Son of God becomes incarnate by the power of the Holy Spirit (Lk 1:26-38). It is the glory of the Lord represented by tongues of fire that rushes down upon the apostles on the feast of Pentecost manifesting God's dwelling presence with his Church (Acts 2:1-13). For von Balthasar, in the Old and New Testaments, it is the glory (beauty) of the Lord that manifests the Father's potent presence in the world through the Son and Holy Spirit and reveals the goodness and truth about his love for the world. The Son of God did not just come to teach or to be useful, he came to reveal God's love.

According to von Balthasar, any engagement with beauty necessitates a theory of vision, that is, a theory about the perception of beauty.[17] Beauty results from the intersection of *species* and *lumen*, that is, form and splendor. At this intersection, beauty, so to speak, happens, and there is a moment in the viewer of beholding and of being enraptured.[18] It is truly an outpouring of the glory of the Lord through the Holy Spirit. To be enraptured by beauty, the form needs to be perceived. Perceiving here in meant in the sense of the German word *Wahr-nehmen*, "to take to be true." When beauty is perceived, goodness and truth are equally present. Beauty is not a competitor to reason or the ethical, but it is in a coordinated relationship manifested God as Being Itself. When a person sees goodness or truth, beauty manifests itself to the beholder. The intersection of form and splendor in an event or

---

[17] Von Balthasar, GL I, 125.

[18] "The form as it appears to us is beautiful only because the delight that it arouses in us is found upon the fact that in it, the truth and goodness of the depths of reality itself are manifested and bestowed, and this manifestation and bestowal reveal themselves to us as being something infinitely and inexhaustibly valuable and fascinating" (Von Balthasar, GL I, 118).

object, and particularly human life, beauty happens and essentially manifests goodness and truth.

If a person wishes to see the whole of beauty, goodness, and truth, he must open himself to the revelation of the divinity of Christ.[19] The first examination of beauty must begin with the Incarnation because it is, according to von Balthasar, "the very apex and archetype of beauty in the world, whether men see it or not."[20] The hypostatic union of the personhood of the divine Son with the fullness of human nature is that of the greatest possible concreteness of an individual form and the greatest possible universality of the epiphany of Being-itself.[21] Jesus Christ is the most beautiful form and splendor because as God he is Beauty itself. The two polarities of form and splendor indissolubly intersect and give the definitive evidence that he is the most beautiful. By the act of faith given through grace, the Christian perceives the perfect beauty of the Incarnation and it will enrapture him. Faith-filled eyes, trained by viewing the perfect form, see that the beauty of life manifests the beautiful glory of God.

With his theological aesthetics, von Balthasar can conclude that when one beholds beauty in the created order, one is actually beholding the glory of God and his glory is enrapturing through its own evidential power of goodness and truth. When one perceives anything that is beautiful, one is also perceiving the perfection of beauty that is being manifested. The perfection of beauty and the full manifestation of the glory of the Lord is the revelation of Jesus Christ as the Son of God.

We must, however, be reminded by von Balthasar that Jesus as the perfect form and splendor of beauty is also the one who experiences the sheer ugliness of death on the cross. The Incarnate One is also the Crucified One. Perfect beauty has been made sin for us. He has been made ugly by us. In the death of Jesus Christ on the cross, Beauty itself has been completely given away, nothing held back, all is surrendered.

---

[19] "Here the circumincession of *pistis* and *gnosis* becomes fully manifest, because it is only through faith in Christ's divinity that one can gain access to this sphere of truth within the Godhead, in which one learns to see and understand the very essence of truth" (Von Balthasar, GL I, 135).

[20] Von Balthasar, GL I, 69.

[21] Von Balthasar, GL I, 234.

Von Balthasar, influenced particularly on this point by the mystic Adrienne von Speyr, believes that since Jesus as the Son of God has surrendered all, he has revealed everything about himself and his Trinitarian relationship with the Father and Holy Spirit. In other words, the paschal mystery of Christ's death on the Cross is the point of the highest revelation to us about who God is. The beautiful thing about the Cross for Christians is that they see in it perfect beauty and the glory of the Lord lovingly given away against the severe backdrop of the ugliness of death. Indeed, on most crucifixes in Orthodox churches, one will not see the sign you will see the title "The Glory of the Lord." For them, the crucifixion is the great manifestation of the glory of the Lord. The Son's complete giving away in the truly perfect surrender of self on the Cross manifests the fullness of beauty as the glory of the Lord.

According to the theological aesthetics of Irenaeus and von Balthasar, I think that we can now conclude that life and the glory of God are connected through the transcendental of beauty. We have seen that theologically life leads to beauty and beauty leads to the glory of God. In short, the theological aesthetic argument for life would say that we should be for life because life manifests the glory of God through the transcendental of beauty.

In the story about the pregnant women who was on her way into the abortion clinic we might ask why was it that she cried when she saw the image of a father holding his sweetly sleeping child. After examining the theological aesthetics of Irenaeus and von Balthasar, I think that she cried because she saw that the life of a child is beautiful and that the living child's beauty reveals the glory of God. In this image, the glory of God overwhelmed her because of its own evidential power. The created beauty of the living child revealed the glory of God who is Beauty, Goodness, and Truth itself. God knows what she did after that moment of tears, but I think that we can say the entryway for her human encounter with God was offered to her through the transcendental of beauty. Although I am desperately aware that I am an inadequate, imperfect father, somehow God used my life and my child's life to open an encounter with himself as Beauty itself.

From the evidence of this episode and the theological aesthetics of Irenaeus and von Balthasar, I think that we should argue for life from the transcendental of beauty because that is how God the Father seeks to convert us through his Son and the Holy Spirit. He attracts us through the beauty of the perfect form of the perfect human being giving himself completely away on the Cross in order to draw us through the Holy Spirit into the Father's love.

About Our Contributors

Samuel W. Calhoun is Professor of Law at Washington and Lee University School of Law, where he teaches contracts, legal writing, commercial law, and a seminar entitled "The Abortion Controversy." His principal areas of scholarly interest are the abortion debate and the interrelationship of law and religion. He received his B.A. from Harvard College and his J.D. from the University of Georgia School of Law.

Robert C. Cetrulo, J.D., is a practicing attorney in Covington, Kentucky and president of the Northern Kentucky Right to Life Committee. He received his legal education at the University of Kentucky College of Law and served as U.S. Magistrate-Judge for the Eastern Judicial District of Kentucky from 1960 to 1975. He has taught political science and constitutional law at the University of Kentucky Northern Community College and lectured at the Salmon P. Chase College of Law. He is the author of various articles, including articles in the *Kentucky Law Journal* and the *Kentucky Bench & Bar Quarterly*.

John J. Conley, S.J. holds the Francis X. Knott Chair of Philosophy and Theology at Loyola College in Maryland. Recent books include *The Suspicion of Virtue: Women Philosophers in Neoclassical France* (Cornell University Press, 2002), *Jacqueline Pascal: A Rule for Children and Other Writings* (University of Chicago Press, 2003), *Madame de Maintenon* (University of Chicago Press, 2004), and *Adoration and Annihilation: The Convent Philosophy of Port Royal* (University of Notre Dame Press, 2009).

Anne Barbeau Gardiner is Professor Emerita in the Department of English at John Jay College, City University of New York. She has published two books on Dryden, including *Ancient Faith and Modern Freedom in John Dryden's The Hind and the Panther* (Catholic University of America Press, 1998). She has also published numerous essays on Milton, Dryden, and Swift, including "Jonathan Swift and the Idea of the Fundamental Church" in *Fundamentalism and Literature*, ed. Catherine Pesso-Miquel and Klaus Stierstorfer (New York NY: Palgrave MacMillan, 2007), pp. 21-43.

Robert Gotcher received his doctorate in theology from Marquette University and has taught theology at Sacred Heart School of Theology in Hales Corners, Wisconsin.

James G. Hanink, Professor of Philosophy at Loyola Marymount University, has been active in pro-life work since 1972. His special interests include Thomism, personalism, and political philosophy. He has contributed essays, editorials and reviews to several publications, both academic and general.

Jeff Koloze received his doctorate in English at Kent State University in 2001 and is Campus College Chair for the College of Arts and Sciences at the Columbus, Ohio Campus of the University of Phoenix. He has taught communications, undergraduate and graduate English, and humanities courses since 1989 at several colleges and universities in the Cleveland, Columbus, and Springfield, Ohio metropolitan areas. His primary research interest is the presentation of the right-to-life issues of abortion, infanticide, and euthanasia in American fiction; most of his publications on these matters are available in conference proceedings and on the web. His most recent book is *An Ethical Analysis of the Portrayal of Abortion in American Fiction: Dreiser, Hemingway, Faulkner, Dos Passos, Brautigan, and Irving*. He can be reached at JeffKolozePhD@sbcglobal.net.

Joseph W. Koterski, S.J. is a member of the Philosophy Department at Fordham University, where he has taught since his priestly ordination in1992. He also serves as the Editor-in-Chief of *International Philosophical Quarterly* and as Master of Queen's Court Residential College for Freshmen. He regularly teaches courses on natural law ethics and on medieval philosophy. He has produced videotaped lecture-courses on "Aristotle's Ethics," on "Natural Law and Human Nature," and most recently on "Biblical Wisdom Literature" for The Teaching Company. Among his recent publications: *An Introduction to Medieval Philosophy: Basic Concepts* (Wiley-Blackwell, 2009).

Richard S. Myers is Professor of Law at Ave Maria School of Law. He is a Phi Beta Kappa graduate of Kenyon College. He earned his law degree at Notre Dame, where he won the law school's highest academic prize. He began his legal career by clerking for Judge John F. Kilkenny of the U.S. Court of Appeals for the Ninth Circuit. Professor Myers taught at Case Western Reserve University School of Law and the University of Detroit Mercy School of Law before joining the Ave Maria faculty. He has also taught as a visitor at Notre Dame Law School. He has published extensively on constitutional law. Professor Myers has co-edited two books: *St. Thomas Aquinas and the Natural Law Tradition: Contemporary Perspectives* (The Catholic University of America Press, 2004) and *Encyclopedia of Catholic Social Thought, Social Science, and Social Policy* (Scarecrow Press, 2007). He is the president of University Faculty for life and the executive secretary of the Society of Catholic Social Scientists. Professor Myers is married to Mollie Murphy, who is a Professor of Law at Ave Maria School of Law. They are the proud parents of six children.

Craig Payne has taught at the college level since 1990, at Indian Hills College in Iowa and Truman State University in Missouri, primarily in the areas of philosophy, religion, and literature. He has had three books published, the most recent being *What Believers Don't Have to Believe: The Non-Essentials of the Christian Faith*. He holds a doctorate in theology and religious studies from the University of Wales, St. David's University College. Craig is married to a professional clown and has two children. All of them live in southeastern Iowa.

Edmund Pellegrino, M.D., is the John Carroll Professor Emeritus of Medicine at Georgetown University Medical Center. He served as Director of the Institute (1983-1989), and the Center for Clinical Bioethics at the Medical Center (1991-1996). Dr. Pellegrino is the recipient of 42 honorary doctoral awards. Author of more than 500 publications, he is best known for his discussions of Christian virtue and medical ethics in the treatment of patients, humanism and the physician, and the philosophical basis of medical treatment. He is the founding editor of *Journal of Medicine and Philosophy*.

Janet E. Smith holds the Michael J. McGivney Chair of Life Ethics at Sacred Heart Major Seminary. She is the author of *Humanae Vitae: A Generation Later* and a *Right to Privacy*; co-author with Christopher Kaczor of *Life Issues, Medical Choices*, and editor of *Why Humanae Vitae Was Right: A Reader*.

She is best known for her talk "Contraception: Why Not." She has published widely on sexual ethics, bioethics, and the principles of moral theology.

Matthew Lewis Sutton, Ph.D. has taught at the College of St. Benedict and St. John's University in Minnesota and now teaches Christian Spirituality and Mysticism at St. John's University in Queens, New York. He has a B.A. in Catholic Studies from the University of St. Thomas in Minnesota, having also studied abroad at the Pontifical Institute of St. Thomas Aquinas, the Angelicum, in Rome, Italy. He earned his M.A. and Ph.D. at Marquette University in Systematic Theology with his dissertation on the Trinitarian Mysticism of Adrienne von Speyr. He is married to Elizabeth and is graced with three daughters, Felicity, Anastasia, and Edith.

Lynn D. Wardle is the Bruce C. Hafen Professor of Law at the J. Reuben Clark Law School, Brigham Young University, where he has taught Family Law, Biomedical Ethics and Law, and other courses since 1978. He is past President (2000-02), Secretary-General (1994-2000) and current Executive Council member (1991-94, 2002-present) of the International Society of Family Law; has been a visiting professor or lecturer at other law schools in Scotland, Japan, Australia, China, and the U.S. He has made academic presentations in more than 25 nations, most dealing with Family Law. He is author or co-author 6 books, editor or co-editor of eight other books (most recently *The Jurisprudence of Marriage and Other Intimate Relationships*, with Professor Scott FitzGibbon of Boston College Law School (Wm. S. Hein & Co. 2010)), and of over 100 articles and chapters, most dealing with family law or biomedical law issues. He is a member of the American Law Institute; and serves on the Boards of Directors or Advisory Boards of national and international legal publications, and other professional and scholarly associations, including University Faculty for Life, and previously of Americans United for Life, and of the National Right to Life Committee.

Christopher Wolfe is Emeritus Professor of Political Science at Marquette University. He currently is Vice-President of the Thomas International Project and Co-Director of the Ralph McInerny Center for Thomistic Studies. He graduated *summa cum laude* from Notre Dame in 1971 with a major in government and went on to study political philosophy at Boston College, receiving his Ph.D. in 1978. During his graduate studies he "migrated" from political philosophy to American Political Thought and Constitutional Law. He taught at Assumption College from 1975 to 1978 and came to Marquette in 1978. Dr. Wolfe's main area of research and teaching for two decades was Constitutional Law, and his books include *The Rise of Modern Judicial Review: From Constitutional Interpretation to Judge-Made Law* (Basic Books, 1986), *Judicial Activism: Bulwark of Freedom or Precarious Security?* (Brooks/Cole, 1991), and *How to Read the Constitution: Originalism, Constitutional Interpretation, and Judicial Power* (Rowman and Littlefield, 1996). He also edited *That Eminent Tribunal: Judicial Supremacy and the Constitution* (Princeton University Press, 2004). In his more recent research, Dr. Wolfe has shifted back to political theory, with studies of natural law and liberalism.

Acknowledgments

Some parts of Prof. Lynn Wardle's paper (mostly historical in nature) overlap with a law review forthcoming in *Ave Maria Law Review* and with a paper under consideration in the *Journal of Law, Philosophy, and Culture*.

The paper by Prof. Samuel Calhoun is reprinted from *The Mississippi Law Journal* with the permission of D. Eric Schieffer, Executive Editor.

The article by Prof. Richard Fehring is an extension of an article published in *Current Medical Research* and in the August 2009 edition of *The Linacre Quarterly*. Our thanks to Dr. Bill Williams, M.D., the Editor-in-Chief of *The Linacre Quarterly* to have permission for it to appear here.

UFL Board of Advisors, 2010-2011*

UFL Board of Directors, 2010-2011*